GARBAGE AND OTHER POLLUTION

Cornelia Blair

INFORMATION PLUS REFERENCE SERIES
Formerly published by Information Plus, Wylie, Texas

GALE GROUP

Detroit
New York
San Francisco
London
Boston
Woodbridge, CT

GARBAGE AND OTHER POLLUTION

was produced for the Gale Group by Information Plus, Wylie, Texas

Information Plus Staff:

Cornelia Blair, Author

Jacquelyn Quiram, Designer

Editorial: Abbey Begun, Barbara Klier, Nancy R. Jacobs, Virginia Peterson, Mei Ling Rein, Mark A. Siegel

The Gale Group Staff:

Editorial: Rita Runchock, Managing Editor; John F. McCoy, Editor

Graphic Services: Randy Bassett, Image Database Supervisor; Robert Duncan, Senior Imaging Specialist

Product Design: Michelle DiMercurio, Senior Art Director; Michael Logusz, Graphic Artist

Production: NeKita McKee, Buyer; Dorothy Maki, Manufacturing Manager

GARBAGE AND OTHER POLLUTION

CHAPTER I

HISTORICAL PERSPECTIVE — GARBAGE THEN AND NOW

Beginning with ancient civilizations, there has always been refuse. There has not always been a refuse problem, however, at least not one of the magnitude that has developed in modern times. — Martin Melosi, *Garbage in the Cities*, 1981

Prehistoric people did not have to worry about garbage. They lived in nomadic tribes that wandered the countryside following the herds of wild animals that they hunted and killed for food and clothing. They were free to leave behind their waste because, after the scavengers and insects had eaten what they wanted, the garbage decayed and returned to the earth.

THE FIRST GARBAGE DUMPS

About 10,000 years ago, prehistoric people began to form villages and become farmers. For the first time they had to live with their refuse. The garbage smelled bad and attracted wild animals, some of which could be very dangerous. Some prehistoric villagers dug pits to toss the garbage into. One of the best ways scientists learn about prehistoric communities is by studying the garbage tossed into pits located in or near their villages.

CLEANING UP ANCIENT CITIES

Residents of the ancient city of Troy left their waste on the floors of their homes or tossed it into the streets. At about the same time, however, the Indus Valley city of Mahenjo-Daro (Pakistan) was built using a plan that called for homes to contain built-in rubbish chutes and trash bins.

In the ancient Egyptian city of Heracleopolis, founded about 2100 B.C.E. (Before the Common Era), the garbage of religious leaders and the wealthy was collected and dumped into the Nile River. At about the same time, in Crete, the bath-

rooms of the kings were connected to sewers. Around 800 B.C.E., Jerusalem had a sewer system to take away wastes.

About 500 B.C.E., the city of Athens, Greece, passed the first garbage dump law in the Western world, requiring that garbage be dumped at least one mile outside the city walls. By the second century B.C.E., sanitary police were gathering up the garbage in major Chinese cities. In the Roman Empire, major cities had sewage and water systems, although the garbage collection system was not always adequate.

During the Middle Ages in Western civilizations, few large cities existed in Europe, so garbage was not considered an important problem. In Edinburgh, Scotland, and in English cities, residents threw garbage into the streets and rivers. In 1388, however, the English Parliament made it illegal to throw garbage into the rivers. Across the English Channel in France, Parisians also tossed their garbage out of windows. By 1400, the piles of garbage outside the city gates of Paris were so high that it was hard to defend the city because the mounds of garbage were as high as the city walls.

THE COMING OF THE INDUSTRIAL REVOLUTION

In Western civilizations, the Industrial Revolution (from the late eighteenth century through the nineteenth century) brought many millions of people to the cities. Small towns became cities and cities grew larger. People lived in crowded housing and the sanitation was poor. For example, in one part of Manchester, England, there was only one toilet for 212 people.

In 1842, an English government commission reported that the terrible sanitation conditions caused disease. By 1869, England had created a Sanitary Commission to improve sanitation and garbage disposal in the English cities.

AND IN THE UNITED STATES . . .

Until recently, most Americans were not concerned about garbage or polluting the environment. The United States was a huge country. People thought there was enough land and water to absorb any amount of garbage they might throw away.

In colonial America, much as in Europe, people dumped their garbage into the streets. Pigs roamed around and ate the garbage. In 1657, New Amsterdam (now New York) became the first city to pass laws against street disposal. Nonetheless, as late as the 1860s, residents of Washington, DC, still threw their garbage into the streets.

When the United States became an industrialized country in the nineteenth century, most Americans did not think that what they were doing could hurt the environment. Factories often dumped their chemicals directly into rivers and lakes. Cities poured their sewage into the same rivers and lakes. Garbage was deposited into nearby garbage dumps without any concern that it might harm the ground water. Ships dumped garbage overboard into rivers, lakes, and oceans.

Postcards proudly showed factories pouring filthy smoke into the air. America was rapidly becoming industrialized, and most people were proud of the factories in their towns. They did not care that the plants were pouring chemicals into the water or pollution into the air. The sky and the rivers were thought to be big enough to absorb anything that might be done to them.

Nonetheless, the result of this lack of concern for the environment led to some serious problems. New Orleans had typhoid epidemics because sewage was poured into streets and canals. Memphis lost nearly 10 percent of its population to yellow fever. Infant mortality was very high in the large cities.

And it was not only people that made garbage. In New York, about 120,000 horses drew carriages, hauled wagons, and pulled streetcars, while Chicago had 83,000 horses doing such work. Every city needed large numbers of horses to do these things. These horses produced thousands of tons of manure that dirtied the streets and had to be cleaned up and dumped somewhere.

EARLY EFFORTS TO
MAKE USE OF TRASH

Most Americans produced little trash until the twentieth century. Women boiled food scraps into soups or fed them to animals, which returned the favor with eggs or meat. Durable items were passed on to the next generation or to people more in need. Objects that were of no further use to adults became toys for children. Broken items were repaired by "handymen" or dismantled for reuse. Many Americans possessed the skills required for repairing. Things that could no longer be used were burned for fuel, especially in the homes of the poor. Even middle-class Americans traded rags to peddlers in exchange for buttons or tea kettles. These ragmen worked the streets, begging or buying for pennies bones, paper, old iron, rags, and bottles. They then sold the junk to dealers who marketed it to manufacturers.

Spending time to prolong the useful lives of items and to use scraps saved money. In 1919, in *Save and Have, A Book of 'Saving Graces' for American Homes* (New York), the University Society discussed habits of thrift for American housewives. The Society recommended keeping cake fresh by storing it with an apple and "turning" worn sheets by tearing them down the middle and sew-

FIGURE 1.1
GARBAGE COLLECTION

Source: *Garbage Then and Now*, National Solid Wastes Management Association, Washington, DC, no date

ing up the good sides. Other suggestions included collecting grease to make soap, reusing flour sacks for dish towels or clothing, using jars for drinking glasses, and keeping a grease can on the stove containing grease that was used over and over.

Besides giving away clothes, mending and re-making them, and using them as rags for work, women reworked textiles into useful household furnishings, such as quilts, rugs, and upholstery. Such activities demonstrated a woman's frugality and creative skill and came to represent an aspect of a woman's "virtue." In 1845, in a mill-workers' magazine, *Lowell Offering*, an author wrote, "How many passages of my life seem to be epitomized in this patchwork quilt." Interestingly, with the invention of the sewing machine, which aided women with handworking skills, handmade patchwork quilts came to be thought of as coarse in comparison with the fine needlework done by machine. Today, quilts are valued once again, but as a form of art and expression rather than housekeeping skill.

Rags were one of the most important materials collected for recycling in factories. Paper mills used rags to make paper, and a growing paper industry made it profitable for thrifty housewives to save rags.

This trade in used goods provided crucial resources for early industrialization. These early systems of recycling began to pass into history around the turn of the century. Sanitary reformers and municipal trash collection did away with scavenging. Technology made available cheap and new alternatives. People made fewer things, and bought more than previous generations had. They saved and repaired less and threw out more. As Susan Strasser, in *A Social History of Trash* (Henry Holt and Co., New York, 1999), describes it,

The rhetoric of convenience, luxury, and cleanliness was potent. It sold a wide variety of products that transformed Americans' relationship to waste and, in general, to the material world. In a few decades, the ideal of the durable and reusable was displaced by aspirations of leisure and luxury, ease and cleanliness. The new ways were entrenched by 1929, in principle if not always in practice, and neither a depression nor the material shortages of a world war were enough to reverse what most people saw as progress.

Old-fashioned reuse and recycling did not cease overnight. During the first decades of the twentieth century, most people still threw away relatively little as old ways still survived in the midst of the new. Nonetheless, as the century progressed, middle-class people learned to throw things away, attracted by the convenience and wanting to avoid any association with scavenging and poverty. Success often meant that one did not have to use second-hand things. As municipalities became responsible for collecting and disposing of refuse, Americans found it easier to throw things out.

DOING SOMETHING ABOUT GARBAGE

Throughout the nineteenth century, many cities passed anti-dumping ordinances, but many people ignored them. Some landowners and merchants resented ordinances, which they considered infringements of their rights. As cities grew, garbage became not only a public eyesore, but also a threat to public health.

City leaders began to recognize that they had to do something about the garbage. By the turn of the century, most major cities had set up garbage collection systems (Figure 1.1). Many cities introduced incinerators to burn some of the garbage. By the time the First World War began in 1914, about 300 incinerators were operating in the United States and Canada.

Cities located downstream from other cities that were pouring their garbage into rivers sued the upstream cities because the water was polluted. As a result, more and more cities stopped dumping their garbage into rivers and began to build landfills or garbage dumps to get rid of their waste. Many coastal cities began to take their refuse out into the ocean and dump it, although much of the garbage they poured into the sea washed back to dirty the beaches.

TABLE 1.1

Per Capita Resource Consumption in the United States, Mid-1990s

Material	Pounds Per Day
Stone and cement	27
Coal	19
Miscellaneous minerals	17
Oil	16
Farm products	12
Wood	11
Range grass	10
Metals	8
Natural gas	1
Total	**121**

Source: John C. Ryan and Alan Thein Durning, *Stuff: The Secret Lives of Everyday Things*, Northwest Environment Watch, Seattle, WA, 1997

Some health officials and reformers knew that pollution was unhealthy and could lead to sickness, but until recently, most people were not concerned about the long-term effects of garbage and pollution on the environment. Over the past decades, more and more Americans have become concerned that garbage and pollution are harming the environment.

In 1965, the United States government passed the Solid Waste Disposal Act (PL 89-272), the first of many solid waste management laws (see below). Over the past 40 years, the number and influence of environmental groups have grown significantly. As a result of this growing concern for the environment, the first Earth Day was celebrated on April 22, 1970.

IN A CONSUMER SOCIETY — A GARBAGE GLUT

The United States generates more garbage than any other nation on Earth, twice as much per person as in Europe. Americans produce about 1,400 pounds of trash per person per year, 4.4 pounds per day per person. As with most of the environmental issues, waste disposal has grown to crisis proportions. The cost of handling garbage is the fourth biggest item — after education, police, and fire protection — in many city budgets. Some 80 percent of the nation's solid waste is being dumped in landfills, but sites are rapidly filling up and many are leaking toxic substances into the nation's water supply.

America is facing a problem with its ever-growing mountains of garbage. Not only are many landfills incapable of holding any more trash, but also as more is learned about garbage, the more apparent it is that trucking garbage to landfills does not necessarily eliminate it. As a result, municipal governments worldwide are struggling to find the best methods for managing waste.

Growing populations, rising incomes, and changing consumption patterns have combined to complicate the waste management problem. Garbage generation expands as a city grows in size. Consumers earn more money and increase their consumption of food, and demands grow for "convenience foods" with their additional packaging. Other convenience items, such as disposable diapers, also add to the mountain of wastes. Before the days of densely populated urban areas, waste disposal was eased by the apparent ability of the surrounding land and water to absorb the wastes. A hundred years ago, farm communities created little waste. Today, farm communities produce waste similar to urban areas, plus the runoff from insecticides and fertilizers used in food-producing fields.

One-Time Use

The widespread human appetite for all materials has defined this century in much the same way that stone, bronze, and iron characterized previous eras. — United States Geological Survey, *Mineral Commodity Summaries,* 1998

The scale of materials use by Americans, Europeans, Japanese, and other industrialized countries dwarfs that of a century ago. Today's stock of materials draws from all 92 naturally occurring elements in the periodic table, compared with approximately 20 at the turn of the century. The United States Geological Survey (USGS) estimates that in the United States alone, consumption of metal, glass, wood, cement, and chemicals has grown 18-fold since 1900. The United States alone uses a third of world materials today.

Much of the waste disposal problem exists, first, because of a growing population and, second, because most consumer goods are designed for short-term use. This contrasts sharply with the practices of earlier eras, when materials were reused or transformed into other uses. Susan Strasser (see above) observed that Kleenex® and Shredded Wheat boxes — the literal throwaways — represented the most extreme form of a relationship to objects that was new at the dawn of the twentieth century. "More and more things were made and sold with the understanding that they would soon be worthless or obsolete," she reported.

The volume of waste increases with income — poor neighborhoods generate lower amounts of solid wastes per capita than richer neighborhoods.

FIGURE 1.2

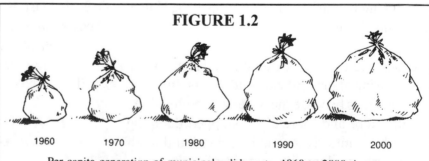

| 1960 | 1970 | 1980 | 1990 | 2000 |

Per capita generation of municipal solid waste, 1960 to 2000, in pounds per person per day. This graph shows waste generation before materials recovery or incineration. Demographic changes, economic factors, and consumer preferences are among the factors contributing to the increase in per-capita generation of MSW.   Adapted from EPA, *Characterization of Municipal Solid Waste in the United States: 1992 Update.*

Source: *The Garbage Primer*, The League of Women Voters Education Fund, Washington, DC, 1993

An inventory of what Americans throw away would reveal valuable metals, paper representing millions of acres of trees, and plastics incorporating highly refined petrochemicals.

A Frontier Mindset

This reckless abuse of the natural environment is the product of a frontier mindset that views materials, and the Earth's capacity to absorb wastes, as practically limitless. — Gary Gardner and Payal Sampat, *Mind Over Matter: Recasting the Role of Materials in Our Lives*, Worldwatch Institute, December 1998

It is indicative of a society's priorities and values that products so rich in raw materials are frequently considered worthless. Northwest Environment Watch, a not-for-profit research center in Seattle, Washington, estimates that every day each American consumes 120 pounds of natural resources extracted from farms, forests, rangelands, and mines. Table 1.1 shows the per capita resource consumption in the United States.

In cultures based on handwork, such as America before the twentieth century, handmade objects are valued because they represent many hours or work, either one's own or someone known to the individual. Today, it is easier to throw away a commercially made dress than it would be to throw away a dress you or your grandmother had sewn.

More recently, the interest in recycling has grown, and most states are making recycling an important part of waste collection and disposal. Nonetheless, the nation's garbage dumps are filling up, and new ones are having to be constructed. Most states send some garbage to other states or even to other countries. Some of these states and countries will no longer accept other people's garbage. (See Chapter II.)

The Sorting Process

Nothing is inherently trash. Trash is produced by sorting, a human behavior. Items in people's lives eventually require a decision — to keep or to throw away. Some things go here; some things go there.

Sorting — or classification — has a spatial dimension; it separates one's private property from the public domain. Journalists and fans believe that items placed outside the walls of a celebrity's house are "fair game," and the Supreme Court has generally upheld that belief. In *California v. Greenwood* (1998), a case that involved evidence found in a drug dealer's rubbish, the Court declared that the borders of a household do not encompass the contents of trash cans. The Court maintained that citizens may not expect their trash to be private and that law enforcement officers do not need a search warrant to search trash.

The sorting process varies from person to person, from place to place, and changes over time. What is considered rubbish changes from decade to decade. Some ethnic groups have probably valued saving things more than others. Nomadic people, who must travel light, save less. Age matters as well — the young have more readily adopted the notions of disposability and convenience and are less likely to conserve.

Sorting is also an issue of class. Trashmaking creates social differences based on economic status. The wealthy can afford to be wasteful, and discarding things is often a way of demonstrating wealth and power.

A Modern Challenge

The moon is littered with astronauts' cast-offs, while tens of thousands of pieces of debris orbit the earth — spent rocket boosters, dead satellites, garbage from manned space missions, and tiny but fast-moving bits of metal and chips of paint. Those of us not responsible for safeguarding the operational spacecraft endangered by this orbiting trash grimace at the very idea of it, but then we shrug. — James R. Chiles, "Casting a High-Tech Net for Space Trash," *Smithsonian Magazine*, January, 1999

At the turn of the millenium, people in developed nations discard things for a reason unheard of in developing nations or in earlier times — because they do not want them. Disposing of out-of-style clothes and outmoded equipment reflects a worship of newness that was not widespread before this century. Dumpsters are filled with "perfectly good stuff" that is simply not new anymore — items the owner has tired of.

Economic growth during the twentieth century has been fueled by waste — garbage produced by disposables, packaging, and "planned obsolescence." A consumer culture depends on a continual supply of new products. Colored plastic trash bags represent the contemporary attitude about trash, far from the homemade soup, darned underwear, and flour-sack dresses of an earlier time.

HOW MUCH GARBAGE?

As the United States became richer, the nation produced more garbage and pollution. The Environmental Protection Agency (EPA), the government agency whose job it is to protect the environment, estimates that the average American man, woman, or child throws away about three-fourths of a ton of garbage a year. The amounts are usually higher in the cities. Since 1960, America's population has grown 34 percent, but the amount of garbage produced has increased 80 percent. Figure 1.2 shows the per capita growth in garbage production from 1960 through 2000.

Most of the waste that people see is produced by ordinary households throwing out their uneaten food, yesterday's newspapers, packaging materials, lawn clippings, and branches from bushes and trees. This garbage, however, is only a fraction of all the wastes that are thrown out.

The EPA can only guess how much garbage is made each year. The EPA estimates that somewhere between 12 and 13 billion tons of garbage are produced annually. Of this figure, about 0.7 billion tons are hazardous waste (Subtitle C) and 11 to 12 billion tons are nonhazardous waste (Sub-

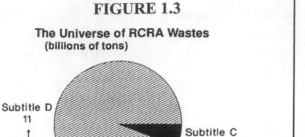

FIGURE 1.3

The Universe of RCRA Wastes
(billions of tons)

Subtitle D 11

Subtitle C 0.7

Excludes mineral processing wastes and some wastewater discharges (see text)

Based on U.S. Environmental Protection Agency, Office of Solid Waste and Emergency Response, *Report to Congress: Wastes From the Extraction and Benefication of Metallic Ores, Phosphate Rock, Asbestos, Overburden From Uranium Mining and Oil Shale*, EPA/530-SW-85-033 (Washington, DC: December 1985); *Report to Congress: Management of Wastes From the Exploration, Development, and Production of Crude Oil, Natural Gas, and Geothermal Energy*, EPA/530-SW-88-003 (December 1987); *Report to Congress: Wastes From the Combustion of Coal by Electric Utility Power Plants*, EPA/530-SW-88-002 (February 1988); *Report to Congress: Solid Waste Disposal in the United States*, vols. 1-2, EPA/530-SW-88-011 (October 1988); *Report to Congress on Special Wastes from Mineral Processing*, EPA/530-SW-90-070C (July 1990); *1987 National Biennial RCRA Hazardous Waste Report*, EPA/530-SW-91-061 (July 1991); *National Survey of Hazardous Waste Generators and Treatment, Storage, Disposal, and Recycling Facilities in 1986, Hazardous Waste Management in RCRA TSDR Units*, EPA/530-SW-91-060 (July 1991).

Source: *Managing Industrial Solid Wastes from Manufacturing, Mining, Oil and Gas Production, and Utility Coal Combustion*, Office of Technology Assessment, Washington, DC, 1992

title D). (See Figure 1.3.) For more information on hazardous waste, see Chapter VII.

Non-Household Wastes

According to the EPA, of the estimated 12 billion tons of wastes the nation produces, about 217 million tons is made up of the garbage that people throw out. (See Figure 1.4. In the figure, city garbage is shown as municipal solid waste.) Over half (57 percent), 7 billion tons, of all wastes resulted from industrial wastes (waste produced by factories that manufacture products we use). Special wastes (mining, oil and gas production, electric utilities, cement kilns, and agriculture) comprised 39 percent of solid waste.

Manufacturing produces huge amounts of waste. The paper industry, which uses many chemicals to produce paper, accounted for the largest proportion of manufacturing wastes — 35 percent of the total. The iron and steel (20 percent) and chemical industries (14 percent) produced most of the rest. Many of the big manufacturing plants have sites on their own property where they can throw waste or treat it so it will not become dangerous. Still others ship it to private disposal sites for dumping or for treatment. Smaller manufacturers might use private waste disposal companies or even the city garbage company.

Mining also produces much waste, most of it waste rock and tailings. Normally, miners have to move waste rock to retrieve the ore or minerals they want to mine. Tailings are left over after miners have sifted through the rocks and dirt for the ore or the minerals.

Chemicals are used to remove minerals from ore. After these chemicals have done their job, they become waste. Sometimes these chemical wastes are liquid, and sometimes they are solid.

Almost all (96 to 98 percent) of the wastes from gas and oil drilling are produced as waters. These waters are pumped out before the oil is found or are mixed with oil. The water is often saltwater. These waters must be separated from the oil and gas before they can be turned into refined oil or gas for automobiles or home heating. The rest of the oil and gas waste comes from mud and rock that comes up from drilling. Most oil and gas companies dispose of their own wastes. When an electric company burns coal to heat water to make electricity, about 90 percent of the coal is burned up. About 10 percent is left in the form of ash, which must then be discarded.

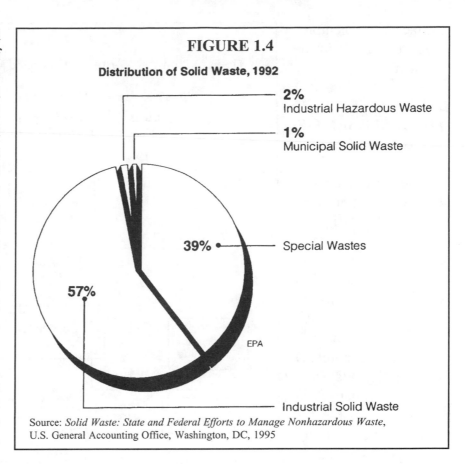

FIGURE 1.4

Distribution of Solid Waste, 1992

2% Industrial Hazardous Waste

1% Municipal Solid Waste

39% Special Wastes

57%

EPA

Industrial Solid Waste

Source: *Solid Waste: State and Federal Efforts to Manage Nonhazardous Waste*, U.S. General Accounting Office, Washington, DC, 1995

HOW DO HUMANS DISPOSE OF GARBAGE?

There are four general ways to get rid of garbage. First, the garbage can be dumped into a landfill or "garbage dump," an area set aside for garbage to be brought to and buried. Second, waste may be poured into a surface impoundment, a large pond in which liquid wastes can be stored and then treated so they can be safely thrown away. Third, waste can be spread out in a "land application," where waste is taken to a designated area and poured on the land. Fourth, the garbage may be dumped onto a waste pile on the ground, where it is stored and may eventually be treated. (See Chapter II for further discussion of these methods.)

Almost all wastes from oil and gas production, mining, and agriculture end up in surface impoundments. Manufacturing uses all four methods to get rid of waste. Almost all of the garbage produced by cities and construction wastes ends up in landfills. Refuse that is incinerated (burned) produces residue that is then processed using one of the four methods.

LAWS GOVERNING THE DISPOSAL OF GARBAGE

The Resource Conservation and Recovery Act (RCRA; PL 94-580), the major federal law on waste disposal, was passed in 1976. This law primarily covers hazardous waste, which is only a small part (approximately 6 percent) of all garbage. State and local governments are mainly responsible for passing laws concerning nonhazardous waste, although the federal government will supply money and guidance to local governments so they can better manage their garbage systems.

Other federal laws cover other areas of waste disposal. For example, the Clean Water Act (PL 95-217) regulates water disposal, the Safe Drinking Water Act (PL 93-523) controls underground injections when waste water is dumped into deep wells, and the Clean Air Act (PL 95-95) governs dirty air. For more information on environmental policy making, see Chapter VIII.

WASTE MANAGEMENT — AMERICA'S NEW GROWTH INDUSTRY

The trash industry is one of the most potentially profitable in the country. Historically, solid waste disposal was regarded as more of a nuisance than a problem requiring a well-thought-out solution. Even recent interest in recycling stems primarily from the high cost of landfill disposal and the health risks of other methods, not from the recognition that environmentally safe waste disposal should be an integral part of any production plan. Recycling is beginning to succeed mainly because there are financial gains to be made. Figure 1.5 shows the roles of households and producers in the flow of products, waste, and recycled materials.

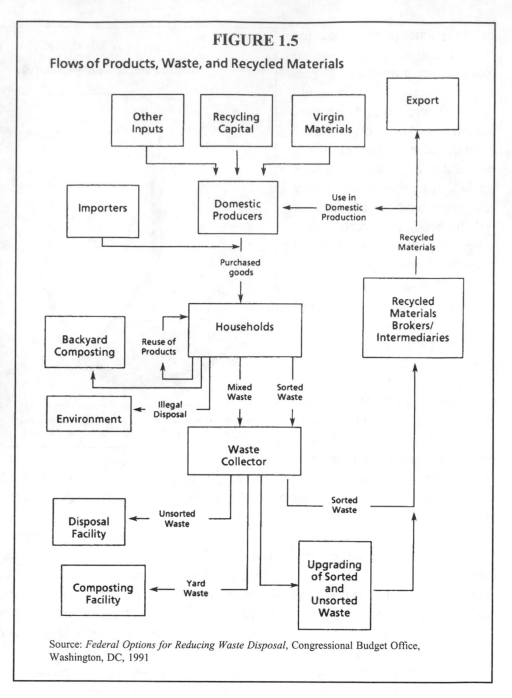

FIGURE 1.5

Flows of Products, Waste, and Recycled Materials

Source: *Federal Options for Reducing Waste Disposal*, Congressional Budget Office, Washington, DC, 1991

10

THE STATE OF GARBAGE IN 2000 — STABILITY

Fueled by legislative mandates, landfill bans on certain items, funding for state recycling programs, and the 1994 federal deadline for the closing of substandard landfills, the early 1990s saw significant jumps in recycling rates, big declines in the number of landfills, and increases in composting of yard trimmings. In the past few years, however, the steep increases and declines have become more gradual, reflecting both saturation and maturation of programs and stabilization of landfill closures. Furthermore, nothing on the horizon is likely to change this steady state. No major federal or state initiatives are anticipated that will significantly alter waste management trends.

CHAPTER II

MUNICIPAL SOLID WASTE

Since human beings have inhabited the earth, they have generated, produced, manufactured, excreted, secreted, discarded, and otherwise disposed of all manner of waste. Among the myriad kinds of rejectamenta, refuse — solid waste — has been one of the most abundant, most cumbersome, and potentially most harmful. — Martin Melosi, *Garbage in the Cities*, 1981

When most people think of garbage, they think of the bags of refuse they put out for the sanitation people who come by once or twice a week. That garbage may include food that was thrown away, yesterday's newspaper, the wrapping that once contained a birthday present, the package a microwave dinner came in, empty soda bottles, diapers, and old math and history tests no longer needed.

Some municipalities require that people separate newspapers, other papers, and used soda bottles so they can be recycled. City governments either pay their own employees or hire private companies to pick up the garbage.

As defined by the U.S. Environmental Protection agency (EPA), municipal solid waste (MSW) includes durable and nondurable goods, containers and packaging, food scraps, yard trimmings, and miscellaneous inorganic refuse from residential, institutional, and industrial sources. MSW does not include wastes from other sources, such as construction and demolition wastes, automobile bodies, municipal sludges, combustion ash, and industrial process wastes that might also be discarded in municipal landfills or incinerators.

A LOT OF GARBAGE

In developed countries such as the United States, almost everything that is sold at supermarkets or department stores is put into packages that will eventually be discarded. Many things are made to be thrown away. A family goes on a picnic and uses paper plates and plastic utensils that are tossed away after the meal. After the doctor uses a needle to give a shot, she immediately throws it into a special trash can. The dentist uses disposable rubber gloves that he puts into the garbage after every patient. Until recently, cassettes and CDs came in large plastic containers that were thrown away after they were bought. Meat and chicken are wrapped in layers of plastic and foam packaging.

Americans discard a huge amount of garbage. (See Figure 2.1.) They toss away 2.5 million plastic bottles every hour, or 22 billion a year, and almost 32 tons of leaves, branches, and grass cuttings from their yards each year. If the discarded paper were built into a 12-foot wall, it would stretch all the way across the country from Los Angeles to New York.

If the aluminum we throw away were made into passenger airplanes, the nation could rebuild all the passenger planes in the United States every three months. Americans throw away over 200 million tires every year. Every two weeks, Americans toss away enough bottles and jars to fill up the twin towers of New York's World Trade Center, each one over one-quarter of a mile high.

FIGURE 2.1

With the aluminum we throw away in 3 months, the United States could rebuild its entire commercial airfleet.

We throw away 2.5 million plastic bottles every hour (22 billion plastic bottles a year).

We throw away over 200 million tires every year (one for every person in the United States).

We throw away 31.6 million tons of yard waste each year.

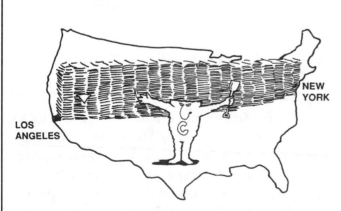

Every 2 weeks, we throw away enough bottles and jars to fill the 1,350-foot twin towers of New York's World Trade Center.

With the office and writing paper we throw away every year, we could build a 12-foot high wall from Los Angeles to New York City.

Source: *Let's Reduce and Recycle: Curriculum for Solid Waste Management*, Environmental Protection Agency, Washington, DC, 1990

TABLE 2.1

GENERATION, MATERIALS RECOVERY, COMPOSTING, COMBUSTION, AND DISCARDS OF MUNICIPAL SOLID WASTE, 1960 TO 1997
(In millions of tons and percent of total generation)

Thousands of Tons								
	1960	1970	1980	1990	1994	1995	1996	1997
Generation	88.1	121.1	151.6	205.2	214.2	211.4	209.2	217.0
Recovery for recycling	5.6	8.0	14.5	29.0	42.2	45.3	46.4	48.6
Recovery for composting*	Neg.	Neg.	Neg.	4.2	8.5	9.6	10.9	12.1
Total Materials Recovery	5.6	8.0	14.5	33.2	50.6	54.9	57.3	60.7
Discards after recovery	82.5	113.0	137.1	172.0	163.6	156.5	151.9	156.3
Combustion**	27.0	25.1	13.7	31.9	32.5	35.5	36.1	36.7
Discards to landfill, other disposal†	55.5	87.9	123.4	140.1	131.1	120.9	115.8	119.6

Pounds per Person per Day								
	1960	1970	1980	1990	1994	1995	1996	1997
Generation	2.68	3.25	3.66	4.50	4.50	4.40	4.32	4.44
Recovery for recycling	0.17	0.22	0.35	0.64	0.89	0.94	0.96	1.00
Recovery for composting*	Neg.	Neg.	Neg.	0.09	0.18	0.20	0.23	0.25
Total Materials Recovery	0.17	0.22	0.35	0.73	1.06	1.14	1.18	1.24
Discards after recovery	2.51	3.04	3.31	3.77	3.44	3.26	3.14	3.20
Combustion**	0.82	0.67	0.33	0.70	0.68	0.74	0.75	0.75
Discards to landfill, other disposal†	1.69	2.36	2.98	3.07	2.75	2.52	2.39	2.45
Population (thousands)	179,979	203,984	227,255	249,907	260,682	263,168	265,253	267,645

Percent of Total Generation								
	1960	1970	1980	1990	1994	1995	1996	1997
Generation	100.0%	100.0%	100.0%	100.0%	100.0%	100.0%	100.0%	100.0%
Recovery for recycling	6.4%	6.6%	9.6%	14.2%	19.7%	21.5%	22.2%	22.4%
Recovery for composting*	Neg.	Neg.	Neg.	2.0%	4.0%	4.5%	5.2%	5.6%
Total Materials Recovery	6.4%	6.6%	9.6%	16.2%	23.6%	26.0%	27.4%	28.0%
Discards after recovery	93.6%	93.4%	90.4%	83.8%	76.4%	74.0%	72.6%	72.0%
Combustion**	30.6%	20.7%	9.0%	15.5%	15.2%	16.8%	17.3%	16.9%
Discards to landfill, other disposal†	63.0%	72.6%	81.4%	68.3%	61.2%	57.2%	55.4%	55.1%

* Composting of yard trimmings and food wastes. Does not include mixed MSW composting or backyard composting.
** Includes combustion of MSW in mass burn or refuse-derived fuel form, incineration without energy recovery, and combustion with energy recovery of source separated materials in MSW (e.g., wood pallets and tire-derived fuel).
† Discards after recovery minus combustion.
Details may not add to totals due to rounding.

Franklin Associates

Source: *Characterization of Municipal Solid Waste in the United States: 1998 Update*, Environmental Protection Agency, Washington, DC, 1999

HOW MUCH GARBAGE AND WHAT IS IN IT?

There is a lot of garbage. Garbage experts estimate statistics on garbage; not all communities and states provide complete information, and many communities and states have different definitions for the types of garbage.

The Environmental Protection Agency (EPA), in its *Characterization of Municipal Solid Waste in the United States: 1998 Update* (1999), reported that, in 1997, Americans produced about 217 million tons of municipal solid waste — 4.4 pounds per person per day— up from 209.2 million tons and 4.3 pounds per person per day in 1996 (Table 2.1). That amount is, however, down from 4.5

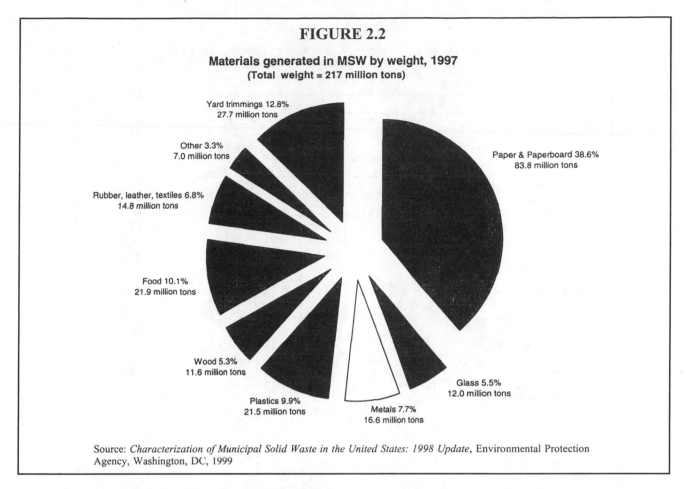

FIGURE 2.2

Materials generated in MSW by weight, 1997
(Total weight = 217 million tons)

Yard trimmings 12.8%
27.7 million tons

Other 3.3%
7.0 million tons

Rubber, leather, textiles 6.8%
14.8 million tons

Food 10.1%
21.9 million tons

Wood 5.3%
11.6 million tons

Plastics 9.9%
21.5 million tons

Metals 7.7%
16.6 million tons

Glass 5.5%
12.0 million tons

Paper & Paperboard 38.6%
83.8 million tons

Source: *Characterization of Municipal Solid Waste in the United States: 1998 Update*, Environmental Protection Agency, Washington, DC, 1999

pounds per person per day in 1990 and 1994. Considering the booming economy of the late 1990s, that decline is significant.

BioCycle Magazine, a waste industry publication, in its annual nationwide survey, "The State of Garbage in America — 1999," compiled from data provided by the individual states, reported the total amount of MSW generated in 1998 at a record 375 million tons. (The *BioCycle* survey included industrial waste, which was not counted in figures compiled by the EPA in its *Characterization of Municipal Solid Waste in the United States: 1998 Update* [above].)

Most garbage is paper. In 1997, 38.6 percent of all MSW by weight was paper, followed by yard wastes (12.8 percent), food wastes (10.1 percent), plastics (9.9 percent), metals (7.7 percent), rubber, leather, and textiles (6.8 percent), glass (5.5 percent), wood (5.3 percent), and miscellaneous other (3.3 percent). (See Figure 2.2.)

As shown in Table 2.2, the proportion of garbage products that come from paper (18.2 percent) has increased only slightly since 1960 (16 percent), although corrugated boxes make up an increasing proportion of paper waste. The amount of plastics has increased steadily and is expected to continue to rise. On the other hand, the proportions of yard wastes, food wastes, and glass have been dropping and are expected to decline even more in the next few years.

FACTORS AFFECTING MUNICIPAL SOLID WASTE GENERATION

A growing population clearly contributes to the increasing amount of MSW. Population, however, is not the only factor leading to more garbage. MSW has increased more rapidly than population. While average population growth over the last 35 years has been 1.1 percent, average annual growth of MSW has been 2.7 percent.

TABLE 2.2

PRODUCTS GENERATED* IN THE MUNICIPAL WASTE STREAM, 1960 TO 1997
(WITH DETAIL ON CONTAINERS AND PACKAGING)
(In percent of total generation)

Products	Percent of Total Generation							
	1960	1970	1980	1990	1994	1995	1996	1997
Durable Goods	11.3%	12.1%	14.4%	14.5%	14.5%	14.7%	15.1%	15.3%
Nondurable Goods	19.7%	20.7%	22.7%	25.4%	26.5%	27.1%	26.5%	27.2%
Containers and Packaging								
Glass Packaging								
Beer and Soft Drink Bottles	1.6%	4.6%	4.4%	2.7%	2.5%	2.4%	2.4%	2.3%
Wine and Liquor Bottles	1.2%	1.6%	1.6%	1.0%	0.8%	0.8%	0.9%	0.8%
Food and Other Bottles & Jars	4.2%	3.7%	3.2%	2.0%	2.3%	2.2%	1.9%	1.8%
Total Glass Packaging	7.0%	9.8%	9.2%	5.8%	5.6%	5.5%	5.2%	4.9%
Steel Packaging								
Beer and Soft Drink Cans	0.7%	1.3%	0.3%	0.1%	Neg.	Neg.	Neg.	Neg.
Food and Other Cans	4.3%	2.9%	1.9%	1.2%	1.4%	1.3%	1.3%	1.3%
Other Steel Packaging	0.3%	0.2%	0.2%	0.1%	0.1%	0.1%	0.1%	0.1%
Total Steel Packaging	5.3%	4.4%	2.4%	1.4%	1.5%	1.4%	1.4%	1.4%
Aluminum Packaging								
Beer and Soft Drink Cans	Neg.	0.1%	0.6%	0.8%	0.8%	0.8%	0.7%	0.7%
Other Cans	Neg.	Neg.	Neg.	Neg.	Neg.	Neg.	Neg.	Neg.
Foil and Closures	0.2%	0.3%	0.3%	0.2%	0.2%	0.2%	0.2%	0.2%
Total Aluminum Packaging	0.2%	0.5%	0.8%	0.9%	1.0%	0.9%	0.9%	0.9%
Paper & Paperboard Pkg								
Corrugated Boxes	8.3%	10.5%	11.3%	11.7%	13.1%	13.6%	13.9%	13.9%
Milk Cartons**			0.5%	0.2%	0.2%	0.2%	0.2%	0.2%
Folding Cartons**			2.5%	2.1%	2.4%	2.5%	2.6%	2.5%
Other Paperboard Packaging	4.4%	4.0%	0.2%	0.1%	0.1%	0.1%	0.1%	0.1%
Bags and Sacks**			2.2%	1.2%	1.1%	0.9%	0.9%	0.9%
Wrapping Papers**			0.1%	0.1%	0.0%	0.0%	0.0%	0.0%
Other Paper Packaging	3.3%	3.1%	0.6%	0.5%	0.5%	0.5%	0.6%	0.6%
Total Paper & Board Pkg	16.0%	17.7%	17.4%	15.9%	17.5%	18.0%	18.3%	18.2%
Plastics Packaging								
Soft Drink Bottles**			0.2%	0.2%	0.3%	0.3%	0.3%	0.4%
Milk Bottles**			0.2%	0.3%	0.3%	0.3%	0.3%	0.3%
Other Containers	0.1%	0.8%	0.6%	0.7%	0.6%	0.6%	0.6%	0.7%
Bags and Sacks**			0.3%	0.5%	0.6%	0.6%	0.7%	0.7%
Wraps**			0.6%	0.7%	0.8%	0.8%	0.9%	1.0%
Other Plastics Packaging	0.1%	1.0%	0.5%	1.0%	1.1%	1.1%	1.1%	1.3%
Total Plastics Packaging	0.1%	1.7%	2.2%	3.4%	3.7%	3.6%	3.9%	4.3%
Wood Packaging	2.3%	1.7%	2.6%	4.0%	3.3%	2.9%	3.1%	3.2%
Other Misc. Packaging	0.1%	0.1%	0.1%	0.1%	0.1%	0.1%	0.1%	0.1%
Total Containers & Pkg	31.1%	36.0%	34.7%	31.4%	32.7%	32.4%	33.0%	33.1%
Total Product Wastes†	62.0%	68.8%	71.8%	71.4%	73.8%	74.2%	74.7%	75.6%
Other Wastes								
Food Wastes	13.8%	10.6%	8.6%	10.1%	10.0%	10.3%	10.4%	10.1%
Yard Trimmings	22.7%	19.2%	18.1%	17.1%	14.7%	14.0%	13.3%	12.8%
Miscellaneous Inorganic Wastes	1.5%	1.5%	1.5%	1.4%	1.4%	1.5%	1.5%	1.5%
Total Other Wastes	38.0%	31.2%	28.2%	28.6%	26.2%	25.8%	25.3%	24.4%
Total MSW Generated - %	100.0%	100.0%	100.0%	100.0%	100.0%	100.0%	100.0%	100.0%

Franklin Associates

* Generation before materials recovery or combustion.
  Details may not add to totals due to rounding.
** Not estimated separately prior to 1980.
† Other than food products.
  Neg. = Less than 5,000 tons or 0.05 percent.

Source: *Characterization of Municipal Solid Waste in the United States: 1998 Update*, Environmental Protection Agency, Washington, DC, 1999

Many reasons have been suggested for the growth in per capita MSW generation: lifestyle changes, more two-income wage earners in households, smaller households, changes in the workplace, and a growing economy. More women in the workforce, who prefer the convenience of pack-

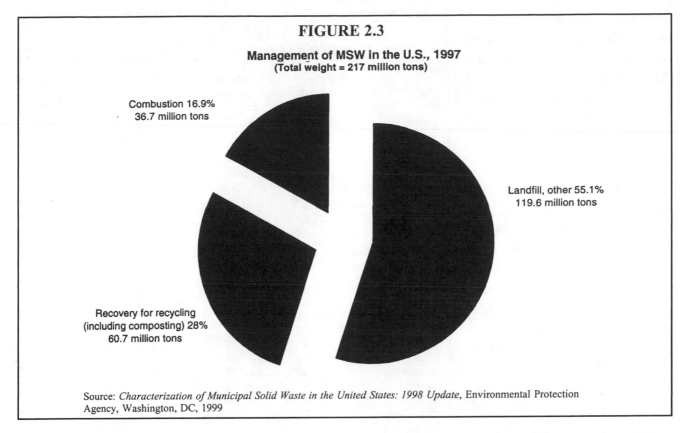

FIGURE 2.3

Management of MSW in the U.S., 1997
(Total weight = 217 million tons)

Combustion 16.9%
36.7 million tons

Landfill, other 55.1%
119.6 million tons

Recovery for recycling
(including composting) 28%
60.7 million tons

Source: *Characterization of Municipal Solid Waste in the United States: 1998 Update*, Environmental Protection Agency, Washington, DC, 1999

aged and fast-food items, produce more garbage. In a strong economy, people are able to buy more, again creating more refuse.

METHODS OF HANDLING SOLID WASTE

The three primary methods of handling municipal solid waste are landfilling, combustion or incineration, and recycling. According to the EPA, in 1997, 55 percent of all wastes went into landfills (down from 62 percent in 1993), 28 percent was recycled (up from 22 percent in 1993), and 16.9 percent was incinerated, roughly the same as in 1993. (See Figure 2.3.) This generally agrees with *BioCycle* in its 1999 "The State of Garbage in America," which found that about 61 percent of the garbage went into landfills in 1998 (down from 71 percent in 1993 and 67 percent in 1995). More than 31 percent was recycled (up from 19 percent in 1993 and 23 percent in 1995), and 7.5 percent was burned in incinerators (down from 11 percent in 1993 and 10 percent in 1995).

Table 2.3 shows how the various states disposed of their garbage. Some states, such as Wyo-

ming (95 percent), Montana (93 percent), and New Mexico (90 percent), got rid of almost all of their garbage by pouring it into landfills. These are less-populated states that often have more space for landfills. Most states in the Northeast, along with Minnesota, Florida, and Hawaii discard less than 50 percent of their waste in landfills. MSW incineration occurs almost entirely east of the Mississippi. Overall use of incineration in 1998 — 7.5 percent — was the lowest since records have been kept. Incineration is generally more costly than using landfills, and many people are concerned about incineration's risk to the environment and human health (see below).

According to *BioCycle*, recycling is becoming more important everywhere in the United States. Minnesota (45 percent), New York and New Jersey (43 percent), Maine, South Carolina, and South Dakota (42 percent each) all recycled a significant part of their garbage in 1998.

LANDFILLS

Landfills are open areas where cities and towns dump their garbage. They were once called "garbage dumps" because cities used to take the garbage to the area and simply dump it. Landfills are the cheapest way to get rid of garbage. In the United States, 55 percent of all municipal solid waste was poured into landfills in 1997. (See Figure 2.3.)

Landfill use fluctuates with changes in the use of alternative management methods. For example, when incineration rates are low and recovery rates are low, the MSW percentage sent to landfills increases. Alternatively, when recovery and incineration of MSW increases, landfill use declines. Since 1990, as incineration, recycling, and composting have increased, landfill disposal has decreased. (See Figure 2.4.)

Decreasing Numbers of Landfills in the United States

Fewer and fewer landfills are available for MSW disposal. In the early 1970s, the number of operating landfills was estimated at about 20,000. In 1995, 2,893 landfills were operating, and by 1998, according to the Environmental Industry Associations, only 2,314 landfills were still open (Table 2.4). Many landfills have closed because they are full, while many more closed because they could not conform to stricter legal requirements. Figure 2.5 shows the estimated years of landfill capacity remaining for the states as of 1996, as reported by the U.S. Environmental Protection Agency (EPA).

TABLE 2.3

Waste generation, recycling and disposal methods (by state)

State	Solid Waste (tons/yr)	Recycled[1] (%)	Incinerated (%)	Landfilled (%)
Alabama[2]	5,630,000	23	5	72
Alaska[2]	675,000	7	15	78
Arizona[3]	5,142,000	17	0	83
Arkansas[4]	3,316,000	36	<1	67
California[2]	56,000,000	33	0	67
Colorado[4,5]	5,085,000	18[6]	<1[6]	82[6]
Connecticut[7]	3,047,000	24	64	12
Delaware[5]	825,000	22	30	48
Dist. of Columbia	250,000	8[6]	92[6]	0
Florida[4,8]	23,770,000	39	16	45
Georgia[3]	10,745,000	33	1	66
Hawaii[5]	1,950,000	24	30	46
Idaho	987,000	n/a	n/a	n/a
Illinois[4,8]	13,300,000	28	1	71
Indiana[4]	5,876,000	23	10	67
Iowa[3,5]	2,518,000	34	<1	66
Kansas[9]	2,380,000	13	<1	87
Kentucky[4]	6,320,000	32	0	68
Louisiana[2,3]	4,100,000	19	0	81
Maine[4,8]	1,635,000	42	40	18
Maryland[4]	5,700,000	30	25	47
Massachusetts[4]	7,360,000	34	45	21
Michigan	19,500,000	25	5	70
Minnesota[4]	5,010,000	45	28	27
Mississippi[2,4]	3,070,000	14	5	81
Missouri[2,4]	7,950,000	30	<1	70
Montana[4,5]	1,001,000	5[6]	2[6]	93[6]
Nebraska[2]	2,000,000	29	0	71
Nevada[4]	2,800,000	14	0	86
New Hampshire[2,4]	880,000	26	20	54
New Jersey[4]	7,800,000	43	20	37
New Mexico[4,6]	2,640,000	10	0	90
New York[4,5]	30,200,000	43	11	46
North Carolina[2,3]	12,575,000	32	1	67
North Dakota[8]	501,000	26	0	74
Ohio[4]	12,335,000	17	0	83
Oklahoma[4,8]	3,545,000	12[6]	10[6]	78[6]
Oregon[4,8]	4,100,000	30	11	59
Pennsylvania[2]	9,200,000	26	22	52
Rhode Island	420,000	27	0	73
South Carolina[2,3]	10,010,000	42	2	56
South Dakota[4]	510,000	42	0	58
Tennessee[4,5]	9,513,000	35	10	55
Texas[4,5]	33,750,000	35	<1	65
Utah[2,4]	3,490,000	22	3	75
Vermont[4]	550,000	30	7	63
Virginia[8]	10,000,000	40	18	42
Washington[4]	6,540,000	33	8	59
West Virginia[3,4]	2,000,000	20	0	80
Wisconsin[4,8]	5,600,000	36	3	61
Wyoming[2]	530,000	5	0	95
Total	374,631,000	31.5	7.5	61

n/a - Information not available; [1]Includes yard trimmings composting; [2] Includes industrial and agricultural wastes as well as C&D debris; [3]Includes industrial waste and C&D debris; [4] Includes C&D debris; [5]Based of FY 1998 data; [6]Based on 1997 data; [7]Based on FY 1997 data; [8]Based on information from the 1998 State of Garbage in America; [9]Based on 1995 data

Source: Jim Glenn, "The State of Garbage in America," *BioCycle*, vol. 40, no. 4, April 1999

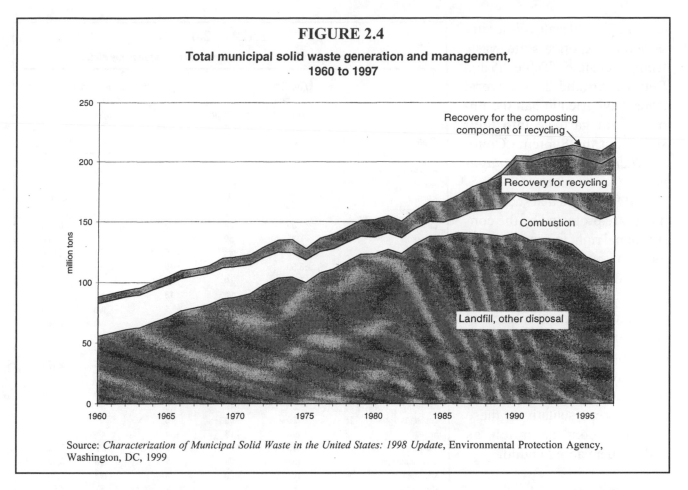

FIGURE 2.4

Total municipal solid waste generation and management, 1960 to 1997

Recovery for the composting component of recycling

Recovery for recycling

Combustion

Landfill, other disposal

Source: *Characterization of Municipal Solid Waste in the United States: 1998 Update*, Environmental Protection Agency, Washington, DC, 1999

New areas for landfills are becoming increasingly hard to find, with some states running out of acreage for landfills. A few states (Connecticut, Massachusetts, New Jersey, and Rhode Island) have insufficient area with soil and water conditions suitable for sanitary landfills. On the other hand, the United States is one of the least crowded (in terms of population density per acre) industrialized nations in the world, and as shown in Figure 2.5, the EPA believes significant acreage is available in the nation's South and West.

Nonetheless, there are significant problems. Most experts believe that the obstacles to new landfills are, first, monetary — landfills are extremely expensive to build since the new regulations (see below) — and, second, psychological and political. Landfills have never been welcome in most neighborhoods. Nobody wants a garbage dump in his or her back yard — the "not in my back yard" syndrome.

Shipping Garbage Somewhere Else — Imports and Exports of Garbage

The Resource Conservation and Recovery Act (see below) went into effect in 1993. Landfills that did not meet the stricter requirements of the law were expected to close down, pay fines, or fix up their landfills. Many landfills closed due to those restrictions.

Because of the drop in the number of landfills, many cities and towns now send their garbage to other states. In 1992, even before the law went into effect, about 19 million tons (9 percent of all garbage created) were sent out of state. By 1995, 25.1 million tons of waste passed over state lines for disposal. This is an especially big problem in the Northeast in states like New York and New Jersey, where some cities must send their garbage very far away. Some are even shipping their garbage to Africa and Latin America.

In 1997, all states either imported or exported solid waste from other states (Table 2.5 and Figures 2.6 and 2.7). Several states have tried to ban the importing of garbage into their states, but the Supreme Court, in *Chemical Waste Management, Inc. v. Hunt* (504 U.S. 334, 1992), ruled that such shipments are protected by the constitutional right to conduct commerce across state borders. Experts point out that the newer, state-of-the-art landfills, which have multiple liners to prevent leaks and equipment to treat emissions, will have to accept waste from a wide region to be financially viable. According to industry representatives, these landfills cost as much as $400,000 an acre to build.

Pennsylvania is by far the largest waste importer, followed by Virginia and Indiana (Table 2.5). Chicago has become a major source of exported waste, despite ample disposal capacity in Illinois. Both Wisconsin and Indiana accept waste from Chicago. Five states — New York, Illinois, New Jersey, Maryland, and Missouri — exported more than one million tons of waste to other states in 1997. New York's large amount of exported waste is dominated by New York City's commercial waste. Furthermore, waste exports from New York are expected to grow rapidly when Fresh Kills Landfill (the city's only landfill) closes in 2001 (see below).

TABLE 2.4

Disposal capacity, number of landfills/incinerators and tipping fees (by state)

State	Number	Landfills Average Tipping Fee ($/ton)	Remaining Capacity (years)	Number	Incinerators Average Tipping Fee ($/ton)	Daily Capacity (tons/day)
Alabama	30	33	10	1	40	700
Alaska	322	50	n/a	4	80	210
Arizona	54	22	n/a	2	n/a	n/a
Arkansas[1]	23	27	20	1	n/a	n/a
California	188	39	28	3	34	6,440
Colorado	68	33	50	1	n/a	<20
Connecticut	3	n/a	n/a	6	64	6,500
Delaware	3	58.50	20	0	–	–
Dist. of Columbia	0	–	0	0	–	–
Florida	95	43	n/a	13	55	18,996
Georgia	76	28	20	1	n/a	480
Hawaii	8	24	n/a	1	n/a	2,000
Idaho	27	21	n/a	0	–	–
Illinois	56	28	15	1	n/a	1,600
Indiana	45	30	n/a	1	27.50	2,175
Iowa	60	30.50	12	1	n/a	100
Kansas	53	23	n/a	1	n/a	n/a
Kentucky	26	25	19	0	–	–
Louisiana	25	23	n/a	0	–	–
Maine	8	n/a	18	4	47	2,850
Maryland	22	48	10+	3	51	3,860
Massachusetts	47	n/a	n/a	8	n/a	8,621
Michigan	58	n/a	15-20	5	n/a	3,700
Minnesota	26	50	9	9	50	4,681
Mississippi	19	18	10	1	n/a	150
Missouri	26	27	9	0	–	–
Montana	33	32	20	1	65	n/a
Nebraska	23	25	n/a	0	–	–
Nevada	25	23	75	0	–	–
New Hampshire	19	55	11	2	55	700
New Jersey	11	60	11	5	51	6,491
New Mexico	55	23	20	0	–	–
New York	28	n/a	n/a	10	n/a	10,350
North Carolina	35	31	5	1	n/a	540
North Dakota	15	25	35+	0	–	–
Ohio	52	30	20	2	n/a	n/a
Oklahoma	41	18	n/a	2	n/a	1,200
Oregon	33	25	40+	2	67	600
Pennsylvania	51	49	10-15	6	69	8,952
Rhode Island	4	35	5+	0	–	–
South Carolina	19	29	16	1	n/a	255
South Dakota	15	32	10+	0	–	–
Tennessee[1]	34	35	10	2	43	1,250
Texas	181	n/a	30	4	n/a	n/a
Utah	45	n/a	20+	2	n/a	340
Vermont	5	65	5-10	0	–	–
Virginia	70	35	20	5	n/a	n/a
Washington	21	n/a	37	5	n/a	n/a
West Virginia	19	48	20	0	–	–
Wisconsin	46	30	6	2	45.50	347
Wyoming	66	10	>100	0	–	–
Total	2,314			119		

n/a - Information not available; [1] Based on 1997 data

Source: Jim Glenn, "The State of Garbage in America," *BioCycle*, vol. 40, no. 4, April 1999

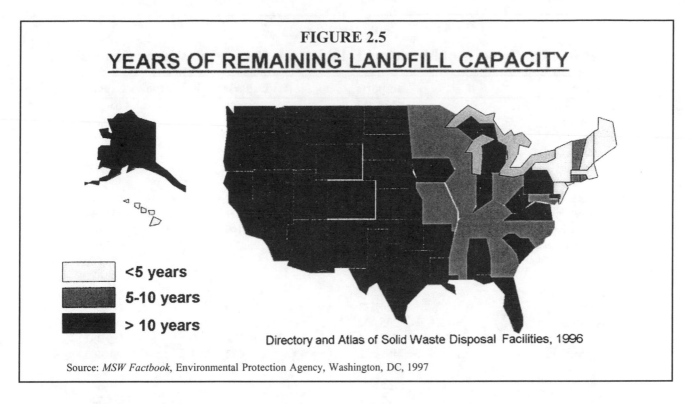

FIGURE 2.5

YEARS OF REMAINING LANDFILL CAPACITY

Legend:
- ☐ <5 years
- ▨ 5-10 years
- ■ > 10 years

Directory and Atlas of Solid Waste Disposal Facilities, 1996

Source: *MSW Factbook*, Environmental Protection Agency, Washington, DC, 1997

In addition, other countries export and import garbage, primarily paper, glass, plastic, or rubber. Canada and Mexico send and receive large amounts of garbage to the United States. Imports to and exports from those countries reflect regional shipments of garbage (as if they were nearby states rather than neighboring countries).

Special Wastes

Certain types of municipal solid waste are particularly challenging to process for waste management facilities, either because of their volume or because they are more toxic than most materials.

Scrap Tires

An estimated 242 million tires are discarded annually (Figure 2.8), 80 percent from passenger cars and the remainder from trucks. This is approximately 1 percent of MSW by weight.

Over 50 percent of the rubber used in the United States is used to make tires. In 1995, approximately 17.5 percent of tires were recycled. The remainder, 3.1 million tons, were landfilled, stockpiled, illegally dumped, or incinerated. The 2 to 4 billion tires that have accumulated in landfills or uncontrolled tire dumps can pose health and fire hazards. Scrap tires are highly combustible, do not compost, and do not degrade easily. The material, primarily hydrocarbons, burns easily, producing noxious, smelly air pollutants and toxic runoff. The tires, which do not compress in landfills, also provide breeding grounds for a variety of pests. In fact, some states ban the disposal of tires in landfills.

Used Motor Oil

A tiny amount of oil can contaminate a lot of water. One gallon — a single oil change — can pollute a million gallons of water. Contaminants often found in used motor oil add to its toxicity.

Approximately 600 million gallons of used motor oil are generated each year in the United States. About 90 percent of the used oil generated by "do-it-yourself" oil changers (200 million gallons) is improperly disposed of. That is equivalent to 18 *Exxon Valdez* spills (see Chapter V) dumped on the ground, poured down the sewers, or thrown in the trash where it will ultimately taint water supplies.

TABLE 2.5

Net Imports/Exports of Municipal Solid Waste, 1997 or latest year (in tons)

State	Imports	Exports	Net Imports/Exports
Pennsylvania	6,340,891	300,000	6,040,000
Virginia	2,800,000	100,000	2,700,000
Michigan	1,691,349	80,356	1,610,993
Indiana	2,116,513	558,827	1,557,686
Oregon	1,136,422	17,000	1,119,422
Kansas	1,150,000	100,000	1,050,000
Wisconsin	1,163,217	191,221	971,996
Mississippi	800,000	15,440	784,560
New Hampshire	817,000	126,000	691,000
South Carolina	453,606	-	453,606
New Mexico	305,529	-	305,529
Nevada	214,683	-	214,683
Alabama	205,000	-	205,000
Kentucky	507,664	308,372	199,292
Connecticut	451,882	261,482	190,400
Tennessee	165,619	4,907	160,712
Ohio	1,018,128	902,388	115,740
Nebraska	122,500	18,203	104,297
Maine	120,000	62,000	58,000
Montana	43,000	-	43,000
West Virginia	254,460	215,000	39,460
Utah	3,511	250	3,261
Georgia	174,772	235,000	-60,228
Iowa	250,000	345,975	-95,975
Florida	-	100,000	-100,000
Idaho	17,000	125,000	-108,000
Rhode Island	-	112,000	-112,000
Texas	104,123	275,000	-170,000
Vermont	-	200,000	-200,000
North Carolina	103,510	326,960	-223,450
Delaware	-	258,860	-258,860
Massachusetts	181,634	502,229	-320,595
Minnesota	-	392,000	-392,000
California	-	453,183	-453,183
Washington	213,336	778,107	-564,771
District of Columbia	-	650,000	-650,000
Ontario, Canada	-	758,000	-758,000
Louisiana	-	800,000	-800,000
Illinois	1,310,306	2,800,000	-1,489,694
Missouri	74,689	1,569,033	-1,494,344
New Jersey	650,000	2,380,683	-1,730,683
Maryland	-	1,832,000	-1,832,000
New York	159,000	3,774,000	-3,615,000

Source: James E. McCarthy, *Interstate Shipment of Municipal Solid Waste: 1998 Update*, Congressional Research Service, The Library of Congress, Washington, DC, 1998

How Garbage Decomposes

In 1992, the Smithsonian Institution reported on its "Garbage Project," an archeological study prepared at the University of Arizona on 14 landfills. Among the findings was the discovery that although *some* degradation takes place initially (sufficient to produce large amounts of methane and other gases), it then slows to a virtual standstill. (Figure 2.9 explains the decomposition process.) The study reported that the volume of old organic matter recovered largely intact turned out to be astonishingly high. Even after two decades, one-third to one-half of supposedly degradable organics remain in recognizable condition. The Smithsonian concluded that well-designed and -managed landfills, in particular, seem more apt to preserve their contents for posterity than to transform them into humus or mulch.

Landfills and the Environment

In this place it takes all the running you can do to keep in the same place. — Red Queen to Alice in *Through the Looking Glass*

Not surprisingly, landfills can lead to many environmental problems. Older landfills were simply big pits dug in the ground into which garbage

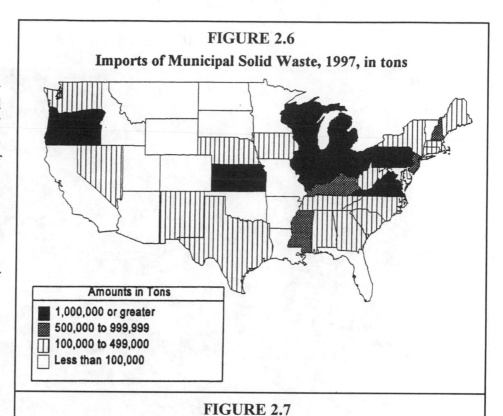

FIGURE 2.6

Imports of Municipal Solid Waste, 1997, in tons

Amounts in Tons
- 1,000,000 or greater
- 500,000 to 999,999
- 100,000 to 499,000
- Less than 100,000

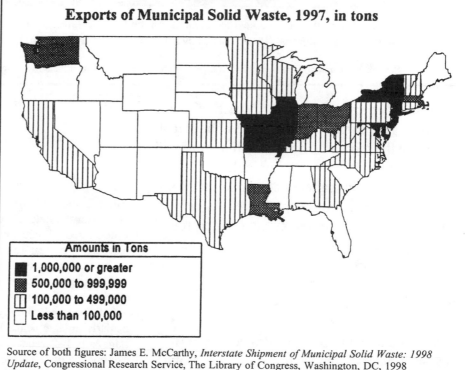

FIGURE 2.7

Exports of Municipal Solid Waste, 1997, in tons

Amounts in Tons
- 1,000,000 or greater
- 500,000 to 999,999
- 100,000 to 499,000
- Less than 100,000

Source of both figures: James E. McCarthy, *Interstate Shipment of Municipal Solid Waste: 1998 Update*, Congressional Research Service, The Library of Congress, Washington, DC, 1998

trucks poured the refuse. When it rained, rainwater dissolved some of the garbage, and it seeped into the ground and contaminated the groundwater. Some water flowed into lakes and rivers, polluting them.

FIGURE 2.8

Of the 242 million tires discarded annually in the United States, many are sent to tire stockpiles and dumps. (Photo by S. Levy, Environmental Protection Agency.)

Source: *The Garbage Primer*, © 1993 League of Women Voters Education Fund. Reprinted with permission.

The most common method of waste disposal is not always the safest. Many experts believe that, even among the most advanced landfills, some will eventually leak. Methane, a flammable gas, is produced when organic matter decomposes in the absence of oxygen. If not properly vented or controlled, it can cause explosions and underground fires that smolder for years. Methane is also deadly to breathe. The Resource Conservation and Recovery Act of 1976 (PL 95-510) requires landfill operators to monitor methane gas.

The Smithsonian "Garbage Project" found that for 15 or 20 years after a landfill stops accepting garbage, the wells still vent methane in fairly substantial amounts. Thereafter, methane production drops off rapidly, indicating that the landfill has stabilized. Increasingly, this gas is being recovered through pipes inserted into landfills and distributed or used to generate energy. Figure 2.10 shows the states that burn methane from landfills for energy.

FIGURE 2.9

HOW GARBAGE DECOMPOSES

Much has been written in the popular press about how garbage does not decompose in a landfill. But it does, eventually, and this is how it happens.

Aerobic Stage: Garbage put in a landfill begins to decompose with the help of oxygen. Aerobic bacteria produce water, carbon dioxide, nitrates, partially degraded organic material, and heat (often 122–158°F). This stage lasts about 2 weeks, until the oxygen is depleted.

Acid Anaerobic Stage: After the oxygen is gone, garbage continues to decompose. Anaerobic bacteria produce carbon dioxide and partially degraded organic material, particularly organic acids. Heat production is reduced. This stage lasts 1–2 years.

Methanogenic Anaerobic Stage: Methane gas is formed as a product of anaerobic decomposition. Methane and carbon dioxide are the dominant chemicals produced. This stage can last several years or decades depending upon landfill conditions (temperature, soil permeability, and water levels). During this stage methane gas can be recovered.

Source: *The Garbage Primer*, © 1993 League of Women Voters Education Fund. Reprinted with permission.

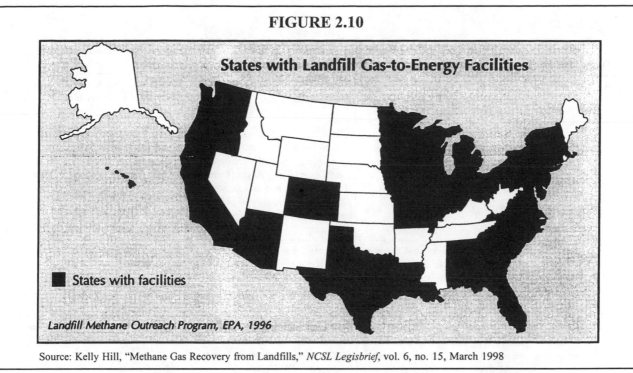

FIGURE 2.10

States with Landfill Gas-to-Energy Facilities

■ States with facilities

Landfill Methane Outreach Program, EPA, 1996

Source: Kelly Hill, "Methane Gas Recovery from Landfills," *NCSL Legisbrief*, vol. 6, no. 15, March 1998

Cadmium

Cadmium is a natural element in the earth's crust that is frequently found in municipal waste. It has many uses, including batteries, pigments, plastics, and metal coatings. The EPA estimates that, by 2000, 2,680 tons of cadmium will be deposited in garbage. Most of that (2,035 tons) will come from batteries. The remainder will come from plastics, consumer electronics, pigments, appliances, glass, and ceramics. When cadmium is ingested by humans through air or water pollution, it can build up in the human body over the years, damaging the lungs, kidneys, nervous system, and stomach. It has also been found to be a carcinogen (causing cancer). (See Table 2.6.)

Lead

Lead, another environmental contaminant, is also found in municipal waste. Lead is a naturally occurring metal found in small amounts in the earth's surface. Humans use lead in batteries, ammunition, solder, pipes, and radiographic X-rays. It can damage virtually every human organ system (Table 2.6). The EPA predicts that by 2000, 281,886 tons of lead will be deposited in municipal waste. That lead comes from lead-acid batter-

ies, consumer electronics, glass and ceramics, plastics, cans, and pigments (Table 2.7). For further discussion of lead, see Chapter IV.

Mercury

Another component of MSW is mercury. Mercury is a naturally occurring metal that may be found both in liquid and gas form. It is used to produce chlorine gas and is used in dental fillings, thermometers, and batteries. Once in ground and surface water, it accumulates in fish that humans may eat. It harms the human nervous system and other body organs (Table 2.6). The EPA estimates that 172.7 tons of mercury will be discarded in garbage in 2000. Most of that will come from household batteries, electric lighting, fever thermometers, electronics, paint residues, and pigments.

Landfills Come Under Regulation

About one-fifth of the hazardous waste sites on the National Priority List for cleanup by Superfund (see Chapter VII — Hazardous Waste) are municipal landfills. Landfills are considered hazardous waste sites because they contain a number of pollutants (Table 2.6).

TABLE 2.6

Some Pollutants Found in the Municipal Waste Stream

Pollutant	Major Health Effects	Some MSW Sources	Comments
Arsenic	Carcinogen. Can cause skin cancer and when inhaled, associated with lung cancer; affects intestines and liver.	Household pesticides, wood preservatives.	Popularly known for its use as a poison in murder mysteries. It is a naturally occurring element used in different household products.
Cadmium	Carcinogen. Damages kidneys; when inhaled, associated with lung cancer.	Nickel-cadmium batteries (used in consumer goods), plastics (used as a stabilizer in polyvinyl chloride (PVC) plastics and as a plastic pigment), paints, enamel pigments, colored printing inks for packaging.	Nickel-cadmium batteries (rechargeable). Batteries account for an estimated 54% of cadmium in the waste stream after recycling (as of 1990).
Chromium	Causes kidney, liver, and nervous and circulatory system damage; respiratory problems; when inhaled, associated with lung cancer.	Pigments for colored papers and paper coating, paints, wood preservatives, batteries: alkaline, lithium cell and zinc-carbon.	A blue-white solid found in rocks and minerals.
Dioxins	Probable carcinogen. Causes liver and kidney damage, gastric ulcers, reproductive and developmental problems.	No natural source. A by-product formed when chlorine-containing products are incompletely burned (e.g., paper, PVC plastics).	EPA is conducting a review of the health risks posed by dioxin, which has been considered a probable carcinogen for many years. The preliminary findings suggest that dioxin may cause damage to immune and reproductive systems and birth defects at very low levels of exposure.
Hydrochloric Acid	Causes respiratory problems and eye irritation.	Paper and PVC plastics.	Hydrochloric acid contributes to the formation of acid rain.
Lead	For children can cause mental retardation and learning disabilities; damages kidneys, liver, brain nerves, and heart; affects blood pressure. Especially toxic to children and pregnant women.	Lead-acid car batteries, electrical equipment, plastics (used as a stabilizer in PVC plastics and as a plastic pigment), colored printing inks for packaging, paints, insecticides.	Although lead-based paints were banned for residential use in 1978, 57 million American homes built before 1980 still contain some lead paint.
Mercury	Causes neurological and kidney damage, blindness; associated with birth defects. Especially toxic to aquatic life.	Most types of consumer batteries, paints, electrical equipment, fluorescent lights, plastics, dyes, thermometers.	Household batteries account for 88% of the total mercury content of municipal solid waste. The use of mercury by U.S. manufacturers declined 33% from 1984 to 1989, primarily due to the virtual elimination of mercury from alkaline batteries.
Methane	Explosive and can cause asphyxiation.	Decomposition of waste in landfills.	Methane is a greenhouse gas.

Sources: Environmental Defense Fund, *Recycling & Incineration: Evaluating the Choices*. INFORM, *Making Less Garbage: A Planning Guide for Communities*, 1990

Under pressure from a lawsuit filed by the Sierra Club, the National Defense Resources Council, and the Friends of the Earth (groups that promote environmental issues), the EPA formulated new standards for landfills that took effect in 1993. Many landfills have subsequently closed. Furthermore, the virtual disappearance of easily affordable environment-impairment liability insurance has forced other dumps to shut down.

TABLE 2.7

SOURCES OF LEAD IN MSW
(in tons)

PRODUCT	1970	1986	2000
Lead -acid batteries	83,525	138,043	181,546
Consumer electronics	12,233	58,536	85,032
Glass & ceramics	3,365	7,956	8,910
Plastics	1,613	3,577	3,228
Soldered cans	24,117	2,052	787
Pigments	27,020	1,131	682
All others	12,567	2,537	1,701
TOTAL	**164,440**	**213,832**	**281,886**

Source: *MSW Factbook*, Environmental Protection Agency, Washington, DC, 1997

The Resource Conservation and Recovery Act (RCRA; PL 95-510) requires landfill operators to do several things to lessen the chance of pollution:

- The most important standard requires landfills to monitor ground water for contaminants.

- Dump sites must have plastic liners, and debris must be covered with soil every day to prevent odors and trash from being blown away. (Figure 2.11 diagrams a modern landfill with liner.)

- Methane gas must be monitored, and a landfill owner is responsible for cleanup of any contamination.

These rules must be observed for a 30-year period after the landfill is closed to prevent pollution of the environment. Some communities were not able to afford the cost of complying with all the regulations and were forced to close their landfills.

Even if cities rely heavily on incinerators (see below) and recycle more, landfills will always play an important role in disposing of garbage. Some waste, such as concrete blocks or steel beams from construction, and appliances, such as old washers and dryers or electric can openers, cannot be burned. Furthermore, if all of the remaining garbage were burned, there would still be tons of ash left over that would have to be dumped into landfills.

Fresh Kills Landfill

Perhaps the most ominous example of the nation's garbage problem sits on New York's Staten Island (Figure 2.12). Listed in the *Guiness Book of World Records* as the largest in the world, the 50-year-old Fresh Kills landfill — New York's one remaining landfill — is about as massive as the largest of the Egyptian pyramids in height and volume. The landfill covers approximately 2,200 acres. More than 500 people work on site 24 hours a day, six days a week. Every day, 18 barges, carrying a total of 10,000 tons of garbage, transport municipal waste from the city's marine transfer stations to the landfill. Approximately 75,000 people live within one mile of the site.

When it closes on December 31, 2001, Fresh Kills will be more than 500 feet tall and will rival

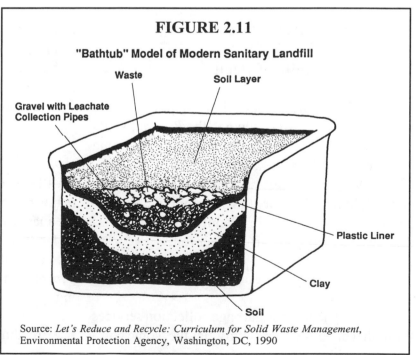

FIGURE 2.11

"Bathtub" Model of Modern Sanitary Landfill

Waste

Soil Layer

Gravel with Leachate Collection Pipes

Plastic Liner

Clay

Soil

Source: *Let's Reduce and Recycle: Curriculum for Solid Waste Management*, Environmental Protection Agency, Washington, DC, 1990

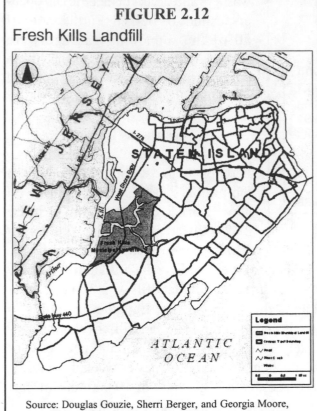

FIGURE 2.12

Fresh Kills Landfill

ATLANTIC
OCEAN

Legend

Source: Douglas Gouzie, Sherri Berger, and Georgia Moore, "Fresh Kills — Teamwork Leads to Better Understanding of Potential Landfill Health Effects," *Hazardous Substances & Public Health*, vol. 8, no. 2, Winter 1998

the Great Wall of China as the largest man-made structure in the world. Fresh Kills, which opened in 1948 on a swampy lowland, will soon be the tallest "mountain" on the Atlantic coast between Florida and Maine. The city plans to turn it into a grass-covered park.

Landfill Tipping Fees

Landfills charge disposal or "tipping fees" to use their facilities. According to the *Biocycle* study (see above), in 1998, the national average tipping fee was $33.60 per ton, an increase of about $2 from 1997. The highest tipping fees are located, in general, in the Northeast; in Vermont, it costs $65 per ton to deposit trash in a landfill. Wyoming has the lowest tipping fee, at $10 per ton.

Pay-As-You-Throw

Rather than pay for garbage collection services through a tax bill or a monthly flat fee, some com-

munities have instituted "unit pricing," a fee for the amount of garbage set on the curb. The unit systems encourage recycling. There are four types of unit pricing systems:

- Can systems — disposal systems based on the number of cans set on the curb.

- Bag systems — prepaid tags and stickers.

- Two-tiered systems — a flat fee for a set number of bags or cans and additional fees for extra bags.

- Weight-based systems — charges based on weight collected.

In the United States today, more than 2,000 communities charge residents by the amount they discard. In 1996, the National Conference of State Legislatures reported that municipalities using unit pricing showed reductions of 25 to 45 percent in the amounts of trash collected and hauled to landfills.

Privatization

Private companies collect more than 80 percent of the nation's garbage, either under contract to government agencies or working for local residents. Approximately 40 percent of all municipalities rely on private collectors for trash collection. Refuse collection by private contractors costs from 28 percent to 40 percent less than what public agencies generally spend for the same service.

Illegal Dumping

Illegal dumping is a growing problem. One major reason is that disposal costs (tipping fees) are increasing. In addition, the declining number of landfills, often at distant locations, has led to increased illegal dumping. Illegal dumping endangers human health and the environment by becoming

- Breeding grounds for pests.

- Safety hazards to children.

- Sources of pollutants.

- Disruptions of wildlife habitat.

Landfills of the Twenty-First Century

Landfills are, and will continue to be, the cornerstone of any U.S. waste service system. A number of changes will likely occur in site design and function. Sites will become more consistent and standardized, especially regarding liners and the collection of landfill gas. This is expected to stimulate the development of new landfill gas-to-energy plants.

The *Biocycle* study reported that the number of landfills declined by 200 in 1998, the smallest reduction since that organization began its study. The toughened standards and the need for operators to provide assurances that they could fund closure, cleanup, and security in the event of contamination caused the decrease in the number of landfills. The slowing rate of decline likely indicates that the remaining landfills meet these tough standards.

According to *Biocycle*, there is as much, if not more, landfill capacity available in the United States as there has been at any time in the past 20 years. Regionally, the West has the greatest capacity. Some states have enough to carry them well into the 2000s. Wyoming, for example, has enough to last 100 years, Nevada for 75 years. On the other hand, the nation is experiencing a dearth of socially and politically acceptable sites to put landfills. Federal, state, and local rules for siting and operating waste facilities, particularly landfills, are becoming more stringent (see Federal Regulation below).

A Changing Landfill

Since it will be difficult to economically justify small-scale local sites, there will likely be fewer, larger, and more regional operations in the next decades. Most waste will move away from its point of generation, resulting in increased interdependence among communities and states in waste disposal. More waste will cross state lines.

Landfilling is expected to continue to be the single most predominant MSW management method. Landfills will provide more diverse services — burial of waste, bioremediation (see Chapter VI), reuse facilities, leachate (fluid drainage) collection, and gas recovery. To make landfills more acceptable to neighborhoods, operators will likely establish larger buffer zones, use more green space, and show more sensitivity to land-use compatibility and landscaping.

COMBUSTION (INCINERATION)

According to the EPA, approximately 16.9 percent of MSW is incinerated. (*BioCycle*'s "State of Garbage in America — 1999," compiled from data provided by the states, reports an incineration rate of 7.5 percent of MSW, down from 10 percent in 1997.) Some observers think incinerators are the best alternative to landfills, and many experts believe they are good additions to landfills in any waste disposal system. In past years, it was common to burn MSW in incinerators to reduce volume. In the 1980s, however, MSW combustion began to incorporate recovery of energy (steam or electricity). Those facilities are called waste-to-energy (WTE) facilities. The resulting energy reduces the amount needed from other sources, and the sale of the energy helps offset the cost of operating the facility.

Industry representatives claim that power produced by incineration is one of the cleanest sources of power. The process destroys bacteria, pathogens, and other elements often found in garbage, and burning cuts MSW volume by about 90 percent. Incinerators, however, produce ash, which can be toxic.

In 1999, there were 119 incinerators in the United States, with an average design capacity of 2,445 tons/day. Although the Northeast had the largest number of incinerators (12), the Midwest had the highest design capacity, at 1,700 tons a day. Another 12 combustors were planned or under construction. They normally operate at an estimated 85 percent capacity over the course of a year. The Northeast had the most combustion capacity, followed by the South. Thirty-nine states have built incinerators or plan to build them in the near future. In addition, there were 112 waste-to-energy (WTE) facilities in the United States, with a design capacity of 101,360 tons per day.

Incinerators vary greatly in size. Smaller ones may burn only about 25 tons of garbage a day, while larger ones may burn up to 4,000 tons of garbage in a single day. Incinerators are very expensive to build. The country's largest incinerator, in Detroit, cost $438 million. This huge incinerator produces enough steam to heat half of Detroit's central business district and enough electricity to supply 40,000 homes. However, most experts agree that energy recovery from MSW has only a limited potential for contributing to the nation's overall energy production. Although the current contribution of waste-derived energy production is less than one-half of 1 percent of the nation's total energy supply, the Department of Energy has set a goal for energy from waste at 2 percent of the total supply by 2010.

Figure 2.13 shows a typical WTE system. At this incinerator, the trucks dump waste into a pit. The waste is moved to the furnace by a crane. The furnace burns the waste at a very high temperature, heating a boiler that produces steam for generating electricity and heat. Ash collects at the bottom of the furnace where it is later removed and taken to a landfill to be thrown out.

The Problem with Dioxin, Mercury, and Other Dangerous Wastes

An emerging body of information suggests that dioxin contamination has reached a level that may pose a large-scale, longterm public health risk. Of particular concern are dioxin's effects on reproduction,

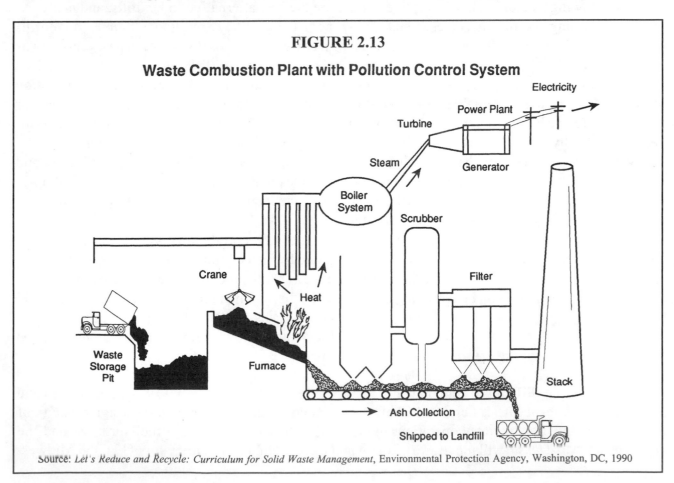

FIGURE 2.13

Waste Combustion Plant with Pollution Control System

Source: *Let's Reduce and Recycle: Curriculum for Solid Waste Management*, Environmental Protection Agency, Washington, DC, 1990

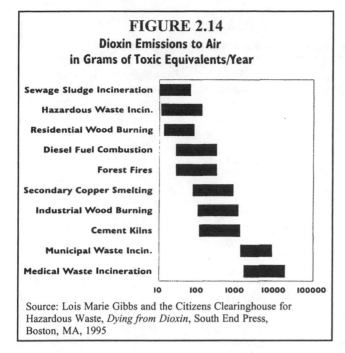

FIGURE 2.14
Dioxin Emissions to Air
in Grams of Toxic Equivalents/Year

Sewage Sludge Incineration
Hazardous Waste Incin.
Residential Wood Burning
Diesel Fuel Combustion
Forest Fires
Secondary Copper Smelting
Industrial Wood Burning
Cement Kilns
Municipal Waste Incin.
Medical Waste Incineration

10   100   1000   10000   100000

Source: Lois Marie Gibbs and the Citizens Clearinghouse for Hazardous Waste, *Dying from Dioxin*, South End Press, Boston, MA, 1995

development, immune system function, and carcinogenesis. — U.S. Public Health Service, *Public Health Reports*, 1996

Most experts, however, believe that incineration can never serve as a primary method of garbage disposal. They contend that incineration can best be used to augment landfill and recycling methods because (1) it produces residue that must then be landfilled and (2) it produces dangerous poisonous gases, primarily dioxin and mercury.

In the process of burning paints, fluorescent lights, batteries, or electronics, mercury is released as a gaseous vapor poisonous to humans and the environment. Mercury is largely impossible to screen with pollution control devices such as scrubbers.

Burning garbage gives off tiny amounts of dioxins and furans, two very dangerous chemicals, and the ash left after the burning also contains dangerous wastes. Ash is a substantial by-product of incinerated garbage. An incinerator that burns 1,000 tons of trash per day can generate between 200 and 250 tons of ash a day as residue.

Dioxin is the common name for a family of approximately 75 chemicals with similar proper-

ties and toxicity. Dioxins are not deliberately manufactured — they are the unintended by-products of industrial processes that involve chlorine or processes that burn chlorine with organic matter. Incinerators provide an ideal environment for dioxin production — plenty of chlorine sources and precursors to dioxin combined with sufficient heat to drive the reactions that produce dioxin. As shown in Figure 2.14, incineration produces dioxin from many different sources.

Dioxin is a stable compound that accumulates in the human body over a lifetime. It was identified in the 1970s as a very potent carcinogen. In 1997, the International Agency for Research on Cancer listed dioxin as a "known" carcinogen. The EPA calculates the average level of dioxin in the body of a middle-aged person to be 9 nanograms (a nanogram is one-billionth of a gram) per kilogram (ng/kg). The EPA believes the minimum level for causing harm in humans is 14 ng/kg. Table 2.8 shows the levels known to produce harm in various organisms.

In the United States, municipal waste incineration is the major known source of dioxin emissions, accounting for 95 percent of dioxin produced. Human exposure occurs principally through eating food, especially meat and fish, that has ingested dioxin. New regulations require that scrub-

TABLE 2.8

Levels of Dioxin Known to Cause Health Problems

Body Burden (ng/kg)	Species	Health Effect
7	Mice	Increased susceptibility to viruses
7	Monkeys	Altered immune response
14	Humans	Altered glucose tolerance
14	Humans	Decreased testes size
19	Monkeys	Learning disability
54	Monkeys	Endometriosis
64	Rats	Decreased sperm count
83	Humans	Decreased testosterone

Source: Lois Marie Gibbs and the Citizens Clearinghouse for Hazardous Waste, *Dying from Dioxin*, South End Press, Boston, MA, 1995

bers, which pull the pollutants out of the smoke, be put on smokestacks to catch the dioxins and furans. The Environmental Protection Agency (EPA) and Congress have not yet decided how to handle the ash.

RECYCLING

Recycling has become more important to towns and cities because of the environmental problems caused by landfills and incinerators. As a result, the proportion of municipal waste handled by recycling has been increasing, rising from 6.7 percent in 1960 to about 28 percent in 1997. *BioCycle*'s 1998 study estimated 31.5 percent of MSW was being recycled (Table 2.3).

Before recyclable materials can be recycled into new products, they must be collected. Most residential recycling involves curbside collection, drop-off programs, buy-back operations, and/or container deposit systems. In 1998, every state except Hawaii had at least one program. That year, there were 9,349 curbside collection programs in the United States, up from 7,000 in 1995. Those programs served 139.4 million Americans, 54 percent of the population. (See Table 2.9.)

Processing recyclable materials is performed at materials recovery facilities (MRFs). There were 380 MRFs in the United States in 1997, up from 310 in 1995. Those MRFs processed an estimated 32,088 tons

TABLE 2.9

Residential curbside recycling and yard trimmings composting sites (by state)

State	Curbside Programs[1]	Curbside Population Served	Percentage of Population Served	Yard Trimming Sites
Alabama	38	1,020,000	23	20
Alaska	1	10,000	2	0
Arizona	32	1,810,000	39	23
Arkansas[2]	41	400,000	16	22
California	511	18,000,000	55	74
Colorado[2]	70	700,000	18	11[2]
Connecticut	169	3,270,000	100	65
Delaware	3	5,000	1	3
Dist. of Columbia	1	250,000	48	0
Florida	315	11,070,000	74	35[2]
Georgia	179	3,988,000	52	169
Hawaii	0	0	0	9
Idaho[2]	6	200,000	16	7[2]
Illinois[2]	450	6,000,000	50	55[2]
Indiana	169	4,133,000	70	51[2]
Iowa	574	1,500,000	52	57
Kansas	101	n/a	n/a	70[2]
Kentucky	43	n/a	n/a	37
Louisiana[2]	33	2,000,000	46	21
Maine	84	400,000	32	50[2]
Maryland	100	4,004,000	78	17
Massachusetts	156	4,758,000	77	250[2]
Michigan	200	2,500,000	25	120[2]
Minnesota	771	3,600,000	76	433
Mississippi	15	420,000	15	9
Missouri	197	2,100,000	39	97
Montana	6	8,000	1	32[2]
Nebraska	15	425,000	26	5
Nevada	8	397,000	23	1
New Hampshire	38	433,000	37	103[2]
New Jersey	510	7,300,000	90	171
New Mexico	3	400,000	23	5
New York	1,472	17,230,000	95	200
North Carolina	271	3,500,000	46	120
North Dakota	25	90,000	14	50
Ohio	372	6,600,000	59	458
Oklahoma	8	639,000	19	4
Oregon	122	1,830,000	56	50
Pennsylvania	879	8,800,000	73	329
Rhode Island	26	860,000	71	21
South Carolina	186	507,000	13	69[2]
South Dakota	3	158,000	21	10
Tennessee	35	n/a	n/a	46
Texas	159	4,700,000	24	166
Utah[2]	14	265,000	13	14
Vermont	80	111,000	19	14
Virginia	79	4,500,000	66	11[2]
Washington	102	5,000,000	88	17[2]
West Virginia	75	500,000	28	22
Wisconsin	600	3,000,000	57	176
Wyoming	2	24,000	5	8
Total	9,349	139,415,000	54	3,807

n/a - Information not available; [1] Municipal, county and other curbside programs available to residents; [2] Based on information from the 1998 State of Garbage in America

Source: Jim Glenn, "The State of Garbage in America," *BioCycle*, vol. 40, no. 4, April 1999

per day. The most extensive use of MRFs was in the Northeast. MRFs vary widely across the nation, depending on the incoming materials and the technology used to sort the materials. The majority of MRFs are classified as low technology, meaning the materials are sorted manually. (For more information on recycling, see Chapter III.)

PACKAGING

The EPA reports that containers and packaging account for 33 percent of all municipal waste (Table 2.2). Containers and packaging are made of a number of materials: paper and paperboard, glass, steel, aluminum, plastics, wood, and small amounts of other materials.

Nearly $1 out of every $12 Americans spend for food and beverage pays for packaging. According to the United States Department of Agriculture, packaging is the second largest portion of the cost of marketing food, accounting for 8 percent of food expenditures. Packaging has become an issue of environmental concern. Many Americans say they would pay more for a product with environmental benefits. Marketing that considers these consumer preferences based on environmental concerns is known as "green marketing."

The increasing numbers of women in the work force and changes in family structure, such as more, but smaller, households and more single adults, have resulted in greater demand for convenience products — carry-out meals, frozen foods, and vacuum-packed foods. Since 1970, the U.S. population has grown by 23 percent, and single-person households increased by 73 percent. MSW discards grew by 43 percent.

The Resource Conservation and Recovery Act (RCRA; PL 95-510) requires that, as of 1993, primary packaging, which includes containers for beverages, soaps, and paints, must be collected by retailers and recycled. To encourage consumers to return the packaging, containers for liquids are subject to deposits. At least 80 percent of all packages must be recycled to the greatest extent possible. The law requires that containers for beer, wine, soft drinks, bottled water, and fruit juice be refillable.

Aluminum

Soft-drink consumption has risen, and along with it, can and plastic container use has increased. Aluminum, the most abundant metal on earth, makes up about 8 percent of the surface of the earth.

TABLE 2.10
PLASTIC RESIN CHARACTERISTICS, MARKETS, AND PRODUCTS

Resin Name	Characteristics	Primary Product Markets	Product Examples
Low–Density Polyethylene (LDPE)	Moisture–proof; inert	Packaging	Garbage bags; coated papers
Polyvinyl Chloride (PVC)	Clear; brittle unless modified with plasticizers	Building and construction; packaging	Construction pipe; meat wrap; cooking oil bottles
High–Density Polyethylene (HDPE)	Flexible; translucent	Packaging	Milk and detergent bottles; boil–in–bag pouches
Polypropylene (PP)	Stiff; heat– and chemical-resistant	Furniture; packaging	Syrup bottles; yogurt tubs; office furniture
Polystyrene (PS)	Brittle; clear; good thermal properties	Packaging; consumer products	Disposable foam dishes and cups; cassette tape cases
Polyethylene Terephthalate (PET)	Tough; shatterproof	Packaging; consumer products	Soft drink bottles; food and medicine containers

Source: *Methods to Manage and Control Plastic Wastes*, Environmental Protection Agency, Washington, DC, 1995

It is not found free in nature; it is always combined with another element, such as oxygen, silicon, and fluorine. Scientists first refined the metal into a valuable product in the 1820s. Its use has continually expanded; beverage cans are currently the largest single use of aluminum. The Aluminum Association reported that, in 1995, approximately half of all aluminum was recovered for reuse.

Plastics

The word "plastics" comes from the Greek word "plastikos," which means "to form." Today, the term refers to a wide range of flexible materials that can be molded or shaped into products such as fast-food packages, compact discs, contact lenses, and surgical sutures.

The advent of low-priced petrochemicals ushered in the age of plastics. The plastics industry in the United States dates from the work of researcher John Wesley Hyatt in the 1860s. In 1939, nylon stockings were introduced at the World's Fair, and, in 1940, plastic ornaments decorated the Christmas tree in Rockefeller Center. World War II spurred the development of new kinds of plastics and a major growth in the industry. The 1955 Corvette was the first car to use plastic parts, and in 1982, Dr. Robert Jarvik designed the first artificial heart made largely of plastic.

The industry today is huge. Several times more plastics — a family of more than 45 types — are now produced in the United States than aluminum and all other nonferrous (non-iron) metals combined. Most of these plastics are non-biodegradable and, once discarded, remain relatively intact for many years. The EPA predicts that the amount of plastic thrown away will continue to increase.

The six most common thermoplastics (the 80 to 90 percent of plastics that are formed by cooling rather than by chemical reactions) are Low Density Polyethylene (LDPE) and High Density Polyethylene (HDPE), Polystyrene (PS), Polypropylene (PP), Polyethylene Terephthalate (PET), and Polyvinyl Chloride (PVC). These types account for 68 percent of all plastics produced in the United States and 97 percent of all plastic used in packaging, the object of most of the debate about plastics in the MSW stream. Table 2.10 shows the characteristics of these types of plastics.

Plastics represent 9.9 percent of MSW by weight (Figure 2.2). One way to reduce the quantity of waste is to trim the amount of packaging. Manufacturing changes in the design of containers have reduced the weight of aluminum and plastic containers. Packaging products in larger containers (with multiple rather than single items) also can reduce the overall amount of plastic packaging used.

Foam Packaging

Foam containers are another environmental threat associated with packaging. One-half of all foam packaging is inflated with chlorofluorocarbons. These chemicals escape into the atmosphere and damage the ozone layer, while the packaging adds to waste disposal problems. Manufacturers of "aseptic" beverage containers ("juice boxes") have been banned in some states on the grounds that the boxes are difficult to recycle because they consist of layers of three different substances — paper, plastic, and aluminum — that must be separated.

In 1990, the McDonald's Corporation, the nation's largest fast-food restaurant, and the Environmental Defense Fund (EDF) formed a joint task force to find ways to reduce McDonald's solid waste by 80 percent through source reduction, reuse, recycling, and composting. One of the task force decisions was to replace the polystyrene "clamshell" with paper-based, polyethylene wraps that reduce packaging waste by more than 70 percent. Many other fast-food restaurants have introduced similar packaging.

How Another Nation Does It — Plastics in Germany

In Germany, the national government took the lead in plastics regulation in 1991, enacting a packaging law based on the principle that those who create packaging are responsible for taking it back. Beginning in 1992, all secondary packaging — blister packs, films, tamper-proof packaging — must be taken back by retailers at the point of sale if the consumer desires. Much of this is plastic.

The Positive Side of Packaging

No one ever buys just a package. The package is a conveyor, a piece of the distribution system that protects, preserves, and holds the product on its journey from the manufacturer to the store and, ultimately, the consumer. Then it is discarded.

Packaging is an integral part of the most efficient distribution system in the world. Packaging has many benefits. In developing countries, 30-50 percent of food is lost between producer and consumer. Approximately 20 percent of China's food supply spoils before reaching the consumer. The United Nations estimates that improved packaging would reduce crop losses by 5 percent.

Packaging helps reduce disease. There are more than 12 million cases of foodborne disease each year. Packaging prevents bacterial growth on food and ensures that medical supplies reach hospitals undamaged. While packaging represents 8 percent of the price of food and beverage, without the protection of packaging, food and beverages would cost even more due to spoilage and damage, perhaps as much as 20 percent. Packaging reduces the amount of inedible food waste in the municipal waste stream and makes "seasonal" produce available nearly year-round.

Packaging protects against tampering of medications and foods, provides convenience in preparing meals, and enables the fast-food industry to give Americans the precious commodity of time. Latchkey children, single adults, and the elderly all benefit from single-serve, small-quantity packages. In addition, the packaging industry employs two million people in the United States, a $75-$80 billion a year business.

Distribution Packaging

Part of the packaging and distribution system is largely unseen. About one-half of all packaging is primary consumer packaging — the familiar bottles, jars, cartons, wraps, and other containers found on a typical store shelf. The other half of packaging is used to transport products from manufacturers to retailers and consumers.

Distribution packaging can take many forms, such as corrugated boxes and trays, wood or plastic pallets, stretchfilm ("shrink-wrap"), molded plastic foam, or plastic and paper bags. Products are routinely sold in quantities by truckloads or pallets.

The primary purpose of distribution packaging is to ensure that products arrive at their destination safely and securely, unharmed by hazards in transport and warehousing — temperature changes, vibration, compression, puncturing, biological contamination, and pilferage.

The fresh meat industry reflects the changes in the U.S. packaging and distribution system. Until a few years ago, beef was shipped from processors to stores as sides of beef on a hook swinging in refrigerated trucks or rail cars. Since fresh meat is sensitive to dehydration, oxygen, and bacterial contamination, shelf life was about one week, and maintaining a large inventory was impossible.

Today, beef is vacuum-packed in thin multi-layer plastic bags with an oxygen barrier. Packaging beef at the processor, instead of at the store, lowers transportation and processing costs since less waste — bones, fat, etc. — is shipped and rail cars can be packed more efficiently. The shelf life for vacuum-packaged beef is four to six weeks. About 95 percent of beef is now shipped in vacuum barrier bags.

About 48 percent of products sold in grocery stores are non-perish-ables packed in cans, bottles, boxes, and jars. To ensure that packages arrive undamaged at the stores, manufacturers use corrugated boxing and wood pallets. While packaging is absolutely essential in getting food to the table, manufacturers are reassessing their delivery systems to see if some packaging can be modified, or even eliminated, to cut down on waste.

(food wastes, yard trimmings) through composting or other on-site alternatives to disposal.

Table 2.11 shows examples of source reduction practices.

SOURCE REDUCTION

Source reduction is gaining more attention as an important option in solid waste management. Often called "waste prevention," source reduction is defined by the EPA as "any change in the design, manufacturing, purchase, or use of materials or products (including packing) to reduce the amount or toxicity before they become MSW. Source reduction means *using less material* in a package, reducing the volume of packaging material that must be recycled or discarded *after* consumption. Prevention also refers to the reuse of products or materials." Source reduction activities affect the waste stream before the point of generation. (See Figure 2.15.)

Source reduction measures include

- Redesigning products or packages to reduce the quantity of materials or the toxicity of materials used, substituting lighter materials for heavier ones, and lengthening the life of products to postpone disposal.

- Using packaging that reduces damage or spoilage to a product.
- Reusing packages or products already manufactured.

- Managing non-product organic wastes

TRENDS IN
SOLID WASTE MANAGEMENT

In the past decade, the management of solid waste has become a major public concern. Municipalities nationwide have upgraded waste management programs and attempted to deal with public concern over waste issues. In most areas of the country, state and local governments have played the lead role in transforming solid waste management. Private waste management firms have also been involved, often under contract or franchise agreements with local governments. Private firms manage most of the commercial waste, which comprises about 40 percent of MSW. Increasingly, they also collect residential waste, the remaining 60 percent of MSW.

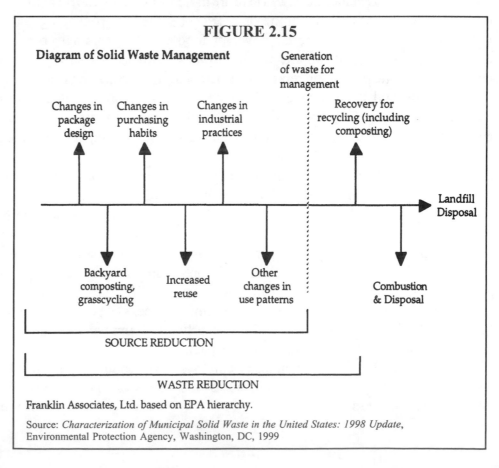

FIGURE 2.15

Diagram of Solid Waste Management

Franklin Associates, Ltd. based on EPA hierarchy.

Source: *Characterization of Municipal Solid Waste in the United States: 1998 Update*, Environmental Protection Agency, Washington, DC, 1999

TABLE 2.11

SELECTED EXAMPLES OF SOURCE REDUCTION PRACTICES

Source Reduction Practice	MSW Product Categories			
	Durable Goods	Nondurable Goods	Containers & Packaging	Organics
Redesign				
Materials reduction	• Downgauge metals in appliances	• Paperless purchase orders	• Concentrates	• Xeriscaping
Materials substitution	• Use of composites in appliances and electronic circuitry		• Cereal in bags • Coffee brick • Multi-use products	
Lengthen life	• High mileage tires • Electronic components reduce moving parts	• Regular servicing • Look at warranties • Extend warranties	• Design for secondary uses	
Consumer Practices				
	• Purchase long lived products	• Repair • Duplexing • Sharing • Reduce unwanted mail	• Purchasing: products in bulk, concentrates	
Reuse				
By design	• Modular design	• Envelopes	• Pallets • Returnable secondary packaging	
Secondary	• Borrow or rent for temporary use • Give to charity • Buy or sell at garage sales	• Clothing • Waste paper scratch pads	• Loosefill • Grocery sacks • Dairy containers • Glass and plastic jars	
Reduce/Eliminate Toxins				
	• Eliminate PCBs	• Soy ink, waterbased • Waterbased solvents • Reduce mercury	• Replace lead foil on wine bottles	
Reduce Organics				
Food wastes				• Backyard composting • Vermi-composting
Yard trimmings				• Backyard composting • Grasscycling

Source: *Characterization of Municipal Solid Waste in the United States: 1998 Update*, Environmental Protection Agency, Washington, DC, 1999

The Federal Role in MSW Management

The federal government, however, does play a key role in waste management. Its legislation has set landfill standards under the Resource Conservation and Recovery Act (see above). The Clean Air Act (PL 91-604 and subsequent reauthorization) set incinerator and landfill emission standards. Table 2.12 shows federal regulations involving waste management.

Some of these laws have been controversial, resulting in legal challenges. Consequently, the federal government has also had an effect on waste management programs through federal court rulings. In a series of recent rulings, including Su-

preme Court decisions, federal courts have held that shipments of waste are protected under the interstate commerce clause of the U.S. Constitution (*Chemical Waste Management, Inc. v. Hunt* [504 U.S. 334, 1992]). As a result, state and local governments may not prohibit landfills from accepting waste from out-of-state, nor may they impose fees on waste disposal that discriminate on the basis of origin.

Flow Control Laws

Flow control laws require private waste collectors to dispose of their waste in specific landfills. State and/or local governments institute these laws to guarantee that any new landfill they build

TABLE 2.12
Federal Regulations on Solid Waste Management

Authority	Regulation	Status	EPA Annual Cost Estimate
RCRA Subtitle D	Municipal Solid Waste Landfill Criteria:	Promulgated 10/9/91, with some subsequent modifications	$330,000,000
	location, design, and operating	effective 10/9/93 for large landfills, 4/9/94 for others	
	groundwater monitoring, and corrective action	requirements phased in; final compliance deadline 10/9/97	
	closure and post-closure care	effective 10/9/93 for large landfills, 4/9/94 for others	
	financial assurance criteria	effective 4/97	
RCRA Subtitle D	Non-Municipal Solid Waste Landfill Criteria	Promulgated 7/1/96; requirements took effect 18 months to 2 years after promulgation	$12,650,000 - 51,000,000
Clean Air Act, Section 111	Air Emissions from Municipal Solid Waste Landfills	Promulgated 3/12/96; effective immediately for new landfills	$94,000,000
Clean Air Act, Sections 111 and 129	Emissions from Municipal Solid Waste Combustors (Incinerators):		
	combustion practices, carbon monoxide, dioxins/furans, particulates, acid gases, nitrogen oxides; applied only to combustors with capacity of 250 tons per day or more	Promulgated 2/11/91; effective 8/12/91	$472,000,000
	maximum achievable control technology for carbon monoxide; dioxins, particulate matter, cadmium, lead, mercury, sulfur dioxide, hydrogen chloride, nitrogen oxides; applies to incinerators with capacity of 35 metric tons per day or more	Promulgated 12/19/95; effective one year after promulgation for combustors with capacity >250 tons per day, three years after promulgation for others	$405,000,000
RCRA Sections 3001 - 3005	Management of Ash from Municipal Waste Combustors (Incinerators)	Supreme Court ruled May 2, 1994, that ash was not exempt from hazardous waste management regulations, despite EPA guidance to the contrary. Hazardous waste testing and management regulations were promulgated 5/19/80, with many subsequent amendments.	not available
Executive Orders 12873 and 13101; RCRA Section 6002	Federal Procurement of Recycled Products	Procurement guidelines for paper, retread tires, used oil and insulation materials took effect in 1988. Executive Orders 12873 (10/20/93) and 13101 (9/14/98) strengthened paper requirements. EPA designated an additional 19 recycled content product categories for procurement preferences 5/1/95; 12 product categories were added 11/13/97; and 19 more were proposed for addition 8/26/98.	not available

Source: James E. McCarthy, *Solid Waste Issues in the 106th Congress*, Congressional Research Service, The Library of Congress, Washington, DC, 1999

will be used. That way, when they sell bonds to get the money to build a new landfill, the bond purchasers will not worry that they will not be repaid. Since 1980, about $10 billion in municipal bonds have been issued to pay to build solid waste facilities. In many of those cases, flow control authority was used to guarantee the investment. Flow control also benefits recycling plants where recycling is financed by fees collected at incinerators or landfills. In the process, however, a monopoly is created, prohibiting facilities outside a jurisdiction from offering competitive services. As a result, there have been a number of court challenges.

In 1994, the Supreme Court, in *C & A Carbone v. Clarkstown* (511 US 383), held that flow control violates the interstate commerce clause. In response, however, many local governments have strongly pushed for the restoration of flow control authority. They have appealed to Congress, with its authority to regulate interstate commerce, to restore the use of flow control. Thus far, proposed bills that addressed flow control have failed.

In 1997, a federal district court, in *Atlantic Coast Demolition and Recycling Inc. v. Atlantic County* (112 F 3d 652), overturned New Jersey's flow control requirements. As a result, much of New Jersey's waste leaves the state because of cheaper disposal elsewhere. In Minnesota, meanwhile, a federal district court, in *Ben Oehrleins, Inc. v. Hennepin County* (GA8 N.96-2120, 1997*)*, ruled in favor of waste haulers who claimed that a county was liable for damages resulting from enforcement of flow control ordinances. The jury awarded the plaintiffs $7.1 million as compensation for the higher costs they were forced to pay as a result of flow control programs.

TABLE 2.13

PROJECTIONS OF MATERIALS GENERATED* IN THE MUNICIPAL WASTE STREAM: 2000 AND 2005
(In thousands of tons and percent of total generation)

Materials	Million tons 2000	Million tons 2005	% of total 2000	% of total 2005
Paper and Paperboard	87.7	94.8	39.3%	39.6%
Glass	11.9	11.2	5.3%	4.7%
Metals	17.6	18.7	7.9%	7.8%
Plastics	23.4	26.7	10.5%	11.2%
Wood	14.0	15.8	6.3%	6.6%
Others	19.7	22.2	8.8%	9.3%
Total Materials in Products	174.3	189.4	78.1%	79.1%
Other Wastes				
Food Wastes	22.5	23.5	10.1%	9.8%
Yard Trimmings	23.0	23.0	10.3%	9.6%
Miscellaneous Inorganic Wastes	3.4	3.6	1.5%	1.5%
Total Other Wastes	48.9	50.1	21.9%	20.9%
Total MSW Generated	223.2	239.5	100.0%	100.0%

* Generation before materials recovery or combustion.
Details may not add to totals due to rounding.
Franklin Associates

Source: *Characterization of Municipal Solid Waste in the United States: 1998 Update*, Environmental Protection Agency, Washington, DC, 1999

Recycling Issues

In 1996, Congress passed the National Highway System Designation Act (PL 104-59), which repealed federal requirements that up to 20 percent of the asphalt pavement used in federal highway projects had to contain rubber-modified asphalt made from scrap tires or other recovered materials. The original provision, contained in the Intermodal Surface Transportation Efficiency Act of 1991 (PL 102-240), was widely opposed by state highway officials and the paving industry.

Also in 1996, Congress passed PL 104-142 (known as the "battery recycling bill"), prohibiting the use of mercury in batteries, requiring labels encouraging proper disposal and recycling, and exempting certain battery collection and recycling programs from some hazardous waste requirements.

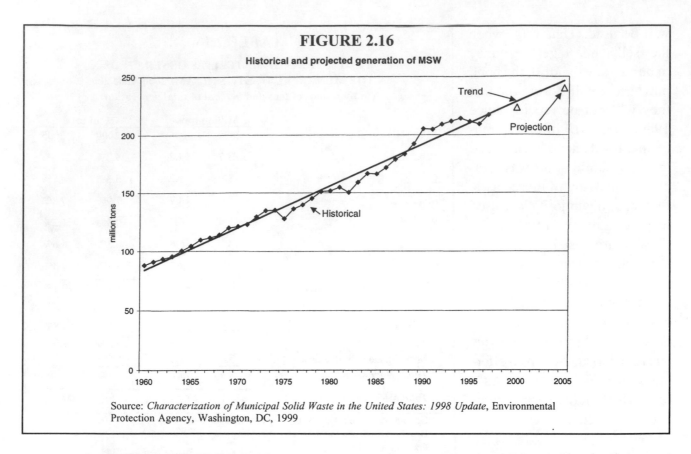

FIGURE 2.16

Historical and projected generation of MSW

Source: *Characterization of Municipal Solid Waste in the United States: 1998 Update*, Environmental Protection Agency, Washington, DC, 1999

PROJECTIONS OF MUNICIPAL SOLID WASTE GENERATION

The EPA expects Americans will produce 223 million tons of garbage a year in the year 2000 and 240 million tons in 2005. Generation of waste made of paper and paperboard, metals, plastics, wood, and other materials, such as rubber and textiles, is projected to increase. Only glass is expected to decline. (See Table 2.13.) Food waste is projected to increase at the same rate as the population. Generation of yard trimmings per capita has been decreasing due to legislation regulating their disposal. Many municipalities will not take yard trimmings. Overall, municipal solid waste generation is projected to increase at a rate of 1 percent per year through 2000, then increase 1.4 percent annually from 2000 through 2005 (Figure 2.16).

CHAPTER III

MATERIALS RECOVERY — RECYCLING, COMPOSTING, AND MATERIAL RECOVERY FACILITIES

Recovery of materials means removing municipal solid waste (MSW) from the waste stream for the purpose of recycling, including composting. Recycling (reusing) urban solid waste can offer many economic advantages. It conserves the energy used in incineration, reduces environmental degradation, lessens the amount of chemical fertilizers that pollute water resources, generates jobs and small-scale enterprise, reduces dependence on foreign imports of metals, and conserves water.

Recycling has become a national issue. State and local governments see it as a way to save money and slow the filling of landfills. Many Americans believe recycling is one way to aid the environment. For example, if paper is recycled, fewer trees have to be cut down to make paper, and landfills will not fill up as quickly. On the other hand, others claim that, in many instances, recycling does not justify the expenditures.

Recovery for recycling continues to be generally considered one of the most effective waste management techniques. Many analysts claim that more than half of consumer waste can be economically recycled. In 1997, recycling (including composting) recovered 28 percent (60.7 million tons) of MSW, up from 25 percent in 1994 and just 6.4 percent in 1960 (Figures 3.1 and 3.2).

THE ROLE OF OBSOLESCENCE IN MUNICIPAL WASTE

In its earliest manifestations, recycling was not the province of municipalities and big waste companies but an activity of counterculture environmentalists. — Susan Strasser, *Waste and Want: A Social History of Trash*, 1999

Manufacturers have not always created products with the intention that they will wear out or go out of fashion soon and have to be replaced. At one time, goods were scarce and were made to last a long time (see also Chapter II). That was considered part of their inherent workmanship. Henry Ford believed that "a Ford was forever." He insisted that his Model T and Model A cars were "so

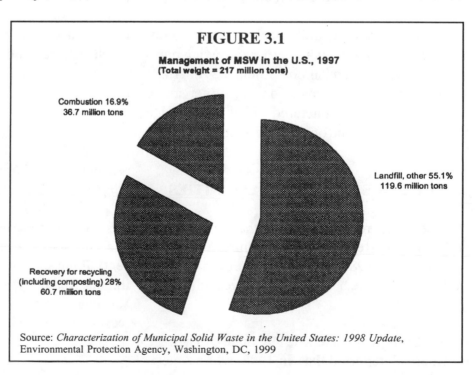

FIGURE 3.1

Management of MSW in the U.S., 1997
(Total weight = 217 million tons)

Combustion 16.9%
36.7 million tons

Landfill, other 55.1%
119.6 million tons

Recovery for recycling (including composting) 28%
60.7 million tons

Source: *Characterization of Municipal Solid Waste in the United States: 1998 Update*, Environmental Protection Agency, Washington, DC, 1999

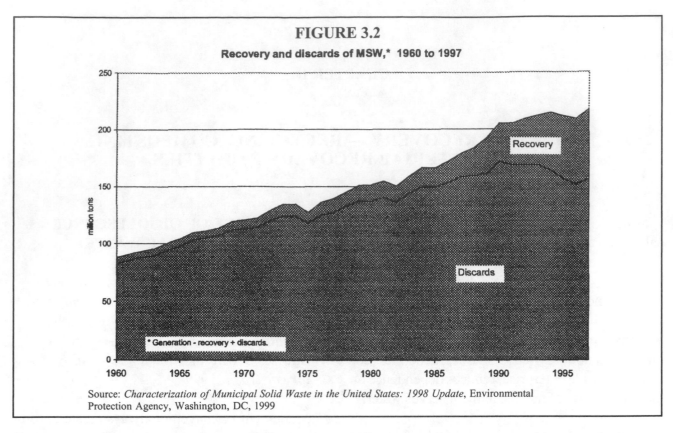

FIGURE 3.2

Recovery and discards of MSW,* 1960 to 1997

Recovery

Discards

* Generation - recovery + discards.

Source: *Characterization of Municipal Solid Waste in the United States: 1998 Update*, Environmental Protection Agency, Washington, DC, 1999

strong and so well-made that no one ought ever to have to buy a second one." Soon, however, it became evident that there was a substantial resale market for secondhand cars. Furthermore, it was quickly recognized that the industry could be more profitable if a person bought nine or 10 cars over his or her lifetime rather than one or two.

By the 1920s, technological and stylistic obsolescence began to characterize a growing number of American consumer products. American society has become based on consumerism in which goods are manufactured with the knowledge that they will become obsolete in a relatively short time.

THE ROLE OF STATES AND CITIES

The oldest recycling law in the United States is the Oregon Recycling Opportunity Act, which was passed in 1983 and went into effect in 1986. Today, every state has some type of recycling program.

BioCycle magazine's 1999 "State of Garbage in America" reported that, in 1998, while Ameri-

cans produced more waste than ever before — 374.6 million tons — they also recycled in record amounts (31.5 percent). Regionally, the highest recycling rate was reported by the Mid-Atlantic states (38 percent), followed by the South (34 percent), the Midwest, New England, and the West (32 percent each), and the Great Lakes (27 percent). Among the states, Minnesota recycled the greatest amount of its waste (45 percent), followed by New Jersey and New York (43 percent each), and Maine, South Dakota, and South Carolina (42 percent each) (Table 3.1).

A growing number of states require that many consumer goods sold must be made from recycled products. In addition, many states have set recycling/recovery goals ranging from 20 percent to 70 percent. Rhode Island (70 percent) and New Jersey (65 percent) have the highest recycling goals of all the states; Maryland has the lowest (20 percent). Eight states — Florida, Georgia, Maryland, Illinois, Kentucky, South Carolina, Tennessee, and Virginia — have exceeded their reduction and/or recycling goals. (See Table 3.2.)

About half of the states with goals have deadlines for the year 2000 or beyond. Some states require that recycled paper be used to make newspapers; many require that recycled materials be used in making telephone directories, trash bags, glass, and plastic containers. Almost all books and pamphlets released by the U.S. Government Printing Office (GPO) are printed on recycled paper. Almost all states bar some materials that can be recycled — car and boat batteries, grass cuttings, tires, used motor oil, glass, plastic containers, and newspapers — from being thrown into landfills.

The states and the federal government also use other incentives for recycling. All states have introduced curbside collection or public drop-off sites for recyclables. Some states provide financial assistance for recycling businesses by making funds available until the market stabilizes. Some states offer incentive money proportional to the tonnage of recyclables recovered. Tax credits, such as investment tax credits, and exemptions are sometimes used to attract and assist recycling businesses. All states have some kind of "buy recycled" program that requires that state funds purchase recycled products when possible. Nine states require newspaper publishers to use a minimum amount of recycled paper.

At the federal level, Executive Order 12873 (1999) requires federal agencies to purchase recyclable goods. Executive Order 13101 (1998) raised the recycled content of copier paper purchased

TABLE 3.1

Waste generation, recycling and disposal methods (by state)

State	Solid Waste (tons/yr)	Recycled[1] (%)	Incinerated (%)	Landfilled (%)
Alabama[2]	5,630,000	23	5	72
Alaska[2]	675,000	7	15	78
Arizona[3]	5,142,000	17	0	83
Arkansas[4]	3,316,000	36	<1	67
California[2]	56,000,000	33	0	67
Colorado[4,5]	5,085,000	18[6]	<1[6]	82[6]
Connecticut[7]	3,047,000	24	64	12
Delaware[5]	825,000	22	30	48
Dist. of Columbia	250,000	8[6]	92[6]	0
Florida[4,8]	23,770,000	39	16	45
Georgia[3]	10,745,000	33	1	66
Hawaii[5]	1,950,000	24	30	46
Idaho	987,000	n/a	n/a	n/a
Illinois[4,8]	13,300,000	28	1	71
Indiana[4]	5,876,000	23	10	67
Iowa[3,5]	2,518,000	34	<1	66
Kansas[9]	2,380,000	13	<1	87
Kentucky[4]	6,320,000	32	0	68
Louisiana[2,3]	4,100,000	19	0	81
Maine[4,8]	1,635,000	42	40	18
Maryland[4]	5,700,000	30	25	47
Massachusetts[4]	7,360,000	34	45	21
Michigan	19,500,000	25	5	70
Minnesota[4]	5,010,000	45	28	27
Mississippi[2,4]	3,070,000	14	5	81
Missouri[2,4]	7,950,000	30	<1	70
Montana[4,5]	1,001,000	5[6]	2[6]	93[6]
Nebraska[2]	2,000,000	29	0	71
Nevada[4]	2,800,000	14	0	86
New Hampshire[2,4]	880,000	26	20	54
New Jersey[4]	7,800,000	43	20	37
New Mexico[4,6]	2,640,000	10	0	90
New York[4,5]	30,200,000	43	11	46
North Carolina[2,3]	12,575,000	32	1	67
North Dakota[8]	501,000	26	0	74
Ohio[4]	12,335,000	17	0	83
Oklahoma[4,8]	3,545,000	12[6]	10[6]	78[6]
Oregon[4,8]	4,100,000	30	11	59
Pennsylvania[2]	9,200,000	26	22	52
Rhode Island	420,000	27	0	73
South Carolina[2,3]	10,010,000	42	2	56
South Dakota[4]	510,000	42	0	58
Tennessee[4,5]	9,513,000	35	10	55
Texas[4,5]	33,750,000	35	<1	65
Utah[2,4]	3,490,000	22	3	75
Vermont[4]	550,000	30	7	63
Virginia[8]	10,000,000	40	18	42
Washington[4]	6,540,000	33	8	59
West Virginia[3,4]	2,000,000	20	0	80
Wisconsin[4,8]	5,600,000	36	3	61
Wyoming[2]	530,000	5	0	95
Total	374,631,000	31.5	7.5	61

n/a - Information not available; [1] Includes yard trimmings composting; [2] Includes industrial and agricultural wastes as well as C&D debris; [3] Includes industrial waste and C&D debris; [4] Includes C&D debris; [5] Based of FY 1998 data; [6] Based on 1997 data; [7] Based on FY 1997 data; [8] Based on information from the 1998 State of Garbage in America; [9] Based on 1995 data

Source: Jim Glenn, "The State of Garbage in America," *BioCycle*, vol. 40, no. 4, April 1999

by federal agencies from 20 percent to 30 percent.

Curbside Programs

Before recyclable materials can be processed and recycled into new products, they must be collected. Most residential recycling involves curbside collection, drop-off programs, buy-back operations, and/or container deposit systems.

The increase in the amount of recycling can be measured by the growth in the number of people receiving curbside recycling service, in which they put garbage to be recycled in special containers. In 1988, when *BioCycle* began its survey, only 1,042 curbside programs were operating in the United States. *BioCycle*'s 1998 "State of Garbage in America" survey reported 9,349 curbside recycling programs in the United States, up from 7,375 in 1995. Such programs served approximately 139.4 million people, 54 percent of the U.S. population. The extent of programs varied greatly by geographic region. The Mid-Atlantic states led in the percent of population served by curbside programs (82 percent), followed by New England (73 percent), the West (56 percent), the Great Lakes (53 percent), the South (52 percent), the Midwest (27 percent), and the Rocky Mountains (23 percent).

Drop-Off Centers

Drop-off centers typically collect residential materials, although some accept commercial waste. They are found in grocery stores, charitable organizations, city-sponsored sites, and apartment complexes. The types of materials accepted vary greatly, although drop-off centers generally accept a greater variety of materials than curbside collection services. Although it is difficult to quantify drop-off centers, the *BioCycle* survey estimated there were 12,694 programs in the United States in 1998.

Commercial Recyclables Collection

The largest quantity of recovered materials comes from the commercial sector. Old corrugated

---

TABLE 3.2

State diversion goals and recovery rates

State	Goal (%)	Rate (%)	Deadline	Mandatory On Local Government
Alabama	25	23	-	No
Arkansas	40	36	2000	No
California	50	33	2000	Yes
Connecticut	40	24	2000	Yes
Delaware	25	22	2000	No
Dist of Col.	45	8	1994	No
Florida	30	39	1994	No
Georgia	25	33	1996	No
Hawaii	50	24	2000	No
Idaho	25	n/a	1995	No
Illinois	25	28	2001	Yes
Indiana	50	23	2000	No
Iowa	50	34	2000	No
Kentucky	25	32	1997	No
Louisiana	25	19	1992	No
Maine	50	42	1998	No
Maryland	20	30	1994	Yes
Massachusetts	46	34	2000	No
Michigan	50	25	2005	No
Minnesota	50	45	1996	No
Mississippi	25	14	1996	No
Missouri	40	30	1998	No
Montana	25	5	1996	No
Nebraska	40	29	1999	No
Nevada	25	14	1995	No
New Hampshire	40	26	2000	No
New Jersey	65	43	2000	Yes
New Mexico	50	10	2000	No
New York	50	43	1997	No
North Carolina	40	32	2001	No
North Dakota	40	26	2000	No
Ohio	25	17	2000	No
Oregon	50	30	2000	Yes
Pennsylvania	35	26	2003	No
Rhode Island	70	27	-	No
South Carolina	30	42	1997	No
South Dakota	50	42	2001	No
Tennessee	25	35	1995	Yes
Texas	40	35	1994	No
Vermont	40	30	2000	No
Virginia	25	40	1997	No
Washington	50	33	2000	No
West Virginia	50	20	2010	No

Source: Jim Glenn, "The State of Garbage in America," *BioCycle*, vol. 40, no. 4, April 1999

TABLE 3.3

MRF PROCESSING EQUIPMENT

Type of Equipment	Description	Purpose
Infeed Conveyors	Z-shaped moving conveyor belts, which usually start below floor level and elevate materials to a certain height above floor level. Usually of steel, apron-pan construction; may also be either chain-driven rubber belts or rubber slider belts.	Move mixed paper and non-paper material from tipping floor into process area, and deposit it onto sorting conveyors or into sorting equipment. Also used to feed sorted materials into the baler(s).
Sorting Conveyors	Horizontal moving rubber belts, of either slider or trough-pulley design. Usually mounted on elevated platforms, below which are storage bins, bunkers, or transfer conveyors.	Hand-sorters stand on one or both sides of the belt and pull specific materials, which are then dropped/tossed into storage bins or bunkers. Negatively-sorted materials are allowed to remain on the belt.
Transfer Conveyors	Moving rubber belts, of slider or trough-pulley design.	Transport loose, separated materials from the sorting area to processing equipment and processed materials from processing equipment to storage bunkers or trailers.
Baling Presses or "Balers"	Machines that compress loose material into dense rectangular blocks or "bales." Typical bale dimensions are 2.5 ft. × 4 ft. × 5 ft. long. The bale is formed by a moving pressure plate, mounted on a hydraulic cylinder or "ram," which packs the material together inside a closed chamber.	Densify recyclables for ease of handling and for more cost-effective shipping.
Magnetic Separator	Typically an electromagnet housed in a moving conveyor belt. The device is mounted above a conveyor carrying commingled recyclables. Ferrous metals, e.g., tin cans, are attracted by the magnet and shoveled onto a transfer conveyor by the moving belt.	Automatically remove ferrous metals from the commingled materials stream.
Eddy-current Separator	Consists of a short belt conveyor that surrounds the eddy current mechanism. The mechanism contains a rotor with rare earth magnets of alternating polarity. As the rotor spins, it creates a magnetic field, which induces eddy currents in non-ferrous metals passing over it. These currents in turn establish a repulsive magnetic force that hurls the metals off the belt at different trajectories than non-metallics. A splitter plate divides the two flows.	Automatically remove aluminum and non-ferrous metals from the commingled materials stream.
"Air Classifier" or "Air Knife"	Normally consists of a blower or suction fan and accompanying tubes and chutes. The air jet created by the blower or fan captures or diverts the lighter materials in the stream from the heavier ones.	Divide the commingled stream into "lights" (aluminum and plastics) and "heavies" (glass). Also may be used to extract paper labels during glass beneficiation processes (described on page 4).
Inclined Sorting Table	A proprietary device that consists of an inclined moving conveyor and a "curtain" of dangling chains that travels along the surface of the conveyor.	Used to separate the commingled stream into lights and heavies.
Trommel Screen	A cylindrical drum with holes of specific size that rotates about its central axis. "Undersize" material (material smaller in diameter than the holes) falls through the holes and is thus separated from "oversize" material.	Most often used to size-classify and remove caps from crushed glass after it is sorted. Also may be used to separate lights from heavies, although this application usually results in unacceptably high glass breakage.
Vibrating or Oscillating Screen	Flat plates, punched with holes, that are mechanically vibrated in one or two dimensions. A similar design is the "finger" screen, which instead of pierced plates employs parallel bars for the screening surface. Undersize materials fall through the holes or between the bars, while oversize material slides across the screening surface.	Separate mixed broken glass from the commingled stream. Also sometimes used to size-classify lights for easier sorting or eddy current separation.
Glass Crusher	Consists of a crushing chamber, with rotating hammers or drums. Many models are sold with attached transfer conveyors and magnetic head pulleys for removal of caps.	Increase density of sorted glass by breaking it into small pieces.
Can Flattener	Consists of one or two rotating drums or wheels mounted inside a crushing chamber. Most models come equipped with an attached blower and blow-tube, which shoot the crushed cans directly into a waiting trailer.	Densify aluminum and/or steel cans for more cost-effective shipping.
Can Densifier	Similar in principle to a baler, but produces small, dense blocks called "briquettes." The briquettes are bundled together with steel strapping prior to shipment.	Densify aluminum and/or steel cans for more cost-effective shipping.
Granulator	Machines which use rotating propeller-like blades to chop plastic bottles into small chips.	Densify plastic for more cost-effective shipping, and to prepare it for remanufacturing.
Plastic Bottle Perforator	A rotating drum upon which spikes are mounted. The spikes pierce the bottles in multiple locations, thus decreasing their resilience.	Make plastic bottles easier to bale. Especially effective on bottles whose caps have been screwed back on.

Source: *The Cost to Recycle at a Materials Recovery Facility*, National Solid Wastes Management Association, Washington, DC, 1992

containers and office papers are widely collected from businesses. Grocery stores and other retail outlets that use corrugated packaging return large amounts of recovered materials.

Buy-Back and Deposit Centers

A buy-back center is usually a commercial operation that pays individuals for recovered materials, such as scrap metal, aluminum cans, or paper. In addition, nine states — Connecticut, Delaware, Iowa, Maine, Massachusetts, Michigan, New York, Oregon, and Vermont — have introduced container deposit systems. In these programs, the consumer pays a deposit on beverage containers when purchased, which is redeemed on return of the empty containers.

Composting

About one-third of trash is organic material — food and yard waste. Composting involves mixing plant and other organic refuse to speed the natural decomposition into fiber and micronutrients. An example would be a compost pile in the backyard where food scraps are deposited and mixed periodically. The product can then be used as fertilizer for the garden. When microorganisms metabolize the waste, organic waste gives off energy in the form of heat and loses between 40 and 75 percent of its original volume in the process. The finished product is often used in landscaping, land reclamation, and landfill cover and to provide high-nutrient soil for farms and nurseries.

Composting is a particularly promising method of disposal of household wastes in developing countries because of the large volumes of water, vegetable, and decaying, degradable matter in those areas. Composting is also very common in Europe. Because composting contains micronutrients, slows soil erosion, and improves water retention, it is an alternative to the use of environmentally dangerous chemical fertilizers.

Yard waste is especially suitable for composting due to its high moisture content. Over the past decade, composting yard trimmings has become an accepted waste management method in many U.S. locations. The practice got a huge boost beginning in the late 1980s when many states banned yard trimmings from disposal facilities. *BioCycle* reported that, by 1998, there were 3,807 public composting facilities in the United States.

MATERIALS RECOVERY FACILITIES (MRFs)

Materials recovery facilities (MRFs) process recyclable materials. An MRF sorts commingled materials collected primarily from homes through curbside pickups and prepares them for shipment to end-user markets. For example, glass recovered from curbside programs may be processed and sold to soft-drink manufacturers for bottling. MRFs vary widely, depending on the incoming materials and the technology and labor used to sort the materials. Most are considered low technology — most sorting is done manually. MRFs classified as high technology sort recyclables using eddy currents (swirling air or water), magnetic pulleys, optical sensors, and air classifiers.

Newspaper is the major paper commodity processed at MRFs, along with corrugated boxes, used telephone books, magazines, and mixed waste paper. Non-paper commingled recyclables consist of aluminum and other metal beverage containers, food cans, glass food and beverage containers, and certain plastics. Most MRFs have separate processing lines for paper and commingled container streams. The type of processing equipment found in a particular plant depends upon the market for which the products are destined and the distance the recyclables have to be transported. Table 3.3 tells about the various processing equipment used in the handling of recyclables.

In 1997, 380 materials recovery facilities helped process recyclables — approximately 32,088 tons per day. Approximately three-fourths of MRFs were private enterprises.

MATERIAL RECYCLING RATES

As the per capita rate of MSW generation rose from 2.68 pounds per person per day in 1960 to 4.44 pounds per person in 1997, the per capita rate of recovery rose from 0.17 pounds per day in 1960 to 1.24 pounds in 1997. Of the remaining 1997 MSW, an estimated 0.75 pounds of discards per person per day were managed through incineration, and 2.45 pounds per person per day went to landfills or other disposal. (See Table 3.4.) Figure 3.3 shows the materials recovered. Fifty-seven percent of recyclables were paper and paperboard, followed by yard trimmings (19 percent), metals (11 percent), miscellaneous other (6 percent), glass (5 percent), and plastics (2 percent).

A large portion (65.4 percent) of metals is recovered. Almost 42 percent of paper can be recovered, while only 5 percent of plastics and wood are generally recovered. (See Table 3.5.)

Laws requiring deposits on soda bottles and the recycling of aluminum cans have led to a significant reduction of litter. In addition, some people collect aluminum cans to earn money and, at the same time, help keep the streets and countryside cleaner.

Figure 3.4 shows how the recovery of materials has affected the amount of the materials that is eventu-ally discarded. Materials that can be recovered at greater rates, such as paper, have been reduced the most by recovery. For example, paper accounted for 38 percent of solid waste generated, but after recovery, paper made up only 32 percent of waste that had to be discarded.

Paper

The paper industry has been at the leading edge of the dramatic expansion in recycling. Paper may be reused several times before the fibers are destroyed and can no longer be used to make paper. As forests have become depleted, wood has be-

---

TABLE 3.4

PER CAPITA GENERATION, MATERIALS RECOVERY, COMBUSTION, AND DISCARDS OF MUNICIPAL SOLID WASTE, 1960 TO 1997
(In pounds per person per day; population in thousands)

	1960	1970	1980	1990	1994	1995	1996	1997
Generation	2.68	3.25	3.66	4.50	4.50	4.40	4.32	4.44
Recovery for recycling & composting	0.17	0.22	0.35	0.73	1.06	1.14	1.18	1.24
Discards after recovery	2.51	3.04	3.31	3.77	3.44	3.26	3.14	3.20
Combustion	0.82	0.67	0.33	0.70	0.68	0.74	0.75	0.75
Discards to landfill, other disposal	1.69	2.36	2.98	3.07	2.75	2.51	2.39	2.45
Resident Population (thousands)	179,979	203,984	227,255	249,907	260,682	263,168	265,253	267,645

Details may not add to totals due to rounding.
Population figures from U.S. Bureau of the Census, Current Population Reports.
Franklin Associates

FIGURE 3.3

Materials recovery,* 1997

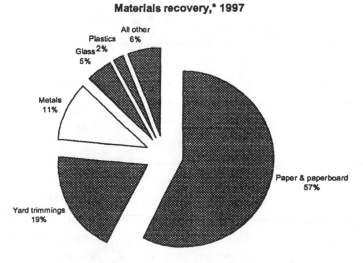

* In percent by weight of total recovery

Source of table and figure: *Characterization of Municipal Solid Waste in the United States: 1998 Update*, Environmental Protection Agency, Washington, DC, 1999

TABLE 3.5

GENERATION AND RECOVERY OF MATERIALS IN MSW, 1997

(In millions of tons and percent of generation of each material)

	Weight Generated	Weight Recovered	Recovery as a Percent of Generation
Paper and paperboard	83.8	34.9	41.7%
Glass	12.0	2.9	24.3%
Metals			
Steel	12.3	4.7	38.4%
Aluminum	3.0	0.9	31.2%
Other nonferrous metals*	1.3	0.8	65.4%
Total metals	16.6	6.5	39.1%
Plastics	21.5	1.1	5.2%
Rubber and leather	6.6	0.8	11.7%
Textiles	8.2	1.1	12.9%
Wood	11.6	0.6	5.1%
Other materials	3.8	0.8	20.2%
Total Materials in Products	164.1	48.6	29.6%
Other wastes			
Food, other**	21.9	0.6	2.6%
Yard trimmings	27.7	11.5	41.4%
Miscellaneous inorganic wastes	3.3	Neg.	Neg.
Total Other Wastes	52.9	12.1	22.8%
TOTAL MUNICIPAL SOLID WASTE	217.0	60.7	28.0%

Includes wastes from residential, commercial, and institutional sources.

  * Includes lead from lead-acid batteries.

** Includes recovery of paper for composting.

Neg. = Less than 50,000 tons or 0.05 percent.

Source: *Characterization of Municipal Solid Waste in the United States: 1998 Update*, Environmental Protection Agency, Washington, DC, 1999

come less plentiful and more expensive. At the same time, landfills are filling, and much of that waste has been paper. Figure 3.5 shows the symbols affixed to paper products that are made from recycled paper or that are recyclable.

The EPA estimates that the amount of paper recovered from U.S. waste grew from 13 million tons in 1985 to 34.9 million tons in 1997. Figure 3.6 shows the growth of paper generation and recovery from 1960 to 1997. Unfortunately, however, many paper purchasers have stopped asking for recycled stock. The percentage of recycled pa-

per produced has fallen from about 10 percent of all paper produced in the early 1990s to about 6 percent in the late 1990s.

Glass

In 1997, glass made up 7.6 percent of municipal solid waste. Glass containers are 100 percent recyclable, and over 30 percent of the glass used in containers is made from recycled glass. (See Figure 3.7.) The Environmental Protection Agency (EPA), in *Characterization of Municipal Solid Waste in the United States: 1998 Update* (1999),

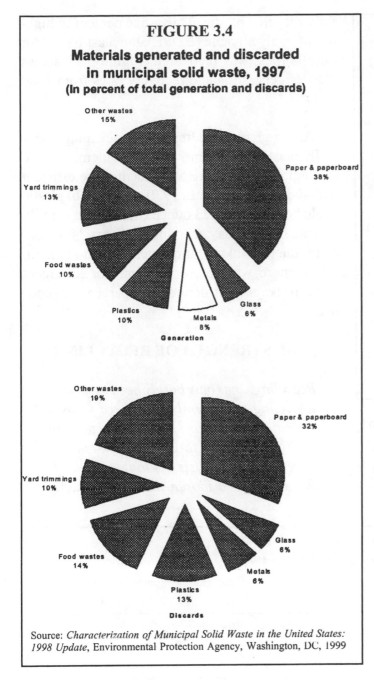

FIGURE 3.4

**Materials generated and discarded
in municipal solid waste, 1997**
(In percent of total generation and discards)

Other wastes
15%

Yard trimmings
13%

Food wastes
10%

Plastics
10%

Metals
8%

Glass
6%

Paper & paperboard
38%

Generation

Other wastes
19%

Yard trimmings
10%

Food wastes
14%

Plastics
13%

Metals
6%

Glass
6%

Paper & paperboard
32%

Discards

Source: *Characterization of Municipal Solid Waste in the United States: 1998 Update*, Environmental Protection Agency, Washington, DC, 1999

melted down in ancient times to make new coins with images of the latest ruler. Metal objects were generally considered valuable and were frequently sold or given away, rarely simply discarded. When metal objects could not be repaired, they could be melted down and fashioned into something else. Lead has a melting point so low it can be heated over a wood fire. Tin melts at an even lower point.

Ferrous metals (iron and steel) are the largest category of metals in MSW. They are used in durable goods, such as appliances, furniture, tires, and other long-lasting goods. Approximately 39 percent of metal MSW was recovered in 1997. (Figure 3.10 shows the increase in the generation and recovery of metals from 1960 to 1997.)

Aluminum and other nonferrous metals make up the remainder of metals recovered from MSW. Aluminum is found in cans and packaging. Lead, zinc, and copper are found in batteries, appliances, and consumer electronics. The EPA reported that 49 percent of all aluminum and 60 percent of aluminum cans were recovered for recycling in 1997. Making new aluminum requires huge amounts of electricity. Turning used aluminum cans into new ones takes 95 percent less energy than making new metal from bauxite, the ore from which aluminum is made.

Plastics

Plastic packaging is the workhorse of source reduction. — William L. Rathje, *The ULS Report*, March-April 1997

More and more manufacturers are using plastics to package their products because plastic is so easy to use and to shape. As a result, plastics are the fastest-growing part of the garbage the nation makes. In 1960, plastics were less than 1 percent of MSW; by 1997, they were 9.9 percent.

Overall recovery of plastics for recycling is relatively small — 5.2 percent in 1997, although

reported that 24.3 percent of all glass was recovered for recycling in 1997. Figure 3.8 shows glass generation and recovery rates from 1960 to 1997.

Recycling saves energy. When glassmakers use 10 percent crushed, recycled glass, they use 5 percent less energy. (Figure 3.9 shows the glass-recycling loop.)

Metals

Metal recycling is as old as metalworking. Coins and jewelry made of gold and silver were

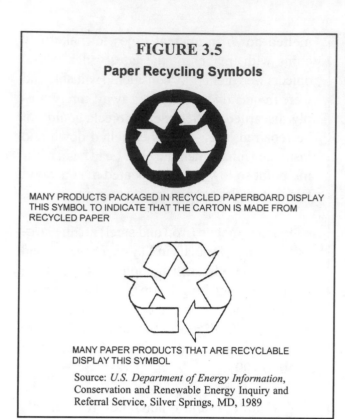

fully recycled plastic. Thirty-one percent of high-density polyethylene (HDPE), the plastic used for milk bottles, was recovered. Figure 3.11 shows plastics generation and recovery rates from 1960 to 1997.

Although people often claim packaging, especially plastic packaging, is "the problem," plastic packaging has become 50 percent more efficient over the past 20 years. In 1970, an ounce of plastic could hold (deliver) 23 ounces of product — milk, aspirin, soda. Today, an ounce delivers 34 ounces of product, thanks to improvements in strength. Furthermore, while plastic accounts for 22 percent of all packaging, it delivers 65 percent of products.

THE STRENGTH OF RECYCLING

Recycling...has only barely been tapped.... Recycling as currently structured focuses on materials that are easily collected and easily stripped of foreign matter and for which a market exists. As long as little effort is made to loosen these parameters,

recovery of some plastics is increasing. In 1995, 37 percent of polyethylene terephthalate (PET), the plastic used to make the bottles that hold soft drinks, was recovered, making it the most success-

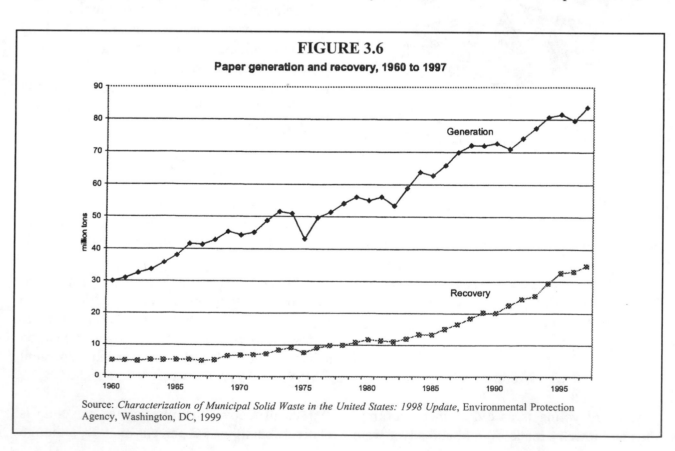

FIGURE 3.6

Paper generation and recovery, 1960 to 1997

Source: *Characterization of Municipal Solid Waste in the United States: 1998 Update*, Environmental Protection Agency, Washington, DC, 1999

recycling will remain a marginal activity. — Gary Gardner and Payal Sampat, *Mind Over Matter: Recasting the Role of Materials in Our Lives*, 1998

Recycling has become a major part of garbage removal in the United States, and it will likely continue to grow, although at a slower pace than in the past. Recycling, however, did not enjoy immediate success. Recycling started out as a "do-good" activity. For a quarter-century after the first Earth Day, recycling advocates pleaded their case to skeptical decision-makers in the interest of environmental benefit. It evolved into a necessary burden for municipal governments.

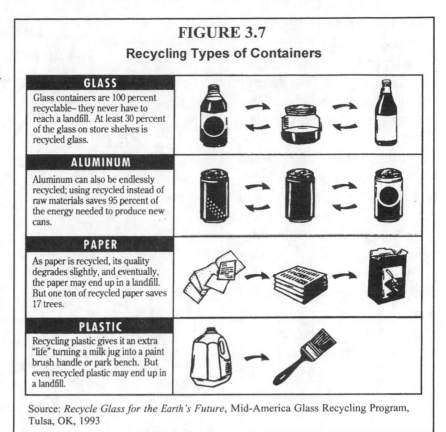

FIGURE 3.7
Recycling Types of Containers

GLASS
Glass containers are 100 percent recyclable– they never have to reach a landfill. At least 30 percent of the glass on store shelves is recycled glass.

ALUMINUM
Aluminum can also be endlessly recycled; using recycled instead of raw materials saves 95 percent of the energy needed to produce new cans.

PAPER
As paper is recycled, its quality degrades slightly, and eventually, the paper may end up in a landfill. But one ton of recycled paper saves 17 trees.

PLASTIC
Recycling plastic gives it an extra "life" turning a milk jug into a paint brush handle or park bench. But even recycled plastic may end up in a landfill.

Source: *Recycle Glass for the Earth's Future*, Mid-America Glass Recycling Program, Tulsa, OK, 1993

In the early years, the economy was unable to use all the plastic, paper, and other things that were recycled. Many private recycling companies were not able to make a profit. Instead of earning money from recycling, the program cost them money. Some cities even started dumping their recycled materials into landfills because they

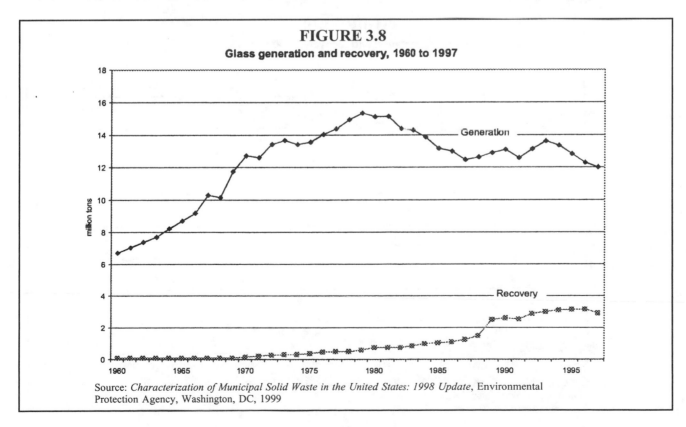

FIGURE 3.8
Glass generation and recovery, 1960 to 1997

Source: *Characterization of Municipal Solid Waste in the United States: 1998 Update*, Environmental Protection Agency, Washington, DC, 1999

51

could not sell them. Philadelphia stopped collecting plastics in order to save money. Many city leaders felt that money could be better used in other areas, such as education.

Critics of recycling pointed to those problems as evidence that recycling programs could not work. Supporters of recycling thought this problem developed because the collection programs were so successful that they recouped more than manufacturers were initially able to handle. Advocates of recycling programs had underestimated the wellspring of support for recycling that existed among the American people.

In fact, by the mid-1990s, that support had translated into

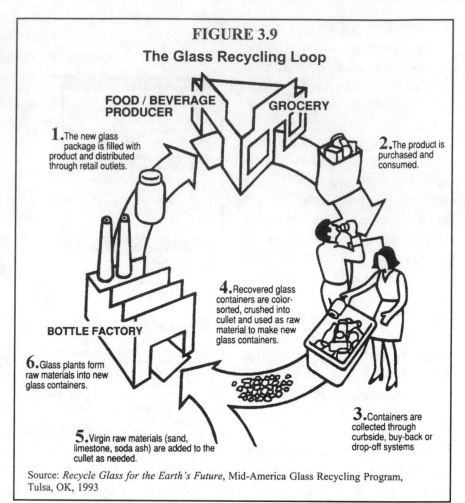

FIGURE 3.9
The Glass Recycling Loop

Source: *Recycle Glass for the Earth's Future*, Mid-America Glass Recycling Program, Tulsa, OK, 1993

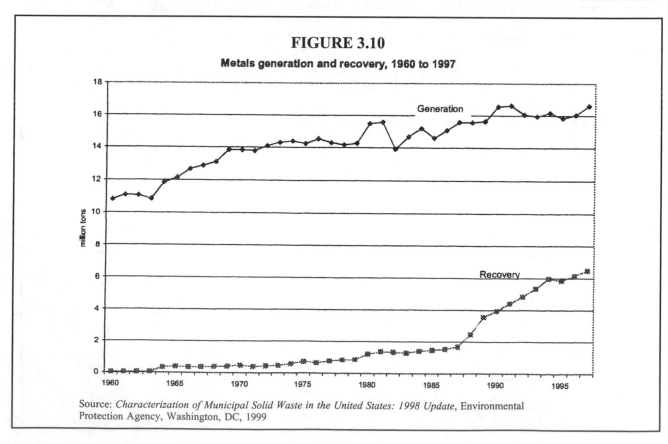

FIGURE 3.10
Metals generation and recovery, 1960 to 1997

Source: *Characterization of Municipal Solid Waste in the United States: 1998 Update*, Environmental Protection Agency, Washington, DC, 1999

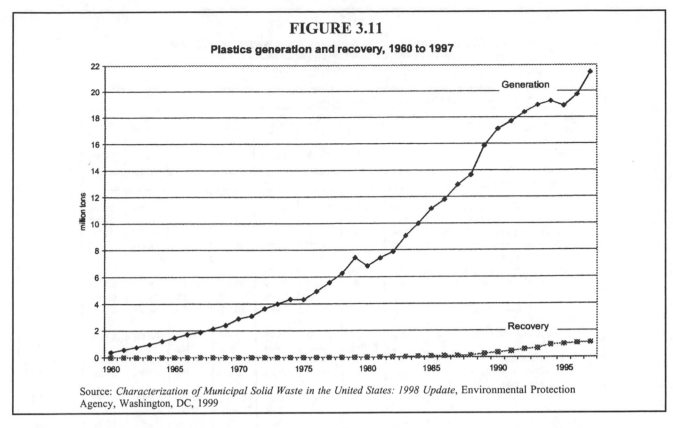

FIGURE 3.11

Plastics generation and recovery, 1960 to 1997

Source: *Characterization of Municipal Solid Waste in the United States: 1998 Update*, Environmental Protection Agency, Washington, DC, 1999

a marketing success. Recycling had become a revenue-producer, and prices for nearly all recyclables skyrocketed. Cities that were once paying to get rid of garbage could earn millions from selling the same material. Recycling programs began to prosper. Theft of recyclables became commonplace. As importantly, private industry began to consider recycling as a way to cut expenses and even add to income instead of as a nuisance that increased overhead costs. Such numbers made recycling increasingly attractive to many city waste administrators. In 1995, the commodities market (the organized buying and selling of future contracts, similar to the stock market) added garbage to its trading options.

As with any business, recycling is subject to the cyclical highs and lows of supply and demand. Recently, the recycling boom has leveled off, and prices have dropped. In the process, however, most Americans now understand that recovery has become a viable industry as well as a necessary service.

There are several barriers, however, that continue to hinder the development of the recycling market:

- Consumers are often unaware of recycled products.

- Consumers often lack confidence in the quality of recycled products.

- The transportation costs of carrying recyclables to processing plants are high.

- Questions about supply and demand deter investors.

- It is difficult to recover or sort certain materials, such as oil, tires, and plastics.

- Recycled products are generally more expensive.

PACKAGING

In almost every case, the lightest package, per unit of contents, is the one with the lowest impact on the environment.... Rather than legislating the choice of material or the required level of recyclability, it makes sense to adopt policies that encourage use

TABLE 3.6

RECOVERY* OF PRODUCTS IN MUNICIPAL SOLID WASTE, 1960 TO 1997
(WITH DETAIL ON CONTAINERS AND PACKAGING)
(in percent of generation of each product)

Percent of Generation of Each Product								
Products	1960	1970	1980	1990	1994	1995	1996	1997
Durable Goods (Detail in Table 13)	3.5%	6.4%	6.2%	11.6%	16.4%	16.1%	16.7%	17.0%
Nondurable Goods (Detail in Table 16)	13.8%	14.9%	13.6%	16.9%	22.2%	23.8%	24.4%	24.8%
Containers and Packaging								
Glass Packaging								
Beer and Soft Drink Bottles	6.4%	2.5%	10.8%	33.5%	31.4%	32.6%	32.9%	31.3%
Wine and Liquor Bottles	Neg.	Neg.	Neg.	10.3%	26.1%	26.3%	24.7%	24.2%
Food and Other Bottles & Jars	Neg.	Neg.	Neg.	12.5%	19.8%	21.6%	25.6%	24.3%
Total Glass Packaging	1.6%	1.3%	5.4%	22.1%	25.8%	27.2%	28.9%	27.5%
Steel Packaging								
Beer and Soft Drink Cans	1.6%	1.3%	9.6%	26.7%	Neg.	Neg.	Neg.	Neg.
Food and Other Cans	Neg.	1.7%	5.3%	23.2%	51.8%	56.1%	58.2%	60.5%
Other Steel Packaging	Neg.	Neg.	Neg.	30.0%	27.3%	23.8%	29.4%	66.7%
Total Steel Packaging	Neg.	1.5%	5.5%	23.9%	50.0%	53.8%	56.5%	61.0%
Aluminum Packaging								
Beer and Soft Drink Cans	Neg.	10.0%	36.5%	63.9%	57.6%	56.6%	58.4%	59.5%
Other Cans	Neg.	Neg.	Neg.	Neg.	Neg.	Neg.	Neg.	Neg.
Foil and Closures	Neg.	Neg.	Neg.	6.1%	8.8%	8.6%	8.3%	8.3%
Total Aluminum Pkg	Neg.	1.8%	25.2%	53.2%	48.6%	47.0%	47.9%	48.5%
Paper & Paperboard Pkg								
Corrugated Boxes	34.4%	21.6%	37.4%	48.0%	57.6%	64.2%	66.7%	67.3%
Milk Cartons**			Neg.	Neg.	Neg.	Neg.	Neg.	Neg.
Folding Cartons**			Neg.	Neg.	19.6%	20.3%	15.8%	10.3%
Other Paperboard Packaging	Neg.	Neg.	Neg.	Neg.	Neg.	Neg.	Neg.	Neg.
Bags and Sacks**			Neg.	Neg.	18.3%	17.2%	12.8%	15.0%
Wrapping Papers**			Neg.	Neg.	Neg.	Neg.	Neg.	Neg.
Other Paper Packaging	7.5%	9.2%	35.3%	Neg.	Neg.	Neg.	Neg.	Neg.
Total Paper & Board Pkg	19.4%	14.5%	27.4%	36.9%	47.0%	52.3%	53.3%	53.6%
Plastics Packaging								
Soft Drink Bottles**			3.8%	32.6%	53.3%	46.2%	40.0%	35.5%
Milk Bottles**			Neg.	3.8%	29.3%	30.6%	30.8%	31.3%
Other Containers	Neg.	Neg.	Neg.	1.4%	10.1%	12.7%	14.8%	13.0%
Bags and Sacks**			Neg.	3.2%	2.3%	3.3%	3.7%	2.6%
Wraps**			Neg.	2.0%	1.7%	2.3%	2.7%	2.3%
Other Plastics Packaging	Neg.	Neg.	Neg.	1.0%	0.9%	0.9%	1.3%	1.8%
Total Plastics Packaging	Neg.	Neg.	Neg.	3.8%	9.0%	9.8%	9.8%	8.7%
Wood Packaging	Neg.	Neg.	Neg.	1.6%	5.1%	7.3%	7.6%	8.4%
Other Misc. Packaging	Neg.	Neg.	Neg.	Neg.	Neg.	Neg.	Neg.	Neg.
Total Containers & Pkg	10.5%	7.7%	16.1%	26.0%	34.9%	39.1%	39.9%	39.4%
Total Product Wastes†	10.3%	9.6%	13.3%	19.8%	26.7%	28.9%	29.7%	29.6%
Other Wastes								
Food Wastes	Neg.	Neg.	Neg.	Neg.	2.2%	2.6%	2.4%	2.6%
Yard Trimmings	Neg.	Neg.	Neg.	12.0%	25.4%	30.3%	37.2%	41.4%
Miscellaneous Inorganic Wastes	Neg.	Neg.	Neg.	Neg.	Neg.	Neg.	Neg.	Neg.
Total Other Wastes	Neg.	Neg.	Neg.	7.2%	15.1%	17.5%	20.6%	22.8%
Total MSW Recovered - %	6.4%	6.6%	9.6%	16.2%	23.6%	26.0%	27.4%	28.0%

* Recovery of postconsumer wastes; does not include converting/fabrication scrap.
** Not estimated separately prior to 1980.
† Other than food products.
Details may not add to totals due to rounding.
Neg. = Less than 5,000 tons or 0.05 percent.

Franklin Associates

Source: *Characterization of Municipal Solid Waste in the United States: 1998 Update*, Environmental Protection Agency, Washington, DC, 1999

---

of the lightest possible package for each product. — Frank Ackerman, *Why Do We Recycle?*, 1997

The American way of life has changed greatly over the past few decades, reflected in increases in the number of households, the elderly and disabled living independently at home, women in the workforce, and "latchkey children." Many products and packages have been developed to meet the changing needs of these American consumers — single-serve meals, easy-to-open bottles and cans, and reclosable containers.

A large proportion of garbage is made up of packaging (see also Chapter II). Therefore, one of the major ways to reduce the amount of garbage is to reduce packaging up front or use materials that will recycle or biodegrade more easily. Until recently, CDs and cassettes were sold in plastic packaging far larger than needed. Many customers and recording artists complained to the manufacturers, who now put CDs and cassettes in smaller packages. Many other industries are also packaging their products in less paper and plastic.

Some states are requiring manufacturers to take back their products after they have been used. For example, in Maryland, car battery makers have to set up a program to take back the batteries they make so they can be recycled. In Minnesota, publishers of telephone books have to set up recycling collection programs so the telephone books will not end up in the garbage dumps.

In 1993, the Clinton Administration issued an executive order directing federal agencies, by 1994, to purchase only office paper products that contain no less than 20 percent recycled paper, increasing to 30 percent by 1998.

The EPA reported that, in 1997, 39.4 percent of packaging and containers were recovered, up from 10.5 percent in 1960. This included 27.5 percent of glass packaging and containers, 61 percent of steel, 48.5 percent of aluminum, 53.6 percent of

TABLE 3.7

NCL Packaging Study, Selected Statistics
Based on Estimated Annual Household Consumption

	Less Filling: **Market Basket 1**	More Packaging: **Market Basket 2**	**Annual Diff.** (Pounds)
Beer	6 Aluminum Cans, LDPE Ring Carrier	6 Glass Bottles, Paperboard Carton	166.30
Cereal, Toasted Oat	PE Bag	Paperboard Box, Plastic Bag	8.58
Cheese, Cheddar	Plastic Bag	Paperboard Carton, servings wrapped in plastic	1.90
Eggs	PS Foam Carton	Paperboard Carton	3.62
Juice	HDPE Jug, 1 Gal	Glass Bottle, 1/2 Gal	66.73
Lunch Meat, Ham	PE Pouch	Paperboard Outer Carton, Inner Plastic Pouch	3.14
Pasta	Plastic Bag, 32 oz.	Paperboard Box, 16 oz.	2.82
Potato Chips	Laminated Bag, 14 oz.	Paperboard Tube, Foil Bags	5.83
Soft Drinks	PET Bottle, 2 liter	12 Aluminum Cans, Paperboard Carton	19.03
Tuna	6 oz. Steel Can	3 Small Cans (8.25 oz.), Paperboard Sleeve	7.98
SAVINGS			285.94

Source: "Great Taste, Less Landfilling," *The ULS Report*, vol. 6, no. 2, April-May-June 1999. Used with permission of *The ULS Report*, Ann Arbor, MI.

paper, 8.7 percent of plastics, and 8.4 percent of wood. (See Table 3.6.)

The National Consumers League (NCL), a private, non-profit consumer advocacy group, studied the amount of waste generated by a typical family consuming a year's worth of 10 common food items. They compared the packaging used to the same products with less packaging. The difference amounted to almost 286 pounds per year. (See Table 3.7.)

"GREEN" PRODUCT DESIGN

Designing and manufacturing products with conservation and consideration for the environment is called "green" product design. Figure 3.12 contrasts conventional and green design methods. Although costs of green design systems are generally greater initially, experts think that long-term expense will be no greater and may be offset by recycling savings.

Some experts believe that issues involving garbage and disposal arise because of inefficiencies in the economy in general. They believe that poor product design, sloppy methods of materials extraction and processing, and a casual attitude about consumption contribute to the tendency of industrial societies to use more materials than necessary to meet their needs.

ENERGY SAVINGS

Disposing of garbage in landfills and by incineration (burning) wastes not only the materials but also the energy embodied in those products. The energy contained in goods and materials is lost permanently when they are landfilled. Studies of the relative energy benefits of recycling and incineration have found that while significant amounts of energy can be recovered through burning (see Chapter II), three to five times more can be saved by recycling municipal solid waste. The Sound Resource Management Group, a private energy research organization, reports that increasing the recovery of materials in U.S. municipal solid waste so that at least 60 percent of materials are recycled could save the energy equivalent of one-fourth the output of U.S. nuclear power plants (*Recycling Versus Incineration: An Energy Conservation Analysis*, Seattle, Washington, 1992).

Policies that encourage production of virgin materials and the easy disposal of wastes promote waste. A major feature of the consumer culture has been the personal sense of freedom in being able to ignore the extent to which raw materials support daily routines. Few people recognize the consequences of constantly acquiring and discarding their plentiful and inexpensive — and excessively packaged — consumer goods.

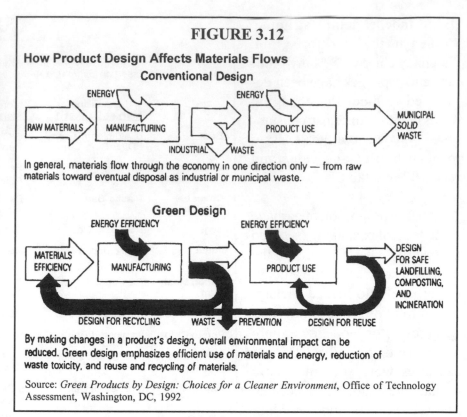

FIGURE 3.12

How Product Design Affects Materials Flows

Conventional Design

In general, materials flow through the economy in one direction only — from raw materials toward eventual disposal as industrial or municipal waste.

Green Design

By making changes in a product's design, overall environmental impact can be reduced. Green design emphasizes efficient use of materials and energy, reduction of waste toxicity, and reuse and recycling of materials.

Source: *Green Products by Design: Choices for a Cleaner Environment*, Office of Technology Assessment, Washington, DC, 1992

RECYCLING AROUND THE WORLD

The United States is not the only country facing garbage problems. Other industrial nations are confronting similar situations. Some landfills in Europe are filling up, and most European countries are passing laws requiring more control over them. Unlike the United States, which still has much undeveloped territory, those nations do not. As a result, many European countries, like many American cities, are sending their garbage to Africa and Latin America.

Some European countries, most notably Germany, require manufacturers to collect and recycle all packaging they use for their products. A green dot is put on products sold in German supermarkets to show that the packaging is recyclable. Between one-half and two-thirds of products carry the green dot. France and Austria have similar laws.

The German government requires most manufacturers to take back and recycle their products after they have been used up. That means, for example, that when a BMW (Bavarian Motor Works)

TABLE 3.8

Worldwide Extended Producer Responsibility Laws

Country	Products	Recycling or Recovery Target
Europe		
EU Directive	Directive on packaging binding on national governments	50% minimum recovery by 2001; 25% minimum recycling rate.
Austria	Batteries, refrigerators, packaging	Various materials, 20%-70% recovery.
Belgium	Appliances, batteries, electronics, packaging	Recovery targets by 2000: 95% ferrous, 85% non-ferrous, 20% plastics; 50% packaging recovery by 1999.
Denmark	Batteries, packaging (voluntary)	54% overall recovery rate by 2000, with 50%-60% industrial waste.
Finland	Packaging	82% of packaging must be recovered.
France	Batteries, packaging	Follows EU directive.
Germany	Batteries, packaging	Various materials 60%-75% recovery targets.
Greece	Packaging	25% recovery by 2001.
Ireland	Packaging	—
Italy	Appliances, batteries, packaging	Recover 30,000 appliances a year; follows EU directive for packaging.
Luxembourg	Packaging	Recovery target: 55%.
Netherlands	Appliances, batteries, packaging	Appliance/battery recovery target: 90%; packaging recycling target: 65%.
Norway	Appliances, batteries, packaging	Appliances: 80% recovery within 5 years; ni-cad battery pilot: 20,000 households; packaging recovery follows EU directive.
Poland	Packaging	Follows EU directive.
Portugal	Packaging	25% recovery by 2001 and 50% recovery by 2005.
Slovakia	Packaging	Follows EU directive.
Spain	Batteries, packaging.	Follows EU directive.
Switzerland	Packaging	Follows EU directive.
United Kingdom	Packaging	Overall target 38%, increasing to 52% by 2001.
Czech Republic	Packaging	Similar to EU directive.
Estonia	Packaging	60% recovery by 2001.
Slovenia	Packaging	Recycling recovery: 48% by 2000, 78% by 2010.
Asia		
China	Packaging	
Japan	Appliances, packaging	
South Korea	Packaging	
Singapore	Packaging (voluntary)	To reduce waste 80% through recycling.
Taiwan	Packaging	
Latin America		
Brazil	Packaging	Specific manufacturers must set up recycling centers for products: combustible oils, cosmetics, etc.

1998 Raymond Communications Inc., www.Raymond.com.

Source: Lynn Scarlett, *Product Take-Back Systems: Mandates Reconsidered*, Center for the Study of American Business, Washington University, St. Louis, MO, 1999

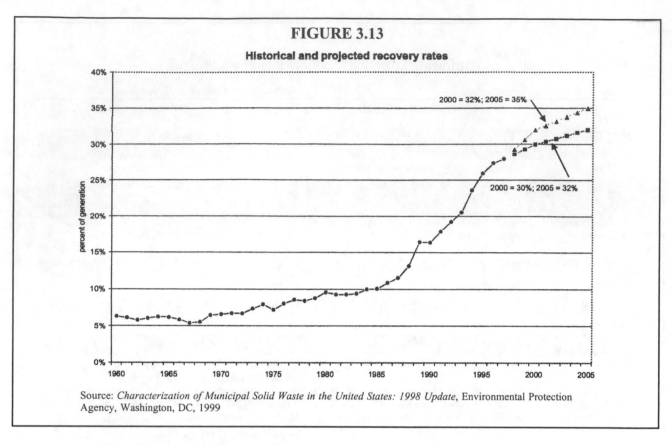

FIGURE 3.13

Historical and projected recovery rates

2000 = 32%; 2005 = 35%

2000 = 30%; 2005 = 32%

percent of generation

Source: *Characterization of Municipal Solid Waste in the United States: 1998 Update*, Environmental Protection Agency, Washington, DC, 1999

motor car can no longer run, the BMW company must take the car, tear it apart, and recycle the parts. A company may throw away a part only if it can prove the part cannot be reused. BMW has found that it can take the windshield out and sell it to glass companies, which can use the glass to make bottles. The engine and other parts can be repaired and sold as spare parts. Plastic bumpers can be melted down and used for door panels.

Sometimes cultural traditions can make it more difficult to control the amount of garbage a country produces. According to a report prepared by the Japan Association of City Mayors, most of Japan's garbage dumps are two-thirds full and will likely be full within six years. One of the major reasons for Japan's growing garbage problem is the huge amount of wrapping and packaging that manufacturers use. Often, the amount of wrapping of a gift shows the amount of respect or love the gift-giver has for the person receiving the gift; the more wrapping, the more respect or love. For example, it is not unusual to have a gift of cookies individually wrapped, laid in corrugated paper, put inside a plastic wrap, covered with nice wrapping

paper, and then delivered in a shopping bag. To change this will require a change in values for many Japanese.

According to the EPA, as of 1995 (although later data exists for the United States, comparative data for the other countries was unavailable), the United States recycled a larger percentage of MSW than many industrialized countries. At a time when Americans recycled 23 percent of its MSW, Switzerland recovered 22 percent; Japan, 20 percent; Sweden, the Netherlands, and Germany, 16 percent each; Spain, 13 percent; and Canada, 10 percent. Italy, France, and the United Kingdom each recycled less than 3 percent of MSW. Table 3.8 shows the recovery goals of various countries in Europe, Asia, and Brazil.

OPPOSING VIEWS

We're not just reusing our garbage; we're performing a rite of atonement for the sin of excess. — John Tierney, *The New York Times Magazine*, 1996

Some observers do not believe that recycling is productive. Some sources claim that recycling is expensive and that programs lose money. According to these observers, recycling benefits politicians, public relations consultants, environmental organizations, and waste-handling corporations, while diverting money from genuine environmental problems. In his article, "Recycling Is Garbage" *(The New York Times Magazine,* June 30, 1996), John Tierney contends, "Recycling may be the most wasteful activity in modern America: a waste of time and money, a waste of human and natural resources."

Tierney also observes that landfills are scarce in just a few places and that where they are scarce, as in the Northeast, it is because of local politics. He claims that human time is the only resource that has become more expensive.

It's wasteful to expend human labor to save raw materials that are cheap today and will probably be cheaper tomorrow. The recycling program consumes resources. It requires extra administrators and a continual campaign explaining what to do with dozens of different products.... It requires extra collection crews and trucks.... Collecting a ton of recyclable items is three times more expensive than collecting a ton of garbage because the crews pick up less material at each stop.

Some other observers also conclude that recycling programs are unprofitable. The Solid Waste Association of North America, a trade organization for waste-management officials, reported that many curbside recycling programs, composting operations, and waste-to-energy incinerators have increased the cost of waste disposal. Some European cities have had similar outcomes, especially Germany, whose recycling program is more unprofitable than New York City's.

On the other hand, Barry McBee, chairman of the Texas Natural Resources Conservation Commission, replied that recycling is "here to stay" because it is profitable for businesses, communities, and individuals. He claims that recycling is now voluntarily practiced by industries because waste is now recognized as a commodity with value in the marketplace, not simply as trash to be buried.

McBee adds that recycling programs can produce savings for local governments. The cost of maintaining landfills has tripled in recent years. Recycling reduces solid waste volume and disposal costs. "Recycling is here to stay because it represents a market-driven solution to our solid waste challenge," he continues. "As is the case with any

TABLE 3.9

GENERATION, RECOVERY, COMBUSTION, AND DISPOSAL OF MUNICIPAL SOLID WASTE: 1997, 2000, AND 2005
(RECOVERY SCENARIOS ASSUMED: 30% IN 2000, 32% IN 2005)
(In thousands of tons and percent of total generation)

	Thousands of tons			% of generation		
	1997	2000	2005	1997	2000	2005
Generation	216,970	223,230	239,540	100.0%	100.0%	100.0%
Recovery for recycling	48,630	53,850	61,840	22.4%	24.1%	25.8%
Recovery for composting*	12,070	13,100	14,900	5.6%	5.9%	6.2%
Total materials recovery	60,700	66,950	76,740	28.0%	30.0%	32.0%
Discards after recovery	156,270	156,280	162,800	72.0%	70.0%	68.0%
Combustion**	36,700	37,200	38,000	16.9%	16.7%	15.9%
Landfill, other disposal	119,570	119,080	124,800	55.1%	53.3%	52.1%

* Composting of yard trimmings and food wastes. Does not include backyard composting.
** Combustion of MSW in mass burn or refuse derived form, incineration without energy recovery, and combustion with energy recovery of source separated materials in MSW. Details may not add to totals due to rounding.

Franklin Associates

Source: *Characterization of Municipal Solid Waste in the United States: 1998 Update,* Environmental Protection Agency, Washington, DC, 1999

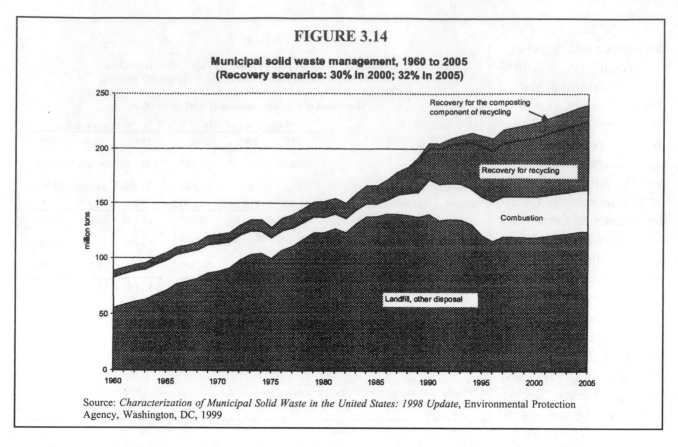

FIGURE 3.14

Municipal solid waste management, 1960 to 2005
(Recovery scenarios: 30% in 2000; 32% in 2005)

Source: *Characterization of Municipal Solid Waste in the United States: 1998 Update*, Environmental Protection Agency, Washington, DC, 1999

commodity, prices for recyclables will rise and fall with demand, but they will have an economic value. Where there is economic value, there is also economic opportunity."

PROJECTIONS FOR SOLID WASTE RECOVERY

Industry experts believe that recovery will increase at between 30 and 35 percent between 2000 and 2005. Because the recycling infrastructure is already in place, growth could approach the upper range. (See Figure 3.13.) On the other hand, recent lower prices do not bode well for expansion in the industry.

The EPA estimates that by 2005, 239.5 million tons of MSW will be generated and that recovery could retrieve 76.7 million tons of MSW. This would mean that landfills and other disposal methods could handle a somewhat smaller percentage of waste (53.3 percent in 2000 and 52.1 percent in 2005) than in 1997 (55.1 percent). (See Table 3.9 and Figure 3.14.)

CHAPTER IV

AIR POLLUTION

For the first time in my life, I saw the horizon as a curved line. It was accentuated by a thin seam of dark blue light — our atmosphere. Obviously, this was not the 'ocean' of air I'd been told it was so many times in my life. I was terrified by its fragile appearance. — Ulf Merbold, West German space shuttle astronaut

THE GLOBAL HEALTH THREAT

It is possible for Americans to avoid the city garbage dumps and even the dirty water. If their drinking water is clean and they do not visit the rivers, the lakes, or the seashore, they can avoid seeing pollution in the waters. If they stay away from the landfills, they can avoid seeing the mountains of garbage building up.

But all Americans must breathe the air, and some of that air is dangerous. Air pollution can make people sick and damage the environment. Trees, lakes, and animals can be harmed by air pollution. Air pollutants have made the ozone layer around Earth thinner, leading to increased skin cancer and cataracts (a disease of the eye that can cause blindness). Air pollution dirties and eats away the stone in buildings, monuments, and statues. Air pollution also causes haze that can make it harder to see.

THE AIR PEOPLE BREATHE

We are evaporating our coal mines into the air. — Svante Arrhenius, Swedish chemist, 1896

Fossil fuels and chemicals have played a major role in society's pursuit of economic growth and higher standards of living. But the burning of fossil fuels and the use of chemicals alter Earth's chemistry and threaten the food, water, and air supplies humans depend on.

FIGURE 4.1

Air pollution in Denver, Colorado, sometimes causes a hazy "brown cloud." Denver has also had problems with carbon monoxide pollution.

Source: *The Plain English Guide to the Clean Air Act*, Environmental Protection Agency, Washington, DC, 1993

Smog

Polluted air is everywhere. In the United States, the list of cities darkened by smog has grown every year since 1970. Smog, a word made up from "smoke" and "fog," is probably the best-known form of air pollution.

Smog is made up mainly of ground-level ozone. Ozone can be good or bad, depending on where it is located. When ozone is high in the atmosphere, it shields the ultraviolet light coming from the sun and protects human health and the environment. When the ozone is at ground level, however, it becomes the most harmful element in

61

smog. Ground-level ozone is produced by the mixing of pollutants from many sources, including smokestacks, cars, and paints. When a car burns gasoline or a painter paints a house, dangerous fumes rise into the air.

Wind often blows smog-forming pollutants away from their sources. The reaction that creates smog occurs while the pollutants are being blown through the air by the wind. This is why smog is often more serious miles away from where the pollutants were created. The smog-forming pollutants are brought together in the sky, and if it is hot and sunny, smog forms more easily. Weather and location determine where smog goes and how bad it will become. When temperature inversions occur (the warm air stays near the ground instead of rising) and winds are calm, such as during the summer, smog may stay in one place for days at a time. As traffic and other pollution sources add more pollutants to the air, the smog gets worse.

Most people connect dirty air with cities and the areas around them. There is good reason for this since some of the worst smog in the country occurs in cities. Figure 4.1, for example, shows Denver, Colorado, a city known for air problems. In a major industrial nation such as the United States, however, smog is not just limited to the cities. On a clear day, the Grand Canyon is one of the most beautiful sites in the world. On bad days, it is hard to see the bottom of the Canyon (Figure 4.2). On the other side of the continent, the Great Smoky Mountains, another beautiful place in the United States, also suffers from smog (Figure 4.3).

As indicated earlier, breathing dirty air is not good for a person's health. The damage this air does to buildings and statues indicates how potent it is. Most television and radio weather reports in major cities include ozone and "air quality" readings as part of the daily weather statistics. Figure 4.4 shows buildings and statues all over the United States that are suffering severe damage from air pollution. (Some of this damage is caused by acid

FIGURE 4.2

Grand Canyon National Park. Top: A clear day. Bottom: Haze.

Source: *The Plain English Guide to the Clean Air Act*, Environmental Protection Agency, Washington, DC, 1993

rain. For more information on acid rain, see *The Environment — A Revolution in Attitudes*, Information Plus, Wylie, Texas, 1998.)

Air pollution has three principal man-made sources — energy use, vehicular emissions, and industrial production — all of which increase with economic growth unless pollution control measures are put in place. In 1998, approximately 113 million Americans lived in areas that failed to meet pollution standards (nonattainment areas). (See Table 4.1 for the number of areas that had nonattainment status in 1998.)

Throughout the world, poor air quality contributes to hundreds of thousands of deaths and diseases each year, to dying forests and lakes, and to corroding buildings and monuments. Mexico City, the capital city of neighboring Mexico, is generally considered to have the worst air in the world. In Paris, France, about 3 million cars enter the capital daily, shrouding the Eiffel Tower in smog and crowding emergency rooms with people suffering from bronchial distress. Air pollution, particularly acid rain, devastates forests, crops, and waterways and works its way into the water cycle and food chains. Table 4.2 shows the pollutants most harmful to plant life.

HEALTH EFFECTS

The quality of the environment plays a role in public health. However, while focusing on the environment is an obvious and often successful approach to improving public health, it is a complex problem. Among the factors that must be considered are the levels of pollutants in the air, the levels of individual exposure to these pollutants, individual susceptibility to toxic substances, and exposure times related to ill effects from certain substances. In addition, attributing health problems to specific pollutants is complicated by the impact of non-environmental causes of the same health effects (for example, smoking, heredity, or diet).

Air pollution is related to a number of respiratory diseases, including bronchitis, pulmonary emphysema, lung cancer, bronchial asthma, eye irritation, weakened immune system, and premature lung tissue aging. The American Lung Asso-

FIGURE 4.3

Great Smoky Mountains National Park. Top: Clear day (photo taken at 7 p.m.). Bottom: haze (photo taken at 3 p.m.).

Source: *The Plain English Guide to the Clean Air Act*, Environmental Protection Agency, Washington, DC, 1993

ciation estimates the annual health costs of exposure to the most serious air pollutants at $40 to $50 billion. In addition, lead contamination causes neurological and kidney disease and can be responsible for impaired fetal and mental development.

The Environmental Protection Agency (EPA) estimates that emissions of toxic materials into the air cause some 2,000 cancer deaths a year. Because

FIGURE 4.4

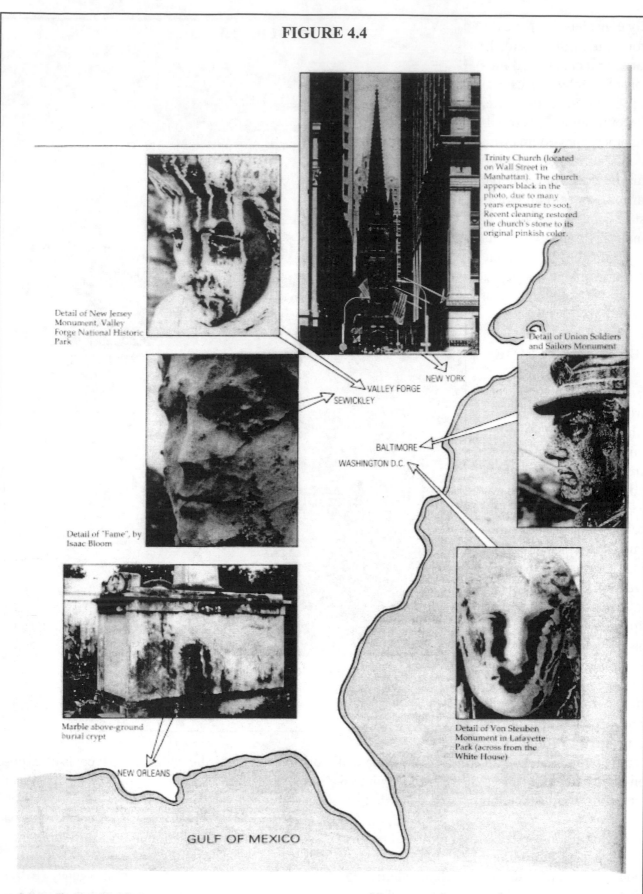

Trinity Church (located on Wall Street in Manhattan). The church appears black in the photo, due to many years exposure to soot. Recent cleaning restored the church's stone to its original pinkish color.

Detail of New Jersey Monument, Valley Forge National Historic Park

Detail of Union Soldiers and Sailors Monument

NEW YORK

VALLEY FORGE

SEWICKLEY

BALTIMORE

WASHINGTON D.C.

Detail of "Fame", by Isaac Bloom

Marble above-ground burial crypt

NEW ORLEANS

Detail of Von Steuben Monument in Lafayette Park (across from the White House)

GULF OF MEXICO

Source: *The Plain English Guide to the Clean Air Act*, Environmental Protection Agency, Washington, DC, 1993

64

research has included only a third of the known carcinogens (and many more have yet to be discovered), this is likely an underestimate. Cancer rates have been known to be higher among persons who live near certain types of factories. The EPA and the Harvard School of Public Health suggest that as many as 50,000 to 60,000 deaths a year are caused by particle (soot) pollution. Scientists report that some types of particles can be fatal even when under the legal limit. In fact, much legislation currently being considered addresses small particle pollution.

WHAT ARE THE AIR POLLUTANTS?

The Clean Air Act of 1970 (PL 91-604; see below) and the Clean Air Act Amendments of 1990 (PL 101-549) address the six pollutants associated with the National Ambient Air Quality Standards (NAAQS). These pollutants — ozone, particulate matter, carbon monoxide, sulfur dioxide, nitrogen dioxide, and lead — are called criteria pollutants and are identified as serious threats to human health. Table 4.3 shows the criteria air pollutants, their health effects, and sources.

The EPA has documented air pollution trends in the United States annually since 1973. Its *National Air Quality and Emissions Trends Report, 1997* (1998) reports two kinds of trends for criteria pollutants. *Emissions* are calculated estimates of the total tonnage of these pollutants released into the air annually. *Air quality concentrations* measure pollutant concentrations in the air at monitoring stations. Nationally, air quality has improved since 1970 for all six pollutants. All criteria pollutant emissions, except NO_x decreased as well. (See Table 4.4.)

TABLE. 4.1

Nonattainment Areas, 1998

Pollutant	1991 # areas	1998 # areas	1998 Population (in 1,000s)
CO	42	20	34,047
Pb	12	10	1,375
NO_2	1	0	0
O_3	100	38	99,824
PM_{10}	70	77	29,890
SO_2	51	34	4,695

Source: *National Air Quality and Emissions Trends Report, 1997*, Environmental Protection Agency, Washington, DC, 1999

Ozone

Ozone (O_3) is the principal component of urban smog. Ozone is a gas formed when energy from sunlight causes hydrocarbons (from industry and automobile emissions) to react with nitrogen oxides (from power plants and automobiles). Ozone has become a persistent problem in many parts of the world. Even the smallest amounts of ozone can cause breathing difficulty. Ground-level ozone is the most complex, pervasive, and difficult to con-

TABLE 4.2

Air pollutants, in order of harm to plants

Pollutant	Primary or secondary pollutant	Form	Major source(s)
Ozone (O_3)	Secondary	Gas	Product of chemical reactions in the atmosphere
Acidic deposition (sulfates and nitrates)	Secondary	Particulate	Product of chemical reactions in the atmosphere
Sulfur dioxide (SO_2)	Primary	Gas	Power generation, smelter operation
Nitrogen dioxides (NO_x)	Primary and secondary	Gas	From direct release and atmospheric transformation
Hydrogen fluoride (HF)	Primary	Gas/ Particulate	Superphosphate production, and aluminum smelters
Ethylene	Primary	Gas	Combustion, natural causes

Source: *Agriculture and the Environment*, U.S. Department of Agriculture, Washington, DC, 1992

TABLE 4.3

Criteria air pollutants, health risks and sources

Pollutants	Health risks	Contributing sources
Ozone[1] (O_3)	Asthma, reduced respiratory function, eye irritation	Cars, refineries, dry cleaners
Particulate matter (PM-10)	Bronchitis, cancer, lung damage	Dust, pesticides
Carbon monoxide (CO)	Blood oxygen carrying capacity reduction, cardiovascular and nervous system impairments	Cars, power plants, wood stoves
Sulphur dioxide (SO_2)	Respiratory tract impairment, destruction of lung tissue	Power plants, paper mills
Lead (Pb)	Retardation and brain damage, esp. children	Cars, non ferrous smelters, battery plants
Nitrogen dioxide (NO_2)	Lung damage and respiratory illness	Power plants, cars, trucks

Environmental progress and challenges: EPA's update

[1] Ozone refers to tropospheric ozone which is hazardous to human health.

Source: Fred Seitz and Christine Plepys, "Monitoring Air Quality in Healthy People 2000," *Healthy People 2000 Statistical Notes*, no. 9, September 1995

---

coal, and natural gas. As a result of the city's efforts to control smog, recent measurements of smog in the Los Angeles area are the lowest in a generation.

In January 1997, chlorofluorocarbons (CFCs) such as Freon, which is used for air-conditioning automobiles, were banned in the United States. CFCs are the prime component in the dissolution of the atmospheric ozone layer. Demand for Freon by American owners of approximately 80 million older cars that use the refrigerant has caused black-market prices to spiral. Federal officials claim the market for contraband Freon is more profitable than cocaine, especially since, in Mexico, Freon is still legal to manufacture and export. A case involving Freon brought the first-ever U.S. felony conviction based on violations of environmental crimes.

Volatile Organic Compounds

Volatile organic compounds (VOCs) are released from burning fuels such as coal, natural gas, gasoline, and wood. Cars are a major source of VOCs. Their health and environmental effects are generally similar to smog. From 1940 through

trol of the six criteria pollutants. In 1998, more than half of all American homes were in areas not in compliance with EPA standards, although since 1988, ozone levels have decreased approximately 20 percent.

Figure 4.5 shows the areas that failed to attain standards set for ozone in 1998. After Southern California, the nation's worst smog problems are in the Chicago, Houston, and New York metropolitan areas. Eleven Atlantic coast states (Maine, New Hampshire, Vermont, New York, Pennsylvania, Massachusetts, Rhode Island, Connecticut, New Jersey, Maryland, and Delaware) and the District of Columbia came under regulatory order to control smog due to their high levels of ozone.

In an effort to raise public awareness, New York is scheduled to get pollution meters, signs that provide pollution readings for the public. California is already under special mandate to reduce emissions because of its high ozone levels. The new regulations require extensive changes to dozens of utility generating stations that use oil,

---

TABLE 4.4

Long-term Percent Change in National Air Quality Concentration and Emissions

	Air Quality Concentration %Change 1978-1997	Emissions % Change 1970-1997
CO	-60%	-32%
Pb	-97%	-98%
NO_2	-25%	+11%
O_3	-30% (1hr)	-37%
PM_{10}	Data Not Available	-75%
SO_2	-55%	-35%

* Includes only directly emitted particles. Secondary PM formed from SO_2, NO_2, and other gases comprise a significant fraction of ambient PM.

Source: *National Air Quality and Emissions Trends Report, 1997*, Environmental Protection Agency, Washington, DC, 1999

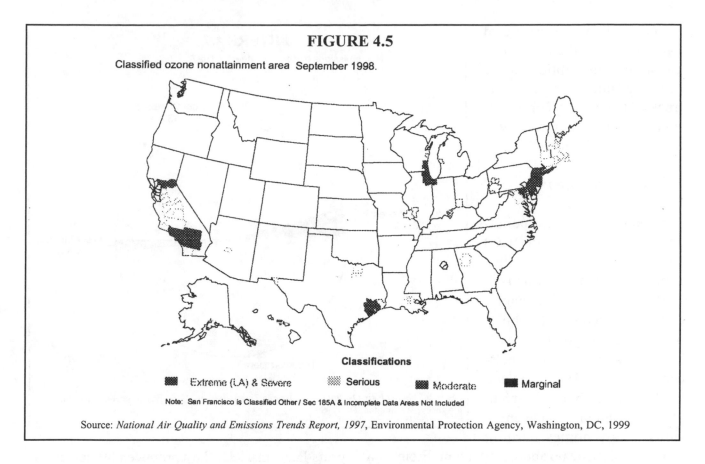

FIGURE 4.5

Classified ozone nonattainment area September 1998.

Classifications

■ Extreme (LA) & Severe   ▨ Serious   ▨ Moderate   ■ Marginal

Note: San Francisco is Classified Other / Sec 185A & Incomplete Data Areas Not Included

Source: *National Air Quality and Emissions Trends Report, 1997*, Environmental Protection Agency, Washington, DC, 1999

1970, VOC emissions increased about 77 percent, mainly because of the increase in car and truck traffic and industrial production. Since 1970, national VOC emissions have decreased as a result of emission controls on cars and trucks and less open burning of solid waste. VOC emissions from highway vehicles dropped 37 percent from 1988 to 1997. Most of the decline has occurred in the transportation area and the burning of fuel. On the other hand, VOC pollution from industry and solid-waste disposal has changed little. Figure 4.6 shows the sources of VOC emissions.

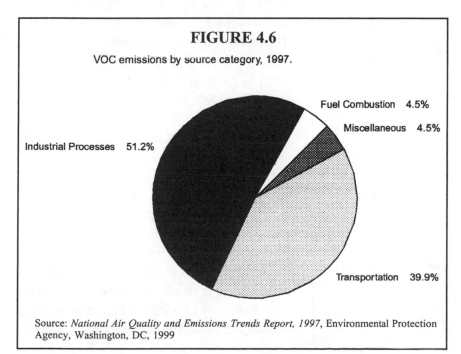

FIGURE 4.6

VOC emissions by source category, 1997.

Fuel Combustion   4.5%

Miscellaneous   4.5%

Industrial Processes   51.2%

Transportation   39.9%

Source: *National Air Quality and Emissions Trends Report, 1997*, Environmental Protection Agency, Washington, DC, 1999

Nitrogen Dioxide

Nitrogen dioxide (NO_2) comes from burning fuels such as gasoline, natural gas, coal, and oil (Figure 4.7). Cars and trucks are a primary source of nitrogen dioxide. Nitrogen dioxide is a major part of smog and causes the same health and environmental effects as smog. Nitrogen dioxide is also in acid rain, which damages trees and lakes and eats away buildings and statues.

From 1940 to 1970, nitrogen dioxide emissions increased

because of more burning of natural gas and the increase in gasoline consumption in the growing number of cars and trucks. Overall NO_2 concentrations fell 14 percent from 1988 to 1997. (See Figure 4.8.)

Carbon Monoxide

Like most criteria pollutants, carbon monoxide (CO) comes from burning gasoline, natural gas, wood, coal, and oil. Carbon monoxide is a dangerous gas that reduces the ability of blood to bring oxygen to the body cells. More than a half-century ago, in 1940, cars and trucks created about 28 percent of the carbon monoxide emissions, while homes burning coal and oil made up about 50 percent. From 1940 through 1970, emissions from cars and trucks nearly tripled. By 1970, cars and trucks accounted for 71 percent of all carbon monoxide, and a dozen years later, in 1982, they produced 80 percent of the total carbon monoxide emissions.

The total amount of carbon monoxide emissions dropped 25 percent between 1988 and 1997 (Figure 4.9), due primarily to an estimated 22 percent drop in emissions from cars and trucks and despite a 25 percent increase in vehicle miles traveled. Transportation now accounts for 76.6 percent of CO emissions (Figure 4.10), down from 81 percent in 1995. Overall CO concentrations fell 38 percent over that time.

Particulate Matter

Particulate matter (PM-10) is the general term for solid or liquid particles — dust, smoke, and soot — that come from burning fuels in industrial plants, from farmland, and from unpaved roads. It also includes particles so small that an electron microscope is required for identification. (See Figure 4.11.) Particulate matter can irritate the nose, throat, and lungs. When

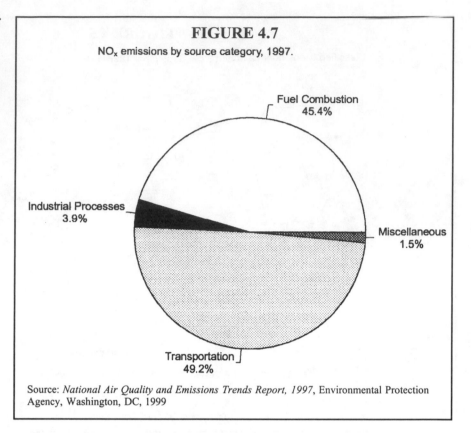

FIGURE 4.7

NO_x emissions by source category, 1997.

Fuel Combustion 45.4%

Industrial Processes 3.9%

Miscellaneous 1.5%

Transportation 49.2%

Source: *National Air Quality and Emissions Trends Report, 1997*, Environmental Protection Agency, Washington, DC, 1999

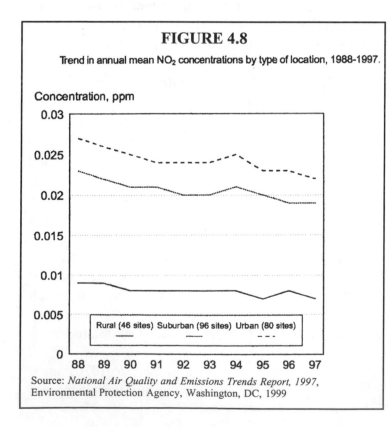

FIGURE 4.8

Trend in annual mean NO_2 concentrations by type of location, 1988-1997.

Concentration, ppm

Rural (46 sites) Suburban (96 sites) Urban (80 sites)

Source: *National Air Quality and Emissions Trends Report, 1997*, Environmental Protection Agency, Washington, DC, 1999

particulate matter hangs in the air, it creates a haze. From 1940 to 1971, particulate matter generally increased. Pollution control laws, however, led to a drop in particulate matter, most of which occurred during the 1970s. Between 1988 and 1997, particulate emissions dropped 12 percent (Figure 4.12). Overall particulate concentration declined 26 percent between 1988 and 1997.

Sulfur Dioxide

Sulfur dioxide (SO_2) is formed when fuel containing sulfur, mainly coal and oil, is burned and during some industrial processes and metal smelting. Inhaling sulfur dioxide can lead to serious breathing problems. Together, sulfur dioxide and nitrogen dioxide are the major components of acid rain, which can damage trees and lakes. From 1940 to 1970, sulfur dioxide emissions increased as a result of the growing use of fossil fuels, especially coal, by industry and electrical utility plants. Since 1970, total sulfur dioxide emissions have dropped because of cleaner fuels with lower sulfur content and the greater use of pollution devices, such as scrubbers, that clean the factory emissions.

As shown in Figure 4.13, most sulfur emissions today still come from fuel combustion. From 1988 to 1997, sulfur dioxide emissions decreased 12 percent (Figure 4.14), and air concentrations declined 39 percent. No counties containing major SO_2 point sources failed to meet the 1997 National Ambient Air Quality Standards (NAAQS).

Lead

Lead poisoning is the most common and most devastating environmental disease affecting young children, according to the Centers for Disease Control and Prevention (CDC). Lead (Pb) can damage the brain and nervous system. Until recently, the main source of lead pollution was leaded gasoline. Today, smelters and battery plants, followed by highway

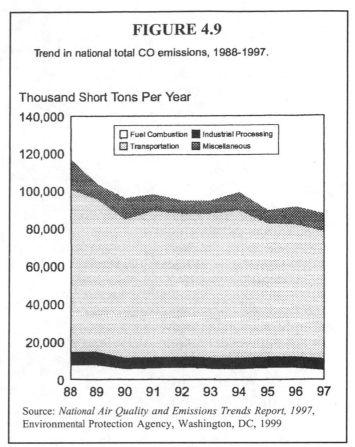

FIGURE 4.9

Trend in national total CO emissions, 1988-1997.

Source: *National Air Quality and Emissions Trends Report, 1997*, Environmental Protection Agency, Washington, DC, 1999

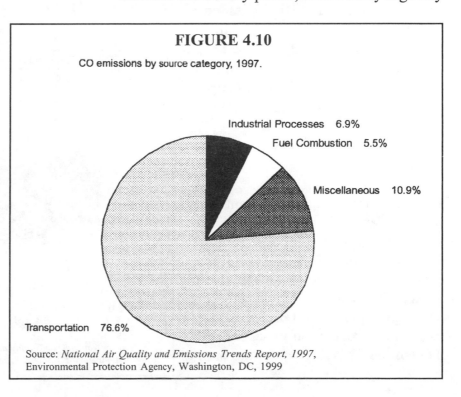

FIGURE 4.10

CO emissions by source category, 1997.

Source: *National Air Quality and Emissions Trends Report, 1997*, Environmental Protection Agency, Washington, DC, 1999

vehicles, are the leading sources of lead emissions (Figure 4.15). From 1988 to 1997, lead emissions decreased 44 percent, primarily because highway vehicles no longer used leaded gasoline. Overall lead concentrations fell 67 percent over that time (Figure 4.16).

The primary cause of the most severe cases of lead poisoning in children is exposure to lead in paint. Lead-based paint was once widely used in housing in the United States. The Office of Housing and Urban Development (HUD) estimates that 57 million, or about three-fourths, of the 77 million privately owned and occupied homes built before 1980 contain lead-based paint. Almost 10 million of these homes are occupied by families with children under 7 years of age, who are the most vulnerable to lead poisoning. In 1997, the EPA and the Department of Housing and Urban Development (HUD) issued a regulation requiring the disclosure of known lead-based paint hazards when homes are sold or rented. In addition, many states have passed laws requiring the disclosure of lead (Figure 4.17).

AIR TOXICS

Hazardous air pollutants, also referred to as air toxics, are pollutants that may cause severe health effects or ecosystem damage. Examples of such toxics are benzene, dioxins, arsenic, beryllium, mercury, and vinyl chloride. The Clean Air Act (CAA) lists 188 substances as hazardous air pollutants (HAPs) and targets them for regulation in section 112 (b) (1) of the CAA. Air toxics are emit-

ted from many sources, including industrial and mobile sources. The air toxics program complements the NAAQS program.

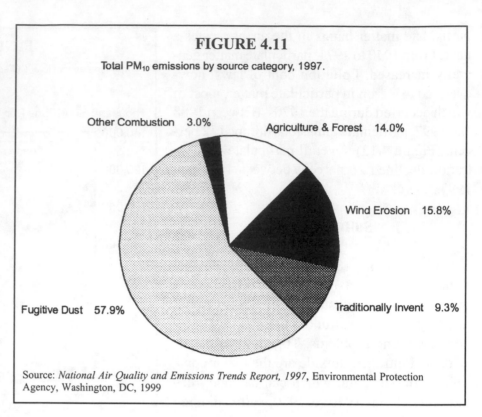

FIGURE 4.11

Total PM$_{10}$ emissions by source category, 1997.

Other Combustion 3.0%
Agriculture & Forest 14.0%
Wind Erosion 15.8%
Fugitive Dust 57.9%
Traditionally Invent 9.3%

Source: *National Air Quality and Emissions Trends Report, 1997*, Environmental Protection Agency, Washington, DC, 1999

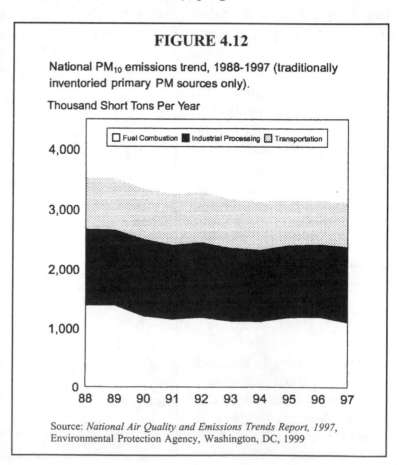

FIGURE 4.12

National PM$_{10}$ emissions trend, 1988-1997 (traditionally inventoried primary PM sources only).

Thousand Short Tons Per Year

☐ Fuel Combustion ■ Industrial Processing ▨ Transportation

Source: *National Air Quality and Emissions Trends Report, 1997*, Environmental Protection Agency, Washington, DC, 1999

Certain manufacturing facilities are required to report their estimated releases of listed chemicals to the EPA each year. These reports have been compiled into a data base called the National Toxics Inventory (NTI), previously the Toxic Release Inventory (TRI), which was established under the Emergency Planning and Community Right-To-Know Act of 1986 (PL 99-499).

The first official results were tabulated in 1988. The list of chemicals that must be reported includes over 300 chemicals in 20 chemical categories. Although the report had limitations — the data is self-reported by the facilities, and certain facilities are not required to participate — TRI estimates generally showed trends in toxic air emissions. Table 4.5 shows the toxic chemical releases by industry from 1988 to 1995. Table 4.6 shows the emissions of 37 selected toxic pollutants, which account for 86 percent of total annual emissions of the 188 HAPs.

The Sector Facility Indexing Project — "Right to Know"

The Clinton Administration has sought to expand "right to know" initiatives — environmental programs designed to inhibit pollution not with legislation and regulation but by exposing polluters to public pressure from a well-informed public. The Sector Facility Indexing Project (SFIP) expands on the National Toxics Inventory (see above) by providing data on the Internet (www.epa.gov/oeca/sfi/) on approximately 640 companies in five industries — automobile, steel, metals, oil refining, and papermaking. The environmental profiles include inspections, noncompliance, enforcement, pollution releases, pollution spills, and demographics on the companies, such as how many people live within three miles of a plant.

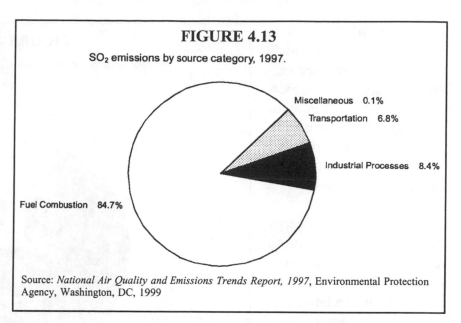

FIGURE 4.13

SO₂ emissions by source category, 1997.

Miscellaneous 0.1%
Transportation 6.8%
Industrial Processes 8.4%
Fuel Combustion 84.7%

Source: *National Air Quality and Emissions Trends Report, 1997*, Environmental Protection Agency, Washington, DC, 1999

THE AUTOMOBILE'S CONTRIBUTION TO AIR POLLUTION

It is the love affair with the automobile, whose numbers are rising faster than the human population, that leads to the most damaging excesses of consumption. Today, motor vehicles account for about a third of global oil consumption. — Shridath Ramphal, *Our Country, Our Planet*, 1992

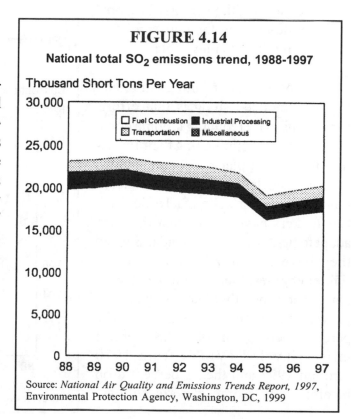

FIGURE 4.14

National total SO₂ emissions trend, 1988-1997

Thousand Short Tons Per Year

Legend: ☐ Fuel Combustion ■ Industrial Processing ⬚ Transportation ⬚ Miscellaneous

Source: *National Air Quality and Emissions Trends Report, 1997*, Environmental Protection Agency, Washington, DC, 1999

Automobiles dominate the transportation sector's share of energy-related carbon emissions. The transportation sector accounts for more than 65 percent of U.S. petroleum consumption and more than 78 percent of carbon monoxide emissions.

Concerns about energy security and air pollution from transportation have encouraged the development of alternative fuel technologies to reduce dependence on traditional gasoline and diesel fuels. Standards established in the 1970s improved efficiency markedly during the 1980s but have since leveled off, leading to a decline in fuel economy. In the absence of tighter standards, emissions from road travel are expected to double by 2020, with much of the increase in developing countries. With industrialization occurring in many Third World countries, the increase in global automobile use and the emissions that accompany them is inevitable.

One of the major failings in reducing auto-induced smog is that efforts have focused on reducing tailpipe emissions instead of eliminating their formation in the first place. Oil and auto industries and legislators have concentrated on mile-per-gallon fuel efficiency. Car makers have shown that they can adapt to tighter emission standards when they have to. They have introduced lighter engines, fuel injection, catalytic converters, and other technological improvements. Figure 4.18 shows the 127 percent increase in total U.S. vehicle miles traveled (VMT) from 1970 through 1997 and the 31 percent drop in emissions. Some experts believe,

however, that efforts could be better spent eliminating emissions altogether and in promoting alternative transportation, such as mass transit systems, carpools, and bicycles.

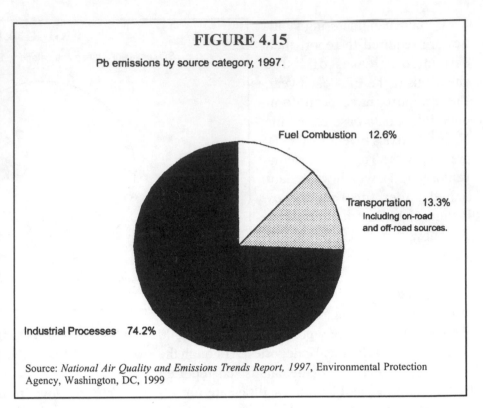

FIGURE 4.15

Pb emissions by source category, 1997.

Fuel Combustion 12.6%

Transportation 13.3%
Including on-road and off-road sources.

Industrial Processes 74.2%

Source: *National Air Quality and Emissions Trends Report, 1997*, Environmental Protection Agency, Washington, DC, 1999

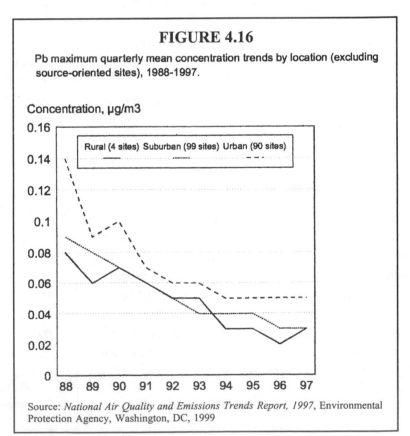

FIGURE 4.16

Pb maximum quarterly mean concentration trends by location (excluding source-oriented sites), 1988-1997.

Concentration, µg/m3

Rural (4 sites) Suburban (99 sites) Urban (90 sites)

Source: *National Air Quality and Emissions Trends Report, 1997*, Environmental Protection Agency, Washington, DC, 1999

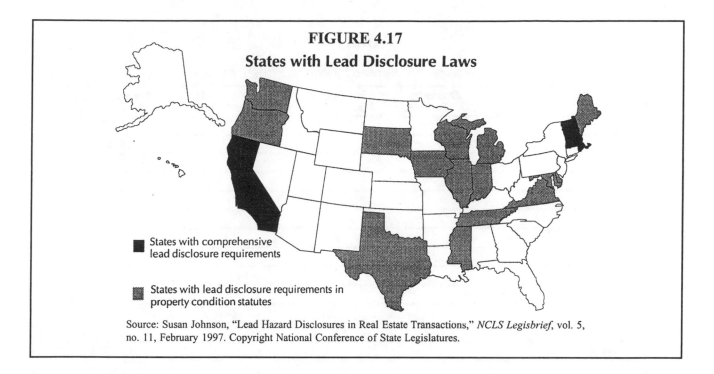

FIGURE 4.17

States with Lead Disclosure Laws

■ States with comprehensive
lead disclosure requirements

▦ States with lead disclosure requirements in
property condition statutes

Source: Susan Johnson, "Lead Hazard Disclosures in Real Estate Transactions," *NCLS Legisbrief*, vol. 5, no. 11, February 1997. Copyright National Conference of State Legislatures.

Those states that do not meet Clean Air Act standards must do something to bring emissions into compliance with national standards. Because of California's extreme air pollution problems, the Clean Air Act Amendments of 1990 (CAAA, PL 101-549; see below) allowed the state to set stricter air quality standards than those required by the amendments. California also requires stricter emission controls than federal standards. The remaining 49 states were given the option of choosing the standards of California or the federal CAAA.

Some states are phasing in tougher tests for auto emissions. In major metropolitan areas, particularly in the Northeast, owners of cars and light trucks will be taking their vehicles to centralized, high-technology inspection stations. The EPA estimates that approximately three-fourths of the vehicles will pass the

inspections on the first try. For those who do not pass, repairs are expected to cost between $38 and $120; repairs for old "clunkers" will likely cost more.

Denver, Colorado, known for its "brown cloud" of pollution, has experienced several winters without violating federal standards for carbon monox-

TABLE 4.5

Toxic Chemical Releases, by Industry: 1988 to 1996

[In thousands of pounds (3,352,959 represents 3,352,959,000). Based on reports filed as required by section 313 of the Emergency Planning and Community Right-to-Know Act (EPCRA, or Title III of the Superfund Amendments and Reauthorization Act of 1986), Public Law 99-499. Owners and operators of facilities that are classified within Standard Classification Code groups 20 through 39, have 10 or more full-time employees, and that manufacture, process, or otherwise uses any listed toxic chemical in quantities greater than the established threshold in the course of a calendar year are covered and required to report]

Industry	1987 SIC[1] code	Core chemicals [2]				Expanded chemical list [3]	
		1988	1994	1995	1996	1995	1996
Total	(X)	3,352,959	1,982,786	1,895,290	1,823,765	2,530,786	2,433,507
Food and kindred products	20	8,378	6,014	5,120	5,121	86,467	83,303
Tobacco products	21	342	135	95	73	2,034	4,153
Textile mill products	22	35,798	16,346	15,656	15,280	18,501	17,328
Apparel and other textile products ..	23	1,026	1,381	1,260	1,742	1,287	1,865
Lumber and wood products.......	24	32,982	32,986	30,435	27,117	34,835	36,243
Furniture and fixtures	25	62,363	52,135	41,530	35,652	41,780	35,877
Paper and allied products	26	207,603	185,334	178,775	172,799	238,317	227,563
Printing and publishing..........	27	61,188	34,387	30,896	28,270	31,156	28,466
Chemical and allied products......	28	1,047,782	537,483	539,600	513,043	844,232	785,178
Petroleum and coal products......	29	72,781	46,877	42,593	43,077	64,141	68,887
Rubber and misc. plastic products ..	30	158,314	125,462	114,765	105,358	127,168	116,409
Leather and leather products......	31	13,024	5,104	4,028	3,814	4,476	4,242
Stone, clay, glass products	32	40,539	17,359	19,053	23,264	32,324	38,740
Primary metal industries	33	629,354	433,886	455,029	496,663	524,041	564,535
Fabricated metals products	34	160,370	99,572	90,441	77,611	97,039	90,254
Industrial machinery and equipment .	35	69,747	27,120	22,852	19,162	26,203	22,061
Electronic, electric equipment	36	132,719	36,672	31,457	33,753	40,456	41,765
Transportation equipment	37	208,392	128,139	114,746	105,232	121,155	111,353
Instruments and related products ...	38	58,085	14,328	12,955	10,359	17,859	15,350
Miscellaneous.................	39	32,593	15,350	13,286	9,843	13,869	10,270
Multiple codes	20-39	308,351	149,011	122,437	91,158	152,531	120,779
No codes...................	20-39	11,229	17,704	8,281	5,377	10,918	8,885

X Not applicable.   [1] Standard Industrial Classification, see text, Section 13, Labor Force.   [2] Chemicals covered for all reporting years.   [3] The Environmental Protection Agency added 286 chemicals and chemical categories to the EPCRA section list of 313 list of toxic chemicals.

Source: U.S. Environmental Protection Agency, *1996 Toxics Release Inventory*.

TABLE 4.6

37 Toxic Pollutants—Ranked by Annual Emissions Totals

Pollutant	Highly Toxic Pollutant[a]	Environmentally Persistent[b]	Effects from Acute Exposure	Ozone Precursor	PM or PM Precursor	National Emissions (tons/year)
Toluene				X	X	1.22E+06
POM (PAHs)	X	X		X	X	7.53E+05
Benzene	X			X		5.72E+05
Formaldehyde			X	X		2.81E+05
Xylenes				X	X	1.87E+05
1,3-Butadiene	X			X		1.23E+05
Tetrachloroethylene			X			1.09E+05
Acetaldehyde				X		9.53E+04
Trichloroethylene				X		5.33E+04
Acrolein	X		X	X		4.93E+04
Methylene chloride		X				4.34E+04
Hydrazine	X			X		3.94E+04
Glycol ethers				X		2.30E+04
Styrene				X		1.67E+04
Arsenic compounds	X	X			X	1.36E+04
Chloroform		X		X		6.93E+03
Nickel compounds	X	X			X	5.36E+03
Lead compounds	X	X			X	3.76E+03
Manganese compounds	X	X			X	1.70E+03
Ethylene dichloride	X			X		1.27E+03
Bis(2-chloroethyl) ether	X					7.90E+02
Cadmium compounds	X	X			X	7.90E+02
Acrylonitrile	X			X		6.98E+02
Ethylene oxide	X	X	X	X		6.52E+02
Vinyl chloride	X			X		5.17E+02
Chromium compounds	X	X			X	2.94E+02
MDI	X			X		2.73E+02
Mercury compounds	X	X			X	2.46E+02
2,4-Toluene diisocyanate	X		X	X		4.50E+01
Antimony compounds	X	X				2.18E+01
Ethylene dibromide	X					1.68E+01
Acrylamide	X			X		1.44E+01
Beryllium compounds	X	X				9.29E+00
Phosgene	X	X	X	X		2.85E+00
2,3,7,8-TCDF	X			X	X	1.44E-02
2,3,7,8-TCDD	X			X	X	1.56E-03
Coke oven emissions	X				X	*

* Coke oven gas emissions not included in Version 2 of the National Toxic Inventory.

a Highly toxic HAP are those HAP with a reference concentration of less than 5.0E-03 mg/m^3 (noncancer effects), a weight of evidence classification of A (known human carcinogen) or B1 (probable human carcinogen); or, a verified unit risk estimate of greater than 2.0 E-05 (ug/m^3)$^{-1}$ and a weight of evidence classification of A or B.

b HAP for which there is potential for persistence in the environment of greater than 14 days.

Source: *National Air Quality and Emissions Trends Report, 1995*, Environmental Protection Agency, Washington, DC, 1996

ide, particulate matter, or ozone. Experts attribute the improvement to automakers' compliance with federal pollution standards. However, the cloud still hangs over the city on windless days, and scientists warn of a possible return to former pollution levels since about half the cars in the city are sport-utility vehicles.

Alternative Approaches

Buses fueled by natural gas take commuters to work. Electric cars recharge in America's garages as their owners sleep. California's smog and Denver's brown cloud are becoming things of the past. Domestic sources account for a substantial portion of the U.S. energy supply. As futuristic as these goals may seem, steps are being taken to achieve them all over the country through the use of alternative fuels and alternative fuel vehicles (AFVs). — National Conference of State Legislatures, A Legislator's Guide to Alternative Fuel Policies and Programs, 1997

One option under consideration to reduce emissions is the introduction of vehicles powered by alternative fuels, such as methanol, ethanol, natural gas, hydrogen, and electricity. Although these fuels offer advantages, their use may substitute one problem for another. For example, methanol reduces ozone formation but increases formaldehyde, a human carcinogen, and is twice as toxic as gasoline if it comes in contact with the skin. Engines require twice as much methanol as gasoline to travel a similar distance. Natural gas reduces hydrocarbons and carbon monoxide but increases nitrogen oxides. In the long run, electricity and hydrogen are likely the most promising of the alternative fuels for vehicles.

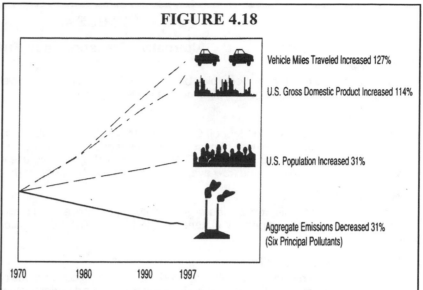

FIGURE 4.18

Vehicle Miles Traveled Increased 127%

U.S. Gross Domestic Product Increased 114%

U.S. Population Increased 31%

Aggregate Emissions Decreased 31%
(Six Principal Pollutants)

1970   1980   1990   1997

Total U.S. Population, vehicle miles traveled, U.S. gross domestic product, and aggregate emissions, 1970-1997.

Source: *National Air Quality and Emissions Trends Report, 1997*, Environmental Protection Agency, Washington, DC, 1999

TABLE 4.7

Percentage of New Fleet Light Duty Purchases That Must Be AFVs

Year	Federal Government	State Government	Fuel Providers	Private/ Municipal⊛
1993	7,500*	-	-	-
1994	11,250*	-	-	-
1995	15,000*	-	-	-
1996	25	-	-	-
1997	33	10	30	-
1998	50	15	50	-
1999	75	25	70	-
2000	75	50	90	-
2001	75	75	90	-
2002	75	75	90	20
2003	75	75	90	30
2004	75	75	90	40
2005	75	75	90	50
2006	75	75	90	60
2007	75	75	90	70

* Actual number of vehicles

⊛ Dependent upon DOE final rulemaking in 2000

Source: Kelly Hill, *A Legislator's Guide to Alternative Fuel Policies and Programs*, National Conference of State Legislatures, Denver, CO, 1997. Copyright National Conference of State Legislatures.

However, electricity generated from non-polluting, renewable sources is not on the immediate horizon, and hydrogen produced by solar cells is still too costly at this time. Many experts believe the most feasible solution in the near future will be a hybrid vehicle using a combination of gasoline and one of the other fuel sources, most likely a fuel cell or hydrogen.

Reformulated Gasoline

Carbon monoxide emissions result from incomplete combustion of fuel. Adding oxygen (*oxygenation*) to the fuel makes combustion more complete, especially in older cars, and carbon dioxide, rather than carbon monoxide, results. The most frequently used oxygenates are ethanol and MTBE (methyl tertiary butyl ether). Reformulated gas means less high-octane fuel and a possible rise in price (4 to 5 cents per gallon to as much as 25 cents per gallon).

The Clean Air Act required those areas with the worst polluted air to sell reformulated gasoline beginning January 1995. Other areas could voluntarily choose to participate. In cities with the highest ozone levels, fuels with oxygen are already required. Customer complaints over price have caused many areas that had voluntarily opted to sell reformulated gas to back out. Some scientists have expressed concern about MTBE, claiming that its safety has not been established.

Converters

Tailpipe catalytic converters are one of the most successful technologies in the history of smog control, eliminating 96 to 98 percent of the carbon monoxide and hydrocarbons. But that can still be improved upon. Researchers are now perfecting new "pre-heating" converters, striving to eliminate pollutants entirely. Converters typically cannot function properly until the car has warmed to a particular temperature; therefore, emissions are greatest during the first few miles. The new converters will function as soon as the car is started.

In 1998, the EPA expressed concerns, however, that catalytic converters rearrange nitrogen-oxygen compounds to form nitrogen oxide, the most common of the global warming gases. Nitrogen oxide levels may increase, at least in part, from the growth in the number of vehicle miles traveled by cars that have catalytic converters.

Government Regulation — Corporate Average Fuel Economy (CAFE) Standards

In 1973, the Organization of Petroleum Exporting Countries (OPEC) imposed an oil embargo that provided a painful reminder to America of how dependent it had become on foreign sources of fuel. Although the United States makes up only 5 percent of the world's population, it consumes approximately one-quarter of the world's supply of oil, much of which is imported from the Middle East. The 1973 oil embargo prompted Congress to pass the 1975 Automobile Fuel Efficiency Act (PL 96-426), which set the initial Corporate Average Fuel Efficiency standards (commonly called the CAFE standards).

The CAFE standards required each domestic automaker to increase the average mileage of the new cars sold to 27.5 miles per gallon (mpg) by 1985. Under the CAFE rules, car manufacturers could still sell the big, less efficient cars with powerful 8-cylinder engines, but to meet the *average* fuel efficiency rates, they also had to sell smaller, more efficient cars. Automakers that failed to meet each year's CAFE standards were required to pay fines. Those that managed to surpass the rates earned credits that they could use in years when they fell below the CAFE requirements.

Faced with the CAFE standards, the car companies became more inventive and managed to keep their cars relatively large and roomy with such innovations as electronic fuel injection and front-wheel drive. Ford's prestigious Lincoln Town Car managed to achieve better mileage in 1985 than its small Pinto did in 1974.

In the aftermath of the Persian Gulf War in the early 1990s, another strong reminder to the United States of its dependence on foreign oil, some members of Congress wanted to raise the CAFE standards to as high as 45 mpg for cars and 35 mpg for light trucks. Those in favor of raising CAFE standards by 40 percent claimed that this would save about 2.8 million barrels of oil a day and noted that if cars became even more fuel-efficient in the future, emissions of carbon dioxide would be significantly reduced. Carbon dioxide has been identified as the main "greenhouse" gas that contributes to global warming. Moreover, with better mileage, the nation's millions of drivers would save money in gas costs.

Opponents to raising CAFE standards believe that the congressional fuel economy campaign saddled American motorists with car features they would not like and would not buy. They have also pointed out that the only way to raise fuel efficiency levels is to manufacture much smaller cars and trucks and to limit the number of larger vehicles. They claim smaller cars would raise the numbers of highway deaths and injuries, limit consumer choice of larger and family-sized vehicles, and place thousands of auto-related jobs at risk.

Legislators have, so far, not passed further legislation to increase CAFE standards. The required efficiency standard has been achieved consistently since then but has not improved further due to America's preference for larger, less-efficient cars, minivans, and sport-utility vehicles. Overall, U.S. new-car fuel economy is now declining, due largely to greater use of sport-utility vehicles. States have also increased speed limits, which lowers fuel efficiency.

Industry officials claim that with each mile added in efficiency, the costs to obtain that improvement increases to an eventual point that it is no longer cost-effective. This is the same objection that is made, in general, about cleaning up many environmental hazards — that the first and most drastic improvements are the least expensive.

In contrast, for 2005, the European Commission (the executive board of the European Union, a league of European countries) has proposed an ambitious target of 47 miles per gallon (mpg) for gasoline-driven cars (compared to the current average of 29 mpg) and 52 mpg for diesel-powered cars.

The Impact of Sport-Utility Vehicles

Big sport-utility vehicles and pickups are the fastest-growing segment of the auto industry, supplying most of the profits for the Big Three auto companies. Currently, such vehicles fall under less stringent emissions standards than automobiles, allowed to emit three times more nitrogen oxides, the main cause of smog. Automakers and buyers of trucks and sport-utility vehicles oppose tightening restrictions on emissions of those vehicles.

In February 1998, President Clinton proposed a research effort with automotive companies to sharply improve the fuel economy of sport-utility vehicles, pickup trucks, and mini-vans. The research is expected to involve switching from an internal-combustion engine to a hybrid system in which a small engine, running on gasoline or diesel fuel, operates steadily to run an electric generator and charge batteries or feed drive motors on the wheels.

In December 1999, the EPA announced tougher pollution regulations on new cars. For the first time, the standards will include sport-utility vehicles, minivans, and light trucks, which currently account for half the new vehicles sold. The new regulations are aimed at slashing tailpipe releases by 90 percent by 2009 and reducing sulfur in gasoline by 90 percent and will take effect with 2004 model cars.

Mandating of Alternative Fuel Vehicles (AFVs)

The Energy Policy Act of 1992 (EPACT; PL 102-486), passed in the wake of the 1991 Persian Gulf War, required that federal and state governments and fleet owners increase the percentages of vehicles powered by alternative fuels. The fleet requirements affect those who own or control at least 50 vehicles in the United States and fleets of at least 20 vehicles that are centrally fueled or capable of being centrally fueled within a metropolitan area of 250,000 or more. (Table 4.7 shows the schedule for AFV purchases.) In doing so, many municipal governments and the U.S. Postal Service have put into operation fleets of natural gas vehicles, such as garbage trucks, transit buses, and postal vans.

Alternative Fuels

Alternative fuel use is expanding worldwide. The use of alternative, nonpetroleum-based fuels in vehicles also offers opportunities to reduce overall energy use and emissions. Table 4.8 shows the variety of fuels under consideration as alternative fuel sources in vehicles.

Gasohol

In 1991, to help reduce the nation's dependence on imported oil, the Congress enacted the National Defense Authorization Act (PL 101-510), which includes a provision directing federal agencies to purchase gasohol (gasoline containing 10 percent ethanol) when it is available at prices equal to or lower than gasoline. Since 1991, federal agencies have taken a number of steps to encourage the use of gasohol.

Executive Order 12759 of 1991 requires federal agencies operating more than 300 vehicles to reduce their gas consumption by 10 percent, an incentive to use gasohol. Despite these measures, however, use of gasohol has increased only slightly because of its cost and frequent unavailability, caused by the high cost of transporting and storing it. While there have been a number of proposals to drop gasohol altogether, senators and representatives from grain-growing states have used their influence to make sure that gasohol remains a part of the nation's fuel mix.

Hydrogen

For decades, advocates of hydrogen have promoted it as the fuel of the future — abundant, clean, and cheap. Hydrogen researchers from universities, laboratories, and private companies claim their industry has already produced vehicles that could be ready to market if problems of fuel supply and distribution could be solved. Other experts contend that economics and safety concerns limit hydrogen's wider use for decades.

But Will They Come?

Many state policies and programs encourage the use of alternative fuels. California, for example, requires the offering of electric vehicles (EVs) by 2003. This has caused vehicle manufacturers to expedite vehicle research and development. In fact, EVs are already selling there (see below), and some rental car agencies now offer EVs to customers at prices only slightly higher than gasoline-powered cars.

Alternative fuel vehicles cannot become a viable transportation option unless a fuel supply is readily available. Ideally, the infrastructure of supplying alternative fuels would be developed simultaneously with the vehicles.

Amoco, a major oil company, built 37 natural gas fueling stations, at a cost of $250,000 to $300,000 each, to service natural gas vehicles. None of the pumps did enough business to recoup the installation charges. The company has closed most of those and will close the remainder when contracts expire. The only station to maintain itself briefly was the one located in Atlanta, Georgia, during the 1996 Olympics, when natural gas vehicles were brought in for show.

Chrysler Corporation stopped making natural gas-powered vehicles after the 1997 model year because it lost money on the vehicles. Chrysler sold only 4,000 such autos since it began production in 1992. General Motors, which had suspended sales of natural-gas vehicles in 1994, resumed sales again in 1997. Ford began selling some natural gas versions of its cars and trucks in 1995. Commercial fleets, not retail customers, are the main buyers of natural-gas vehicles.

The market success of alternative fuels and AFVs depend upon public acceptance. People are accustomed to using gasoline as their main transportation fuel, and it is easily available. Perhaps, as federal and state requirements for alternative fuels increase, so will their visibility to the general public.

Electric Cars — Promise and Reality

While technological dreams do not always come true, the electric car now seems to have more than a fighting chance. The major limitations of today's models are within sight of being overcome; indeed, a host of companies are betting billions of dollars on their ability to make that happen. And they cannot but be pleasantly surprised by the initial response to the EV1: according to Saturn dealers, the waiting list of several hundred hopeful leaseholders continues to grow. — Sean Dunn, Worldwatch, 1997

The electric car is not a new invention. Popular during the 1890s, the quiet, clean, and simple vehicle was expected to dominate the automotive market of the twentieth century. Instead, it quietly disappeared as automobile companies chose to invest billions of dollars in the internal combustion engine. It has taken a century, but the electric car has returned.

Energy standards have created a clear market for alternative-energy cars. The combination of government mandates to reduce emissions and encouraging market opportunities has altered the automobile industry — most car manufacturers either have an electric car on the roads or in testing.

The primary difficulty facing the development of electric vehicles (EVs; Figure 4.19) lies in inadequate battery power. The batteries must be recharged often. Currently, these cars use lead-acid or nickel-cadmium batteries and have a range of 50 to 100 miles on a single charge. The range is reduced by factors such as cold temperatures, the use of air conditioning, vehicle load, and steep terrain.

In addition, electric vehicles are expensive, although the prices are coming down. In general, they cost less than luxury cars but more than the average mid-size American car. In California, some car rental companies offer electric vehicles for rent at rates only slightly more than gas-powered vehicles.

Despite their current high price, electric cars have many advantages. They are relatively noiseless and simple in design and operation. They cost

FIGURE 4.19

THE GENERAL MOTORS ELECTRIC CAR

Source: *Electric Vehicles: Likely Consequences of U.S. and Other Nations' Programs and Policies*, U.S. General Accounting Office, Washington, DC, 1994

less to refuel and service, and have fewer parts to break down. Their owners are likely to spend less time on maintenance, and if they recharge at home, will rarely have to go to the service station. These time savings have real value in today's busy world. Over time, the cost gap between cars that pollute and electric cars that do not is not all that great. With another decade of battery development, the gap could close entirely.

Car experts believe electric cars will assume a "second car" role for commuters and for short trips, much like the microwave oven has become not a replacement for, but an addition to, conventional ovens for cooking.

California has led the development of electric vehicles. In 1990, the California Air Resources Board (CARB), facing severe air pollution in Los Angeles and other cities, passed the toughest auto emissions standards in the world. Most notable was the requirement that 2 percent of cars sold in the state by the seven major carmakers in 1998 be "zero-emission," and that proportion would rise to 10 percent by 2003. Auto-industry lobbyists protested, and the 1998 mandate was lifted. The big automakers are still required to achieve the 10 percent target in 2003. If the automakers actually achieve the goal, and this is a huge if, approximately 800,000 zero-emission cars would be on California roads by 2010, up from 2,000 in use in the entire country in 1997.

In 1997, a federal judge ruled that the State of New York could order automobile manufacturers to sell thousands of electrically powered vehicles in New York in 1998, making New York the only state that mandates the sale of electric cars.

Industry officials have announced plans to produce hybrid vehicles by 2005 that operate on gasoline in conjunction with fuel cells. Such vehicles would overcome the problem of fuel availability by use of conventional fuel and abundant refueling stops and yet burn fuel twice as efficiently as with current technology. For more information on alternative vehicles, see *Transportation — America's Lifeline*, Information Plus, Wylie, Texas, 1999.

AIRPLANES

Air travel in affluent nations is rising and causing a number of environmental problems. The average American flies 1,739 miles a year. Europeans, though they fly fewer miles, have the world's most crowded skies. The most rapid growth in flying has been in Asia. Most air travel is done by a small portion of the world's people.

Flying carries an environmental price; it is the most energy-intensive form of transport. In much of the industrialized world, air travel is replacing more energy-efficient rail or bus travel. Despite a rise in fuel efficiency of jet engines, jet fuel consumption has risen 65 percent since 1970.

Another problem with air travel is its impact on global warming. Airplanes spew out nearly 4 million tons of nitrogen oxide, much of it while cruising in the tropospheric zone five to seven miles above the earth where ozone is formed. Some experts estimate that air traffic accounts for 8 percent of all global greenhouse warming.

On the other hand, the EPA and the Federal Aviation Administration (FAA) believe that jet aircraft currently contribute a minor amount to pollution in the upper atmosphere, especially considering contributions from other sources. In 1995, the now defunct Office of Technology Assessment (OTA) estimated that aircraft emissions represent about 5 percent of the 1.4 billion tons of air pollution produced annually from all sources. Nitrogen oxide emissions in the stratosphere (60,000 to 90,000 feet) currently have a small impact on upper-level ozone depletion. Jet emissions of carbon dioxide and nitrogen oxides, however, could be a concern in the future.

Although each generation of airplane engines gets cleaner and more fuel-efficient, there seems to be little that can be done about the increased amount of flying. There have been, however, modifications in other engines on the trucks, cars, and carts that service airplane fleets. Electric utility companies, including the Edison Electric Institute and the Electric Power Research Institute, launched a program in 1993 to electrify airports. By converting terminal transport buses, food trucks, and baggage-handling carts to electricity, airports hope to reduce air pollution.

BOATS

Boat engines have not changed much since the 1930s. Running an outboard motor for an hour is estimated to pollute as much as driving 800 miles. In 1996, the Environmental Protection Agency (EPA) adopted standards to slash emissions from boats and other water vehicles, such as jet skis, which on some days in some places, according to EPA, can account for up to 15 percent of total smog. The new standards set a goal of a 75 percent emissions reduction by 2006. Under the new regulations, engine prices have risen approximately 14 percent but will save on gas.

In 1998, air-quality regulators in California proposed rules tougher than federal standards to limit emissions from personal watercraft and motorboats. California is the nation's second largest boating state, behind Michigan.

REDUCING EMISSIONS — BUT NOT ENOUGH

The most widespread technological invention to reduce emissions has been the introduction of electrostatic precipitators (electrical cleaning systems) and filters to control emissions from power plants. These reduce particulate emissions from smokestacks by 99.5 percent, but they do nothing about gaseous emissions. The primary technique used to reduce sulfur dioxide has been the use of scrubbers, which remove 95 percent of the sulfur dioxide residue. In general, new power plants are tightly regulated in most industrialized countries. The problem comes in modifying existing facilities. The available technologies have their own problems — they create scrubber ash, a hazardous waste, and they do nothing to control carbon dioxide emissions.

California Leads the Way

California, with the worst air pollution in the nation, has the unique power among the states to set its own emission standards. The states' standards are frequently stricter than federal law mandates. The stringent standards imposed in California have resulted in the introduction of scanners and sensors to detect and monitor emission levels at the source. These sensors are installed in each smokestack, and the results are transmitted directly to a regulatory agency.

Reactive gases from products such as paints and solvents can be scanned with bar-code scanners, much like those used in the retail industry for pricing. The data collected can be transmitted electronically to air-quality agency computers. Many government employees in California work four-day weeks to reduce smog, although some studies conclude that ozone reductions are not as great as claimed.

In a state known for its noxious smog, pollution measurements show that cleanup efforts are reducing air contamination. Thirty-five years ago, California's ozone exceeded health standards on four out of five days. Today, that ozone standard (0.12 parts per million air parts) is exceeded fewer than two of every five days. Since 1988, there has not been a "Stage 2" alert (ozone above 0.35 parts per million), when industries and driving are curtailed and school children are removed from playgrounds.

Not since 1974 has there been a "Stage 3" alert (0.50 parts per million), when a general holiday is ordered. Linda Waade, executive director of the Coalition for Clean Air, a California public interest group, has expressed concern that governmental budget cuts now sweeping the United States could result in a loosening of the strict health standards that made California the national leader in environmental cleanup.

California, particularly the border city of San Diego (classified as a serious ozone nonattainment area), has experienced emissions from unregulated vehicles used by commuters driving from Mexico. Roughly 7,000 commuter vehicles registered in Mexico cross the border into San Diego County each day. (Another 50,000 vehicles cross the border daily, but these include commercial vehicles, vehicles registered in the United States, and Mexican vehicles crossing the border for reasons other than commuting.) In 1998, Congress enacted PL 105-286, an amendment to the Clean Air Act, to control "border smog" emissions from vehicles entering southern California from Mexico. The law limits entry of foreign passenger cars unless they comply with California's vehicle inspection and maintenance requirements.

The Dollar Value of Air Pollution

Putting a dollar value on the health costs of air pollution is very difficult because it requires judgments about the value of good health and human life. Health expert Thomas Crocker of the University of Wyoming estimated the cost to be as high as $40 billion annually in health care and lost productivity. The American Lung Association calculated the direct and indirect health-care costs associated with air pollution to be $16 to $40 billion a year.

The United States Is Missing Its Goals

The Clean Air Act of 1970 imposed controls on certain types of emissions but left others unregulated. As a result, progress in cutting pollution has been uneven. Although reductions in emissions of the six criteria pollutants have occurred, the U.S carbon dioxide emissions continue to rise. Carbon dioxide is the product of burning fossil fuels and is believed to be the major cause of global warming.

Although a car built today produces only one-tenth the pollution per mile traveled as one built two decades ago, fuel efficiency standards have not been tightened in years, Americans are buying less efficient vehicles, and total miles traveled increase each year. The State Department has stated that, fed by an economic boom that has stalled improvements in energy efficiency, affordable gas, and gas-guzzling vehicles, the United States will likely continue to increase emissions of carbon dioxide. This is just the opposite of what was promised at the 1992 United Nations Conference on the Environment in Rio de Janeiro. The U.S. goal of reducing carbon dioxide emissions to 1990 levels by 2000, as agreed at the Conference, will not be reached. Other industrialized nations also expect to fall short of the treaty goal.

The 1997 Kyoto Global Warming Treaty

In December 1997, the United Nations convened a 160-nation conference on global warming in Kyoto, Japan, in hopes of producing a new treaty on climate change that would place binding caps on industrial emissions. However, wide gulfs existed between rich and poor countries, even among rich countries. The European community contended the United States has not done enough to reach its goals.

The treaty, called the Kyoto Protocol to the United Nations Framework Convention on Climate Change, binds industrialized nations to reducing their emissions of six greenhouse gases below 1990 levels by 2012. Each country has a different target for reducing carbon dioxide, hydrofluorocarbons, methane, nitrous oxides, sulfur dioxides, and perfluorocarbons. The United States must cut emissions by 7 percent, most European nations by 8 percent, and Japan by 6 percent. Reductions must begin by 2008 and be achieved by 2012. Developing nations are not required to make such pledges.

The United States had proposed a program of voluntary pledges by developing nations, but that section was deleted, as was a tough system of enforcement. Instead, each country will decide for itself how to achieve its goal. The treaty provides market-driven tools, such as buying and selling credits, for reducing emissions. It also sets up a Clean Development Fund to help poorer nations with technology to reduce their emissions. Countries will decide on their own whether to sign and ratify the treaty.

Although it is the first time nations have made such sweeping pledges, many sources expect difficulty in getting ratification. In the United States, the treaty must be signed and then ratified by the Senate. Within the United States, business leaders believe the treaty goes too far, while environmentalists believe standards do not go far enough. Some experts doubt that any action emerging from Kyoto will be sufficient to prevent doubling of greenhouse gases. Dr. Michael Oppenheimer, a climate scientist with the Environmental Defense Fund (a private environmental agency), considers the pact a victory, although not a complete one. Representatives of the oil industry and business contend the treaty will spell economic pain for the United States.

In November 1998, in a follow-up on the Kyoto Protocol, negotiators from 150 countries meeting in Buenos Aires set a deadline of two years for adopting rules for cutting emissions. Argentina became the first developing country to announce that it would assume binding targets and timetables for emissions. Kazakhstan and Honduras followed, and some African nations expressed interest in more involvement.

While some sources considered the summit a success on those grounds, others discounted any progress made. They note that the two biggest and most influential developing countries, India and China, refused to be involved in the program. In addition, the United States has not ratified the protocol. The fossil-fuel industry and conservative politicians portray the protocol as unworkable and too costly to the American economy. Under the rules of ratification, the protocol cannot go into effect if the United States does not approve it. The conferees set late 2000 as the deadline for adopting rules for putting the Kyoto Protocol into effect.

NO MORE CHEAP FIXES

Increasingly, a major problem with the effort to reduce air pollution further, and some other types of pollution as well, is that most of the relatively cheap fixes have already been made, and many economists argue the expensive ones may not be worth the price. The very premise of cleanup — that smog can be reduced to such levels that it no longer poses any health risk at all — is now being questioned by some academics as well as by industry.

Virtually all gains in the war on ozone have been achieved by reducing auto emissions. But costs for future air quality improvements may likely exceed the value of any improvement made, and the disparity may only get worse over time. "There are only so many times you can go back to the well and expect a full bucket," said Robert Hahn, an economist at the conservative American Enterprise Institute.

With automobiles, for example, by 1994, the tailpipe pollution standard reduced the exhaust of VOC pollutants by 98 percent. Getting the figure down to 99.5 percent will at least double the cost.

Some experts believe that producing zero-emissions electric vehicles with the range and performance of today's cars would require a technological revolution.

California, which has its own emissions standards (see below), has recently retreated from its commitment to a tough mandate for electric cars, citing the problems faced with the increasingly stringent demands of the federal Clean Air Act. This battle of electric cars is only one of many signs that the time of easy solutions is over.

The conservative Center for the Study of American Business expressed the concerns of those who believe that the costs have exceeded the benefits of further cleanup. "The goal of the [Clean Air] Act should be to protect the public against *unreasonable* risk of *significant* adverse health effects," claims Kenneth Chilton and Christopher Boerner. "The United States is already spending more taxpayer and consumer dollars on reducing ozone levels than the public considers worthwhile."

THE CLEAN AIR ACT

In 1948, fog trapped acid fumes over the town of Donora, Pennsylvania, sickening 6,000 residents and killing 19. Those were the first known American deaths from air pollution and vivid proof that pollution can kill. A weather phenomenon called an inversion, in which a cold air mass traps warm air near the ground, mixed sulfur dioxide emissions from a nearby U.S. Steel plant with the fog to form a sulfuric acid mist. U.S. Steel paid multiple out-of-court settlements to survivors, and eventually the plant was closed.

In 1970, the U.S. Congress passed the landmark Clean Air Act (PL 91-604), proclaiming that it would restore urban air quality. It was no coincidence that the law was passed during a 14-day Washington, DC, smog alert. The law has had mixed results. Since its adoption, airborne lead has declined 90 percent, primarily due to the reduced sale of leaded gasoline, and most other measured emissions have also decreased.

Nonetheless, 30 years later, many cities are still not in compliance with the law, and Congress has had to repeatedly draft revisions. Efforts to clean the air have been only partly successful. They have focused on specific measures to combat individual pollutants rather than addressing the underlying social and economic structures that create the problem — for example, the distance between many Americans' residences and their places of work.

The overall goal of the Clean Air Act Amendments of 1990 (PL 101-549) was to reduce the pollutants in the air by 56 billion pounds a year — 224 pounds for every man, woman, and child — when the law is fully phased in by the year 2005. Other aims were to cut acid rain in half by the year 2000 (a goal that may not be reached), reduce smog and other pollutants, and protect the ozone layer by phasing out chlorofluorocarbons (CFCs) and related chemicals.

The Bill Clinton Administration initially committed the United States to a reduction in greenhouse gas emissions to 1990 levels by the year 2000. In 1997, Clinton proposed reducing carbon emissions to 1990 levels between 2008 and 2012. Whether even that can be accomplished with the current budget cuts is questionable.

Resistance to CAA Leads to Federal Concessions

During the mid- to late-1990s, a number of states began balking at strict auto emissions testing that seemed imminent in order to comply with the Clean Air Act. Under the law, if a reduction does not come from auto emissions, it would have to be made up by other sources, for example, smokestack industries. The states are free to implement whatever methods they choose to cut pollution, but most states with serious air quality problems had previously chosen, with EPA encouragement, the stricter car inspection programs. Many states were faced with testing that many consumers considered overly restrictive and expensive.

The EPA had counted on enforcing the program through the sanctions specified by the 1990 CAA — cutting off highway money and other federal aid to the states. But some state legislatures seemed willing to forego such aid in what some sources considered an act of civil disobedience. Rather than provoking a confrontation between the EPA and the states, the EPA chose to allow greater flexibility in auto emissions testing.

The Anti-Regulatory Rebellion

During the early 1990s, there were strong signs of growing dissatisfaction with government regulation. The Republican-led Congress, as part of its "Contract with America," took steps to put brakes on what they considered growing environmental regulation. As a result, funding for environmental protection, including the Clean Air Act, the Clean Air Amendments, the Clean Water Act, the Safe Drinking Water Act, and other environmental statutes, was cut. Subsequent budgets have continued those cuts by many millions of dollars.

Moreover, efforts to balance the federal budget have led to further cuts, many having to do with pollution. In order to combat acid rain, Title IV of the Clean Air Act Amendments of 1990 set goals for reducing sulfur dioxide and nitrogen oxide emissions. However, with less funding available for that program, the agency missed some deadlines established by the Clean Air Act Amendments of 1990.

Smog and Soot — Political Fallout and New Standards

Mountains of evidence led the EPA to the conclusion that air quality standards developed in the 1970s had to be updated for the 1990s. — Carol M. Browner, Administrator of the U.S. Environmental Protection Agency, 1997

The Clinton Administration has dealt with two highly charged political issues — global warming and how to tighten the Clean Air Act. Although the two issues are linked because they both involve the burning of fossil fuels, the American public is less interested and compelled by global warming

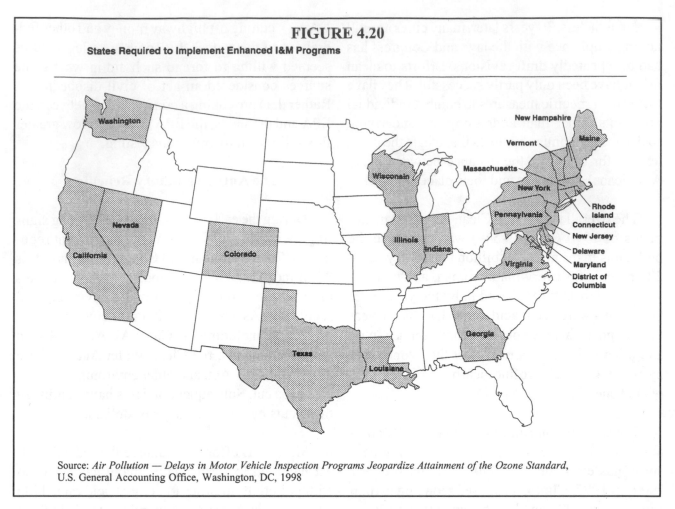

FIGURE 4.20

States Required to Implement Enhanced I&M Programs

Source: *Air Pollution — Delays in Motor Vehicle Inspection Programs Jeopardize Attainment of the Ozone Standard*, U.S. General Accounting Office, Washington, DC, 1998

than by the smog they breathe and the way tiny particles can harm their loved ones. Many people have, on the one hand, applauded Clinton's tightening of Clean Air Act standards while discounting the less immediate concern about eventual rising sea levels and scientific questions about subtle global warming.

The Clean Air Act requires the EPA to review public health standards at least every five years to ensure they reflect the best current science. In 1997, in response to what many consider compelling scientific evidence of the harm caused by ozone and fine particles to human health, the EPA issued updated air quality standards for ozone and particulate matter. These are the first revisions in ozone standards in 20 years and the first-ever standard for fine particulates.

The provisions tighten the standard for ground-level ozone from the current level of 0.12 parts per million (ppm) at the highest daily measurement to 0.08 ppm average over an eight-hour period. The particulate matter standard now includes particles less than 2.5 microns (micron — one millionth of a meter) in diameter, in addition to the previous standard of those over 10 microns.

Despite improvements in ozone levels in recent years, almost no large urban areas and many smaller population centers in the United States comply with current ozone standards. States will be forced to take further pollution control measures to comply in the next several years. Title I of the Clean Air Act Amendments of 1990 require states with the most serious ozone and carbon monoxide problems — 23 states have been cited — to implement enhanced inspection and maintenance (I&M) programs to reduce emissions from motor vehicles (Figure 4.20).

Areas that exceeded the national standards have been given future dates to comply, depending upon the severity of their ozone problems, ranging from

3 to 20 years. Among the reasons for their delays were opposition to the program, problems obtaining the necessary equipment, delays by the EPA, problems with state legislature approvals, and difficulties in certifying inspection centers and technicians (Figure 4.21).

Some critics contend that the standards are either unattainable or not worth the cost. The Global Climate Coalition, a business and trade organization, claim the administration's plan would "damage the U.S. economy while producing no lasting environmental benefit."

A Major Loophole — Grandfather Clause

As many as two-thirds of the nation's power plants are exempt from pollution-control laws, such as the Clean Air Act, because they were in operation before the law was enacted. The exemption, known as "grandfathering," is believed to be a major reason the industry creates two-thirds of the acid rain, one-third of the gases that form smog, and one-third of the global warming gases.

Environmental groups have made updating the plants a top priority, especially in areas that have been unable to meet air quality standards. Politicians have sometimes balked at closing the loopholes that permit old plants to operate because the power industry and its supporters have contributed heavily to political races. Some states have asked for voluntary improvements instead.

States Are Divided

Many states in the Northeast already have stricter standards for ozone pollution than the federal government requires. They believe that Midwestern states should also be held to a stricter standard, particularly in light of the possibility that ozone is being transported on westerly winds from the Midwest to the East Coast.

UTILITY DEREGULATION'S EFFECT ON AIR POLLUTION

Regulated for decades as "natural monopolies," electric utilities are in the midst of a radical shift toward increased competition. As in the case of airline, trucking, natural gas, and telecommunications industries, more efficient technology and increasing demand for lower rates have led regulators to consider some form of deregulation. The Federal Energy Policy Act of 1992 (PL 102-486) has given other electricity generators access to the market. Industrial customers are eager to buy cheaper electricity from new sources or to build their own sources of power.

Industry no longer considers electricity expenditures as a non-negotiable cost of doing business; it is a commodity they can provide for themselves or shop for. Under deregulation plans, utilities are

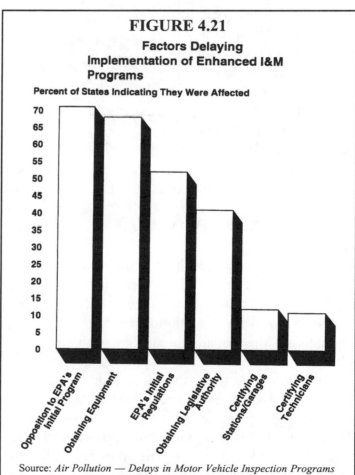

FIGURE 4.21

Factors Delaying Implementation of Enhanced I&M Programs

Percent of States Indicating They Were Affected

Source: *Air Pollution — Delays in Motor Vehicle Inspection Programs Jeopardize Attainment of the Ozone Standard*, U.S. General Accounting Office, Washington, DC, 1998

free to market electricity anywhere. Most state legislatures have either approved or are considering allowing utilities to compete for customers.

Environmental groups and some utilities have warned that deregulation may, by prompting increased competition, cause coal-fired plants to produce more electricity and send more pollutants into the air. The Natural Resources Defense Council cautioned that deregulation could lead to as many as 500,000 tons of increased emissions of nitrogen oxides per year. Responding to those concerns, EPA administrator Carol Browner agrees that the open access rule could lead to future increases in carbon dioxide emissions and admits that the EPA has to work closely with the Energy Department and the states to monitor the results of open access.

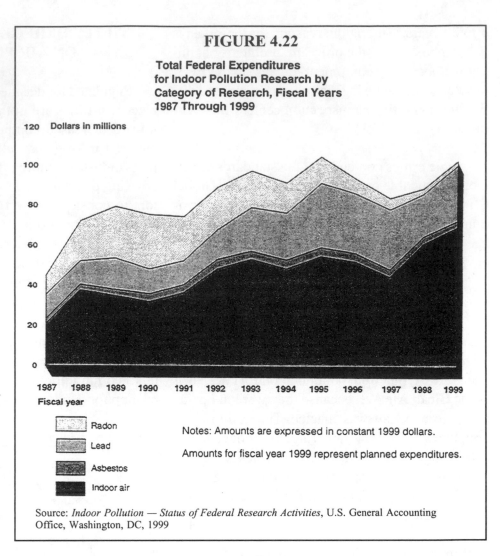

FIGURE 4.22

Total Federal Expenditures for Indoor Pollution Research by Category of Research, Fiscal Years 1987 Through 1999

Dollars in millions

Fiscal year

Radon
Lead
Asbestos
Indoor air

Notes: Amounts are expressed in constant 1999 dollars.

Amounts for fiscal year 1999 represent planned expenditures.

Source: *Indoor Pollution — Status of Federal Research Activities*, U.S. General Accounting Office, Washington, DC, 1999

INDOOR AIR QUALITY

Although most people think of the *outdoor* air when they think of air pollution, recent studies have shown that indoor environments are not necessarily safe havens from air pollution. In fact, certain pollutants are often found at greater concentrations indoors than out, especially important since 90 percent of people's time is spent in indoor environments, including residences, workplaces, public transportation, and public and commercial establishments. Particularly vulnerable groups, such as infants, the elderly, and the ill, may be inside virtually all the time.

Modern indoor environments contain a variety of sources for pollution, including synthetic building materials, consumer products, and dust mites (minute insects that live on house dust and human skin residue). People, pets, and indoor plants also contribute airborne pollution. Efforts to lower energy costs by tightly sealing and insulating buildings have also increased the likelihood that pollutants will accumulate.

Reports of illness and allergy among building occupants have become commonplace. Scientific evidence suggests that respiratory disease, allergy, mucous membrane irritation, nervous system defects, cardiovascular symptoms, reproductive problems, and lung cancer may be linked to exposure to indoor air pollution. Scientists consistently rank indoor air pollution among the top environmental

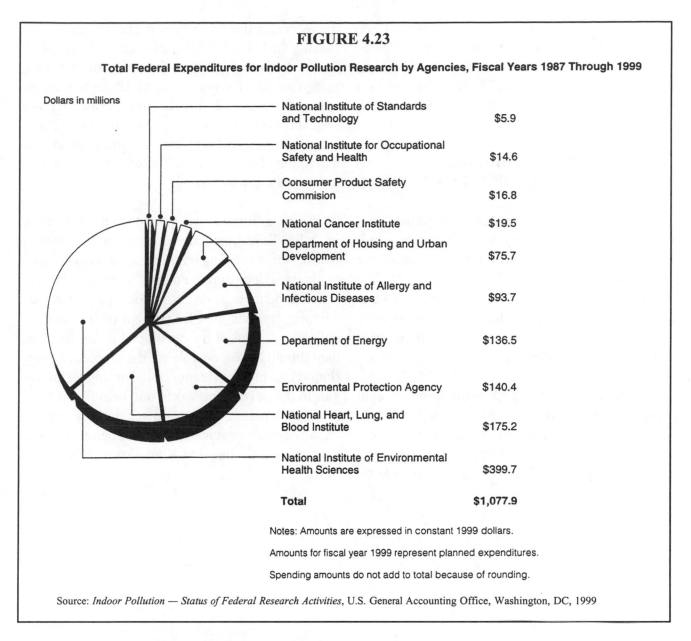

FIGURE 4.23

Total Federal Expenditures for Indoor Pollution Research by Agencies, Fiscal Years 1987 Through 1999

Dollars in millions

National Institute of Standards and Technology	$5.9
National Institute for Occupational Safety and Health	$14.6
Consumer Product Safety Commision	$16.8
National Cancer Institute	$19.5
Department of Housing and Urban Development	$75.7
National Institute of Allergy and Infectious Diseases	$93.7
Department of Energy	$136.5
Environmental Protection Agency	$140.4
National Heart, Lung, and Blood Institute	$175.2
National Institute of Environmental Health Sciences	$399.7
Total	**$1,077.9**

Notes: Amounts are expressed in constant 1999 dollars.

Amounts for fiscal year 1999 represent planned expenditures.

Spending amounts do not add to total because of rounding.

Source: *Indoor Pollution — Status of Federal Research Activities*, U.S. General Accounting Office, Washington, DC, 1999

health risks, although public opinion polls report that most Americans do not perceive the risks of indoor pollution to be great.

Providing healthful air quality is not only a complex scientific and technical issue, but also a complicated issue of public policy in determining the proper role of the government in safeguarding people's health. For example, the EPA estimates that exposure of nonsmokers to cigarette smoke may cause as many as 3,000 lung-cancer deaths annually in the United States. It also contributes to a wide range of diseases, including asthma, pneumonia, and bronchitis, and incurs enormous ex-

pense in work-time loss and medical and insurance expenses.

How does the government protect the rights of one person without denying those of another? Many states now have levied restrictions on smoking in public places. Lead and asbestos are pollutants that have also posed serious and costly problems in indoor settings.

Federal agencies spent $1.1 billion on indoor-related research from 1987 through 1999. Most of that amount went for the study of indoor air, the remainder for the study of radon, lead, and asbestos in the indoor environment. (See Figure 4.22.) Figure 4.23 shows the agencies that participated in such research. (For a complete discussion of radon, lead, and asbestos, see *The Environment — A Revolution in Attitudes*, Information Plus, Wylie, Texas, 1998.)

FOSSIL FUEL USE
IN THE DEVELOPING WORLD

Mounting evidence indicates that global atmospheric warming is a likely result of human activities, especially from the production of gases from the combustion of coal, oil, and natural gas. The developing countries stand on the brink of huge economic growth. That explosion will undoubtedly be fueled by fossil fuels, as was the case in America and Europe decades earlier.

China, especially, faces a dilemma — coal harms the environment but fuels growth. China's heavy reliance on coal, along with its inefficient and wasteful patterns of energy use, will make it the largest single producer of carbon dioxide by the second or third decade of the next century, surpassing the United States. Between 1970 and 1990, energy consumption rose 208 percent in China, compared to an average rise of 28 percent in developed countries during the same period. In order to quadruple the nation's economic output by 2000, more than five million Chinese participate in coal extraction, feeding China's enormous and growing appetite for energy.

China's situation is repeated, on a lesser scale, in India, Brazil, and the rest of the developing world, where meeting environmental goals is generally considered a rich country's luxury. Chinese officials believe, as do leaders in many other developing nations, that 80 percent of the world's pollution is caused by developed countries, and they should be responsible for the problems. They should also pay for cleaner coal-burning technologies in the developing world and help finance hydroelectric plants, nuclear power stations, and alternative energy sources. It is those beliefs that are in conflict at the ongoing Kyoto Protocol negotiations.

CHAPTER V

CONTAMINATION OF SURFACE WATER — OCEANS, LAKES, AND RIVERS

Water is as important to living things as the air they breathe. No plant or animal can live very long without water. Factories use water to make steam for electricity to power their machinery and to cool down machines when they get too hot. They use water to make chemicals or to clean the dirt away from ores to make metals like copper, iron, and gold.

Most farmers must water their crops if they are to make a living. Cities take water from rivers and lakes so they can clean it and send it to their residents for household use. Fishermen sail onto rivers, lakes, and oceans in search of fish so they can make a living and bring fish to America's dinner tables. Barges and freighters carry goods from one city to another in the United States and to foreign countries across the ocean.

Water also provides opportunities for recreation. Americans go swimming, fishing, water skiing, and boating in the nation's waters. Others go bird-watching or take pictures of America's thousands of beautiful lakes and rivers. Many like to sit by the seashore or lakeshore while reading a good book, getting a suntan, or simply relaxing.

Water plays a very important part in everyone's life. This is why it is extremely serious when water becomes polluted. At one time, Americans were not concerned about pouring wastes and emptying garbage into rivers, lakes, and oceans. They believed the waterways were so vast they could easily absorb all the garbage that was put into them. Or they did not care.

MORE GROWTH AND MORE POLLUTION

As America grew bigger and richer and cities increased in size, pollution worsened. Factories

---

TABLE 5.1

Pollution Source Categories Used in This Report

Category	Examples
Industrial	Pulp and paper mills, chemical manufacturers, steel plants, metal process and product manufacturers, textile manufacturers, food processing plants
Municipal	Publicly owned sewage treatment plants that may receive indirect discharges from industrial facilities or businesses
Combined Sewer Overflows (CSOs)	Single facilities that treat both storm water and sanitary sewage, which may become overloaded during storm events and discharge untreated wastes into surface waters.
Storm Sewers/ Urban Runoff	Runoff from impervious surfaces including streets, parking lots, buildings, and other paved areas.
Agricultural	Crop production, pastures, rangeland, feedlots, animal operations
Silvicultural	Forest management, tree harvesting, logging road construction
Construction	Land development, road construction
Resource Extraction	Mining, petroleum drilling, runoff from mine tailing sites
Land Disposal	Leachate or discharge from septic tanks, landfills, and hazardous waste sites
Hydrologic Modification	Channelization, dredging, dam construction, flow regulation
Habitat Modification	Removal of riparian vegetation, streambank modification, drainage/filling of wetlands

Source: *National Water Quality Inventory: 1996 Report to Congress*, Environmental Protection Agency, Washington, DC, 1998

poured their wastes directly into the rivers. Big cities, with huge amounts of garbage and waste, dumped their refuse into big holes in the ground. Pollution from that garbage seeped into the ground water. Many cities poured their sewage directly into rivers. Other cities loaded their waste onto big barges that sailed out into the ocean and dumped the trash there.

Farmers, wanting to raise more food for the growing nation, used increased amounts of pesticides and fertilizers. When they watered their fields or when it rained, some of the pesticides and fertilizers ran off with the excess water into the lakes and rivers.

In cities, streets became coated with oil and other chemicals from cars and trucks. Homeowners used fertilizers to make their lawns grow. When it rained, some of the oil and fertilizer ran off with the rain into storm sewers. Melting snow also carried pollutants, including the salts used to melt ice on streets and roads, into storm sewers. Eventually, storm sewers emptied into rivers or lakes. Table 5.1 gives the standard definitions of the various categories used to describe where pollution comes from.

THE NEED FOR POLLUTION CONTROL

Just as animals gather at watering places, people have always congregated on the shores of oceans, lakes, and rivers. They established permanent homes, then towns, cities, and industries, benefiting from the many advantages of nearby sources of water. One of these advantages has been that lakes or rivers were convenient places to dispose of wastes. As technological societies developed, the amount of wastes became enormous and, even worse, contained synthetic and toxic materials that could not be assimilated by the waters' ecosystems. Millions of tons of sewage, pesticides, chemicals, and garbage were dumped into waterways until (in the United States and other industrialized countries) there were few that were not contaminated to some extent. Some were (and remain) contaminated to the point of ecological "death," unable to sustain life.

THE CLEAN WATER ACT

On June 22, 1969, the Cuyahoga River in Cleveland burst into flames, the result of oil and debris that had accumulated on the river's surface. Five-story-high flames destroyed two bridges and thrust the problem of environmental pollution into the public consciousness. Many people became aware — and wary — of the nation's polluted waters, and in 1972, Congress passed the Federal Water Pollution Control Act (PL 92-500), commonly known as the Clean Water Act (CWA).

The objective of the CWA was to "restore and maintain the chemical, physical, and biological

TABLE 5.2

Levels of Summary Use Support

Symbol	Use Support Level	Water Quality Condition	Definition
	Fully Supporting All Uses	Good	Water quality meets designated use criteria.
	Threatened for One or More Uses	Good	Water quality supports beneficial uses now but may not in the future unless action is taken.
	Impaired for One or More Uses	Impaired	Water quality fails to meet designated use criteria at times.
	Not Attainable	———	The State, Tribe, or other jurisdiction has performed a use-attainability analysis and demonstrated that use support is not attainable due to one of six biological, chemical, physical, or economic/social conditions specified in the *Code of Federal Regulations*.

Source: *National Water Quality Inventory: 1996 Report to Congress*, Environmental Protection Agency, Washington, DC, 1998

FIGURE 5.1

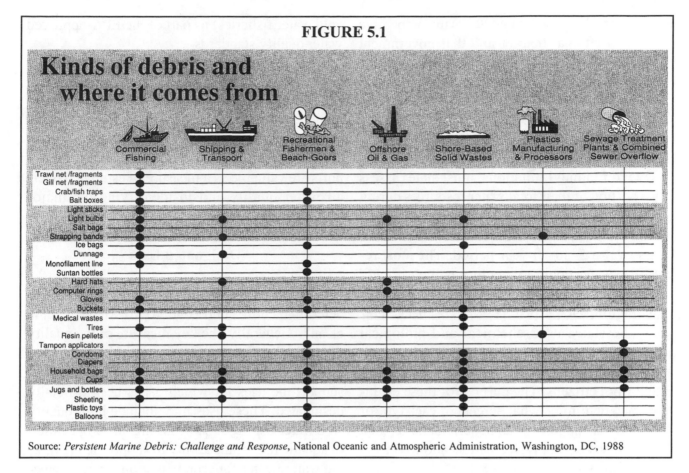

Kinds of debris and where it comes from

	Commercial Fishing	Shipping & Transport	Recreational Fishermen & Beach-Goers	Offshore Oil & Gas	Shore-Based Solid Wastes	Plastics Manufacturing & Processors	Sewage Treatment Plants & Combined Sewer Overflow
Trawl net /fragments	●						
Gill net /fragments	●						
Crab/fish traps	●		●				
Bait boxes	●						
Light sticks	●						
Light bulbs	●	●	●	●	●		
Salt bags	●						
Strapping bands	●	●				●	
Ice bags	●		●		●		
Dunnage	●	●	●				
Monofilament line	●		●				
Suntan bottles			●				
Hard hats				●			
Computer rings				●			
Gloves	●	●	●	●			
Buckets	●		●	●	●		
Medical wastes					●		
Tires	●	●			●		
Resin pellets						●	
Tampon applicators			●				●
Condoms			●				
Diapers			●				●
Household bags	●	●	●	●	●		●
Cups	●	●	●	●	●		●
Jugs and bottles	●	●	●	●	●		●
Sheeting		●		●	●		
Plastic toys			●		●		
Balloons			●				

Source: *Persistent Marine Debris: Challenge and Response*, National Oceanic and Atmospheric Administration, Washington, DC, 1988

integrity of the Nation's waters." It called for ending the discharge of all pollutants into the navigable waters of the United States and for achieving "wherever possible, water quality which provides for the protection and propagation of fish, shellfish, and wildlife and provides for recreation in and on the water." The second provision was that waters be restored to "fishable/swimmable" condition.

Section 305(b) of the CWA required that each state prepare and submit to the Environmental Protection Agency (EPA) a report on

- The water quality of all navigable waters in the state.

- An analysis of the extent to which the waters provide for the protection and propagation of marine animals and allow recreation in and on the water.

- A review of the extent to which pollution has been eliminated or is under control.

- A description of the sources and causes of pollutants.

Congress stated in the CWA that these reports, known as *National Water Quality Inventories* (see below), must be submitted every two years (biennially) to the EPA.

Both conservatives and environmentalists credit the CWA with reversing, in a single generation, what had been a decline in the health of the nation's water since the mid-nineteenth century. Since 1995, however, conservative politicians, as part of a crusade against federal regulations, have proposed legislation to change the CWA, giving more authority to the states and more weight to economic considerations.

The proponents of change (conservative politicians and their supporters and coalitions of industry, agriculture, and state and local governments) argue that enough has been accomplished and that now it is time to make the law more flexible. They claim the huge cost of maintaining clean

93

water risks making the United States uncompetitive in the international market and that government regulations demand more than is necessary to maintain drinkable water.

THE EPA'S 1996 NATIONAL WATER QUALITY INVENTORY

Due to funding limitations, most states assess only a portion of their total water resources during each two-year reporting cycle required under the Clean Water Act, with the goal of assessing all their waters over a 5- to 10-year period. The most recent EPA water quality inventory is the *National Water Quality Inventory: 1996 Report to Congress* (Washington, DC, April 1998). To check their water, the states used chemical and biological monitoring and other types of data, such as surveys of fisheries, water quality models, and information from citizens. The purpose of these evaluations is to determine what percent of each type of water body is supporting its beneficial uses (such as drinking water supply, recreation, and warm and

cold water fisheries) as part of the EPA-approved water quality standards.

Because of the sparse reporting by the states and differences in support criteria and measurement techniques between states, a completely accurate assessment of the quality of the nation's surface waters is not possible. However, the reports are valuable as a measure of estimated overall water quality and in identifying the major sources and causes of pollution.

Designated Uses

Defining water quality is a little like trying to determine "how good is good?" or "how clean is clean?" Generally, the key measure of the quality of any body of surface water — river, lake, or estuary — is the degree to which the water is able to support the uses for which it has been officially designated. These uses may include high-quality cold water fishing and swimming, the propagation of aquatic life, or the ability to supply clean drinking water, water for crop irrigation, or hydroelectric power production.

Under federal mandate, each state must specifically designate a use for the rivers, streams, lakes, and estuaries within its boundaries. Following EPA guidelines, the states then determine whether the bodies of water meet the standards set for their use. It is not uncommon for a water body to have more than one designated use. However, most water bodies are designated primarily for recreation, drinking water supplies, and the support of fish populations. Table 5.1 defines the levels of use support reported by the states.

Point and Nonpoint Sources of Pollution

The main reason that a body of water cannot support its designated uses is that it has become polluted. There are a vast number of pollutants that can make water "impaired," but in order to control a specific pollutant, it is necessary to find out where it is coming from. Although there are many ways in which contaminants can enter waterways,

FIGURE 5.2

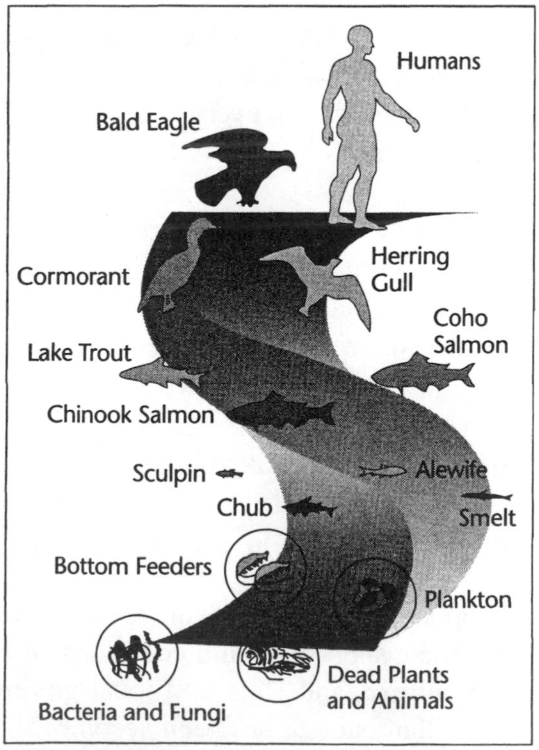

Source: *Persistent Marine Debris: Challenge and Response*, National Oceanic and Atmospheric Administration, Washington, DC, 1988

sources of pollution are generally categorized as *point sources* and *nonpoint sources*.

Point sources are those that disperse pollutants from a specific source or area such as a sewage drain or an industrial discharge pipe. Pollutants that are commonly discharged from point sources include bacteria (from wastewater treatment plants and sewer overflow), toxic chemicals, and heavy metals from industrial plants.

Nonpoint sources are those that are spread out over a large area and have no specific outlet or discharge point, for example, agricultural and urban runoff, runoff from mining and construction sites, and accidental spills, as when a train or truck carrying toxic chemicals derails or overturns, releasing its contents. Some spills are not accidental but the deliberate dumping of toxic wastes, usually at night and in relatively remote areas. Illegal dumping is usually done by individuals or companies that will not pay to have their wastes disposed of safely or whose wastes were the result of operations that were already in violation of environmental regulations.

Nonpoint source pollutants can include pesticides, fertilizers, toxic chemicals, and asbestos and salts from road construction. The EPA estimates that as much as 65 percent of surface water pollutants come from nonpoint sources.

THE QUALITY OF OCEAN WATERS

The oceans are huge, and much of the American coast is beautiful and clean. Many parts of the coast, however, show the results of the abuse of

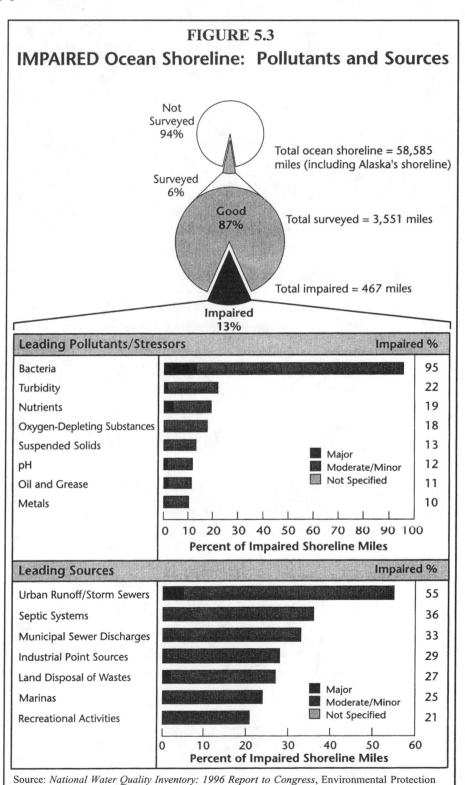

FIGURE 5.3

IMPAIRED Ocean Shoreline: Pollutants and Sources

Not Surveyed 94%

Surveyed 6%

Good 87%

Impaired 13%

Total ocean shoreline = 58,585 miles (including Alaska's shoreline)

Total surveyed = 3,551 miles

Total impaired = 467 miles

Leading Pollutants/Stressors	Impaired %
Bacteria	95
Turbidity	22
Nutrients	19
Oxygen-Depleting Substances	18
Suspended Solids	13
pH	12
Oil and Grease	11
Metals	10

Major
Moderate/Minor
Not Specified

0 10 20 30 40 50 60 70 80 90 100
Percent of Impaired Shoreline Miles

Leading Sources	Impaired %
Urban Runoff/Storm Sewers	55
Septic Systems	36
Municipal Sewer Discharges	33
Industrial Point Sources	29
Land Disposal of Wastes	27
Marinas	25
Recreational Activities	21

Major
Moderate/Minor
Not Specified

0 10 20 30 40 50 60
Percent of Impaired Shoreline Miles

Source: *National Water Quality Inventory: 1996 Report to Congress*, Environmental Protection Agency, Washington, DC, 1998

FIGURE 5.4
Runoff from Urban Areas

Source: *National Water Quality Inventory: 1994 Report to Congress*, Environmental Protective Agency, Washington, DC, 1995

the environment. Some previous studies have reported more than 10 tons of garbage per mile of coastline.

Many types of things are thrown into the water. Over half the garbage is made of plastic. Much of the garbage consists of metal, glass, plastic foam, paper, bags, lids, bottles, and rings used to hold six packs of beer and soda together. People also discard toys, egg cartons, shoes, diapers, and even hard hats in the ocean waters. This is the trash that floats. Much of the garbage that is tossed away does not float and sinks

FIGURE 5.5
Schematic of Physical, Chemical, and Biological Processes

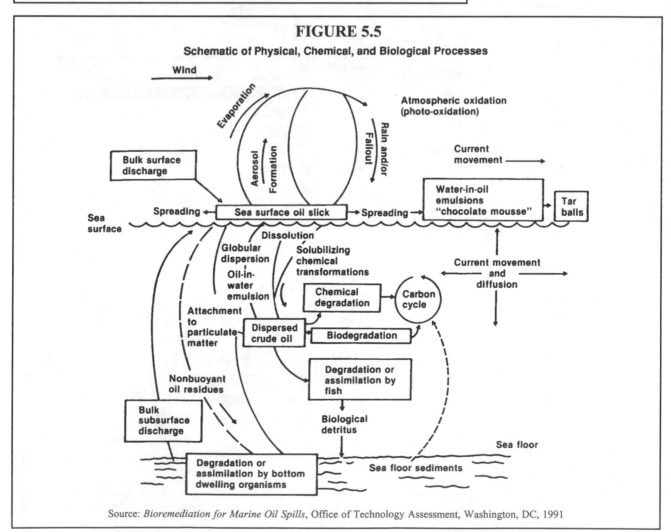

Source: *Bioremediation for Marine Oil Spills*, Office of Technology Assessment, Washington, DC, 1991

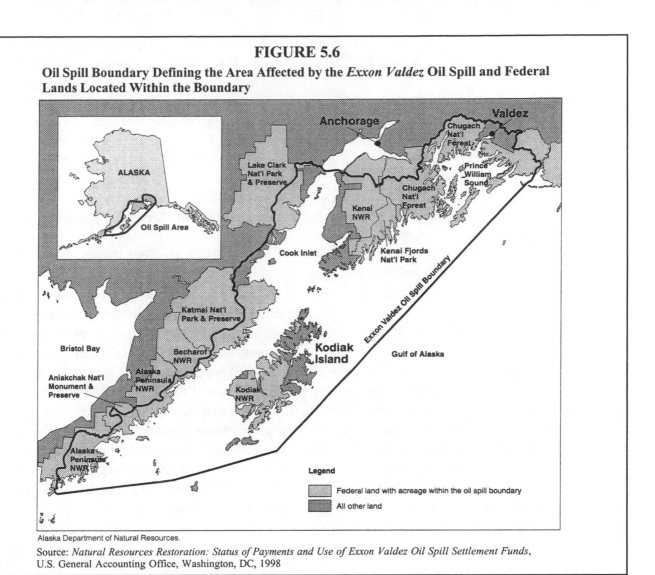

FIGURE 5.6

Oil Spill Boundary Defining the Area Affected by the *Exxon Valdez* Oil Spill and Federal Lands Located Within the Boundary

Alaska Department of Natural Resources.

Source: *Natural Resources Restoration: Status of Payments and Use of Exxon Valdez Oil Spill Settlement Funds*, U.S. General Accounting Office, Washington, DC, 1998

to the bottom of the ocean where it stays, perhaps to be eaten by fish and other sea life or to eventually disintegrate and further pollute the oceans.

Where Does the Garbage Come From?

The floating ocean garbage that washes up on the nation's beaches comes from many places. Manufacturing plants pour their wastes into the ocean. City sewer systems dump their sewage. Garbage barges throw away the trash from the cities. Freighters toss trash over the side, as do many people living and working on offshore oil and gas rigs. Commercial fishermen leave old nets behind, or some of their fishing equipment falls apart and disappears into the ocean. People visiting beaches to swim or sunbathe toss their trash into the water. People in boats who fish or just have a good time throw their trash overboard.

Figure 5.1 shows where particular types of garbage come from. Almost all sources of garbage produce jugs, bottles, and cups. Commercial and recreational fishermen leave fishing line and bait boxes behind. Plastic toys, diapers, and tires can be found in the garbage that barges carrying city wastes dump into the sea. Freighters dump light bulbs and hardhats, while people on offshore oil and gas rigs toss in buckets, bags, and human waste. Just about every part of society and everything that people do produces trash.

Garbage Is a Danger to Sea Animals

The garbage found in the ocean can be a great danger to creatures living in the ocean. An animal, such as a seal, might get trapped in a net, rope, or line and drown. In fact, some scientists think this might be the reason why the seal population has declined over the past two decades. Whales and dolphins also get caught in old fishing nets.

Ocean garbage can be a serious threat to seabirds and shorebirds. They become caught in fishing nets, fishing line, or plastic beer and soda container rings and drown or choke to death. Sometimes pelicans get fishing line or plastic beer container rings caught around their beaks so they cannot catch food. As a result, they starve to death. Pelicans and egrets sometimes get fishing line caught around their wings and legs so they cannot fly. They, too, starve to death. Some birds and sea turtles eat little pieces of plastic, thinking it is food.

And a Danger to Human Beings

Skindivers and scuba divers have been caught by old nets and fishing lines. Fishing nets can wrap around boat propellers, making it impossible for boats to operate. Fish and shellfish that live in polluted waters can become very dangerous to eat. In fact, many states have issued warnings not to eat the fish taken from many lakes and rivers for fear that people who eat them will become sick or die. Figure 5.2 shows the movement of chemicals through the food chain.

The junk washed up on shores fouls beaches and makes them less attractive to visitors. Swimming in polluted waters can make people sick. Pollution can hurt the economy of those who depend on the beach because fewer people will want to visit the beach if it is littered and the water is dirty.

In its 1996 *National Water Quality Inventory* survey of U.S. ocean coastal waters, the Environmental Protection Agency (EPA) reported that 10 of the 27 coastal states had rated the water quality of their ocean shorelines. The states had assessed 16 percent of ocean waters excluding Alaska or 6 percent of U.S. waters including Alaska. Of the waters assessed, 79 percent fully supported their designated uses, 9 percent fully supported uses but were threatened by pollution, and 13 percent were impaired for one or more designated uses. (Figures add up to 101 percent due to rounding.)

Figure 5.3 shows the major pollutants to U.S. oceans. Pathogens (bacterial or viral microorganisms that cause disease) were the leading contaminant, followed by turbidity (muddy or unclear) and nutrients. The leading sources of contamination were urban runoff/storm sewers, septic systems, municipal sewer discharges, and industrial point sources.

Sources of Ocean Contamination

Medical Waste

Sometimes trash can be dangerous. During the summers of 1987 and 1988, medical wastes from hospitals, including containers of blood and syringes used to give shots, floated onto the shore along the East Coast, mainly in New York and New Jersey. Some of this trash was infected with HIV (the virus that causes AIDS) and hepatitis, both very dangerous viruses. As a result, the government closed the beaches in these areas for several weeks. In 1988, medical trash also washed up on shore along the Great Lakes, and those beaches had to be shut down.

Although the public's fear of contracting disease from this contaminated material was largely unjustified, medical wastes called attention to the fact that many by-products of modern technology are not easily disposable. Despite the fact that many contamination problems are much more serious,

---

TABLE 5.3

Bioremediation: Potential Advantages and Disadvantages

Advantages:
- Usually involves only minimal physical disruption of a site
- No significant adverse effects when used correctly
- May be helpful in removing some of the toxic components of oil
- Offers a simpler and more thorough solution than mechanical technologies
- Possibly less costly than other approaches

Disadvantages:
- Of undetermined effectiveness for many types of spills
- May not be appropriate at sea
- Takes time to work
- Approach must be specifically tailored for each polluted site
- Optimization requires substantial information about spill site and oil characteristics

Source: *Bioremediation for Marine Oil Spills*, Office of Technology Assessment, Washington, DC, 1991

the sensational nature of medical wastes prompted quick legislation. A public outcry prompted Congress to pass the 1988 Medical Waste Tracking Act (PL 92-532), requiring producers of medical waste to be held accountable for safe disposal of the waste or face up to $1 million in fines and five years in prison.

However, in 1990, the Agency for Toxic Substances and Disease Registry (ATSDR), a division of the U.S. Department of Health and Human Services, concluded that medical waste presents little danger to the general public. According to Dr. Maureen Lichveld, senior medical officer at the agency and coordinator for the research project, the most pressing concern for future medical waste disposal comes from in-home health care products from persons with chronic diseases, out-patient AIDS victims, and nursing homes, not from hospital medical wastes disposed in the oceans. "We know a lot about what hospitals generate, but we don't know much about home health care — what is generated, or where it goes," she stated.

The ATSDR investigation tried to determine how many people came in contact with medical waste and what was the incidence of disease. The study involved three population groups: health care providers, waste handlers, and the general public. The study concluded that the general public does not normally come in contact with medical waste unless it originates from home health care and is carelessly discarded. The public may also be at risk when encountering needles and syringes discarded by illegal intravenous drug users. Furthermore, despite all the furor raised by the public over medical waste, studies by the Marine Conservancy indicate that it accounts for only .01 percent of all waste collected and analyzed on the nation's beaches. "Most of the waste [on beaches]," said Dr. Lichveld, "is plastics."

Plastics

One of the greatest solid waste threats to marine life is the plastic products that are dumped daily along with other garbage by oceangoing vessels, commercial and recreational fishing boats,

TABLE 5.4
Pathogens and Swimming-Associated Illnesses

Pathogenic Agent	Disease
bacteria	
E. coli	Gastroenteritis
Salmonella typhi	Typhoid fever
Other salmonella species	Various enteric fevers (often called paratyphoid), gastroenteritis, septicemia (generalized infections in which organisms multiply in the bloodstream)
Shigella dysenteriae and other species	Bacterial dysentery
Vibrio cholera	Cholera
viruses	
Rotavirus	Gastroenteritis
Norwalkvirus	Gastroenteritis
Poliovirus	Poliomyelitis
Coxsackievirus (some strains)	Various, including severe respiratory disease, fevers, rashes, paralysis, aseptic meningitis myocarditis
Echovirus	Various, similar to coxsackievirus (evidence is not definite except in experimental animals)
Adenovirus	Respiratory and gastrointestinal infections
Hepatitis	Infectious hepatitis (liver malfunction), also may affect kidneys and spleen
protozoa	
Cryptosporidium	Gastroenteritis
Giardia lambia	Diarrhea (intestinal parasite)
Entamoeba histolytica	Amoebic dysentery, infections of other organisms
Isospora belli and Isospora hominus	Intestinal parasites, gastrointestinal infection
Balantidium coli	Dysentery, intestinal ulcers

Source: Reprinted with permission of Natural Resources Defense Council, originally printed in *Testing the Waters*, Volume VI, Copyright 1996

TABLE 5.5

U.S. Ocean, Bay, and Great Lakes Beach Closings and Advisories, 1988-1998

	1988	1989	1990	1991	1992	1993	1994	1995	1996	1997	1998*
AL	No regular monitoring of ocean/bay beaches for swimmer safety										
CA	Limited monitoring of ocean/bay beaches for swimmer safety										
	**	at least 64	at least 338	745 + 5(p)	609 + 1(e) + 1(p)	1397*** + 2(e)+ 2(p)	at least 910 + 2 (e)+ 6(p)	at least 1305 + 3 (e) + 11(p)	at least 1054 + 7 (e) + 9(p)	at least 1141 + 1 (e) + 37(p)	***** at least 3273 + 30(e) + 12(p)
CT	**	at least 103	218	293 + 1(e)	223	at least 174	at least 162 + 1 (e)	at least 251 + 1(e)	at least 196 + 2(e)	at least 214 + 1(e)	at least 272
DE	1	62	11	11	5	0	0	0	16	3(p)	14
FL	Limited monitoring of ocean/bay beaches for swimmer safety										
	**	**	303	299	772**** + 1(e)	101a + 1(e)	at least 215 + 1 (e)	at least 830	at least 174 + 2(e) + 1(p)	at least 706 + 5(e) + 4(p)	at least 1868 + 3(e) + 5(p)
GA	No regular monitoring of ocean/bay beaches for swimmer safety in 1998										

	1988	1989	1990	1991	1992	1993	1994	1995	1996	1997	1998*
Guam	**	**	**	**	**	0	0	2 + 1(e)	**	688 + 7 (e) + 2(p)	**
HI	Limited monitoring of ocean/bay beaches for swimmer safety										
	at least 9	at least 23	at least 22	106	29	6	22	13***	70	1	0
IL	**	**	**	**	**	73	36	55	66	at least 90	38
IN	**	**	**	**	**	at least 30	36	14	34	30	154 + 1(p)
LA	No regular monitoring of ocean/bay beaches for swimmer safety (since 1988)										
	**	**	**	1(p)	1(p)	1(p)	1(p)	1(p)	1(p)	1(p)	4(p)
ME	Limited monitoring of ocean/bay beaches for swimmer safety										
	**	1	30 + 1(e)	47 + 3(p)	at least 3(p)	35 + 3(p)	at least 15 + 3(p)	at least 10 + 3(p)	at least 20 + 3(p)	20+ 3(p)	25 + 1(p)
MD	Limited monitoring of ocean/bay beaches for swimmer safety										
	0	0	0	24 + 3(p) + 2(e)	at least 6 + 3 (p) + 2(e)	at least 106 + 1(e) +3(p)	82 + 3(p)	200	at least 24 + 3(p)	307 + 4(p) + 1(e)	10
MA	Limited monitoring of ocean/bay beaches for swimmer safety										
	at least 75	at least 60	at least 59	at least 59	at least 60	at least 61	at least 58	at least 132 + 1(p)	at least 152 + 2(p)	78 + 1(e)	231 + 1(e) + 2(p)
MI	Limited monitoring of Great Lakes beaches for swimmer safety										
	**	**	**	**	**	**	26 + 3(e) + 2(p)	96 + 1(e)	at least 18 + 1(e) + 1(p)	236	227 + 1(p)
MN	Limited monitoring of Great Lakes beaches for swimmer safety										
	**	**	**	**	**	0	0	0	0	0	0

(continued)

offshore oil and gas platforms, and military ships. As they drift toward land, plastic bags and pellets are ingested by fish, turtles, birds, and marine mammals.

Other types of plastic debris come from land sources — factory wastes, sewer overflows, illegal garbage dumping, and human littering. Dead whales and dolphins have been found with their stomachs full of plastic bags. Adult birds eat small plastic pellets resembling fish eggs and feed them to their young. An estimated two million sea birds and 100,000 marine animals die each year as a result of ingesting or becoming entangled in plastic.

Commercial fishing nets, once made of natural materials, are now made mainly of durable, non-degradable plastic. When they are lost or discarded in the water, they pose a particular hazard to seals, dolphins, whales, and diving birds, which can become entangled in the nets. One scientist reported that 56 percent of endangered whales pho-

TABLE 5.5 (Continued)

	1988	1989	1990	1991	1992	1993	1994	1995	1996	1997	1998*
MS	Monitoring of ocean/bay beaches for swimmer safety began in 1997, no closure/advisory program in place in 1998										
NH	**	**	**	1(e)	0	0	0	0	0	0	0
NJ	126	266	228	108	112	88	238	86	87	42	31
NY	Limited monitoring of Great Lakes beaches for swimmer safety										
	273 + 1(p)	473 + 5(p)	383 + 3(p)	314 + 2(e) + 3(p)	799b	at least 212c + 1(e)	227 + 1(e) + 24 days of restricted use	283 + 3(e)	219 + 4(e)	273 + 1(e)	178 + 3 (e)
NC	Monitoring of ocean/bay beaches for swimmer safety began in 1997										
					28					44 +1(p)	279 + 4 (e) + 7 (p)
OH	**	**	**	**	**	0	96	67	119	100	288

	1988	1989	1990	1991	1992	1993	1994	1995	1996	1997	1998*
OR	No regular monitoring of ocean/bay beaches for swimmer safety										
PA	Limited monitoring of Great Lakes beaches for swimmer safety										
	**	**	**	**	**	19	14	10	6	0	18
PR	No regular monitoring of ocean/bay beaches for swimmer safety										
		**	**	**	**		1(e)			**	**
RI	Limited monitoring of ocean/bay beaches for swimmer safety										
	0	0	0	0	0	0	0	0	0	0	191
SC	**	**	**	**	2						0
TX	Limited monitoring of ocean/bay beaches for swimmer safety, no public notification program.										
	**	**	**	0	1 medical advisory	42	0	0	0	0	0

	1988	1989	1990	1991	1992	1993	1994	1995	1996	1997	1998*
Virgin Islands	Limited monitoring of ocean/bay beaches for swimmer safety (quarterly)										
	**	**	**	**	**	0	0	0	4	43	**
VA	Limited monitoring of ocean/bay beaches for swimmer safety										
	**	**	**	2	0	0	0	0	0	3	0
WA	No regular monitoring of ocean/bay beaches for swimmer safety										
WI	Limited monitoring of Great Lakes beaches for swimmer safety										
	**	**	**	**	**	at least 94	at least 148	at least 114 + 1(e)	at least 120	at least 137	139 + 3(p)
Total	at least 484+ 3 (p)	at least 1,052+ 5 (p)	at least 1,592+ 4 (p) + 1 (e)	at least 2,008+ 14 (p)+ 7 (e)	at least 2,619+ 8 (p) + 6 (e)	at least 2,438+ 9 (p) + 5 (e)	at least 2,279+ 15 (p) +12 (e)	at least 3,522+ 16 (p) + 9 (e)	at least 2,596+ 20 (p) + 16 (e)	at least 4,153 + 55 (p) + 17 (e)	at least 7,236 + 36 (p) + 41 (e)

NOTES	
**	No data were gathered by NRDC for this year.
***	This increase appears to be due to 700 San Diego County closings/advisories due to heavy winter storms.
****	This increase appears to be due to 506 warnings in Dade County against swimming after heavy rains caused sewage spills.
*****	This increase appears to be due to 2,937 closings and advisories in sourthern California due to heavy El Niño rains.
(e)	Extended beach closure (6–12 weeks)
(p)	Permanent beach closure (12 or more weeks)
a	The decrease in the number of Florida closings/advisories appears to be due to significantly less rainfall in 1993 compared with 1992, particularly in Pasco and Dade Counties.
b	Included in this total are 706 rainfall advisories issued in New York City.
c	The decrease in New York closings/advisories appears to be due to less rainfall in 1993 compared with 1992 and a change in New York City's standing rainfall advisory which covered fewer beaches for a shorter time.

NRDC counts every day of an advisory/closure as one "beach closing." Because of inconsistencies in monitoring and closing practices among states and over time, it is difficult to make comparisons between states or to assess trends over time based on the closing data.

Source: Sarah Chasis and Mark Dorfman, *Testing the Waters — 1999: A Guide to Water Quality at Vacation Beaches*, Natural Resources Defense Council, NY, 1999

tographed by the New England Aquarium had scars from plastic gill nets or lobster gear entanglement. In yearly cleanups of the beaches in Texas, the garbage collected has contained large amounts of plastics.

In 1988, 31 nations ratified an agreement making it illegal for their ships to dump plastic debris, including fishing nets, into the ocean. As part of that agreement, the U.S. enacted the Marine Plastics Pollution Research and Control Act (PL 100-220), which, among other things, imposed a $25,000 fine for each violation. (For more information on plastics, see Chapter II.)

Dredging

Every year, millions of tons of materials are dredged from the bottoms of harbors and coastal areas to clear or enlarge navigational channels or for development purposes. This material ends up in U.S. marine waters, most of it in the Gulf of Mexico. Dredged materials may contain high concentrations of pesticides, metals, and toxic chemicals. During dredging or when the dredged material is dumped, pollutants that have settled into the sediment are stirred up and released into open water and have a greater potential to harm marine life.

Urban Runoff/Storm Sewers

There are over 85,000 miles of shoreline in the lower 48 states. Rain and floodwaters flow into coastal waters, bringing with them debris and contaminants (Figure 5.4). Salt and chemicals spread on snowy roads during the winter run into streams and lakes. Runoff of pesticides and fertiliz-

ers from agricultural and domestic use is of special concern. Most fertilizers are not toxic, but they do contribute nutrients that can cause algae buildup and lead to oxygen depletion.

Some pesticides, especially chlorinated hydrocarbons, are very toxic and extremely durable. DDT, banned in the United States for most uses more

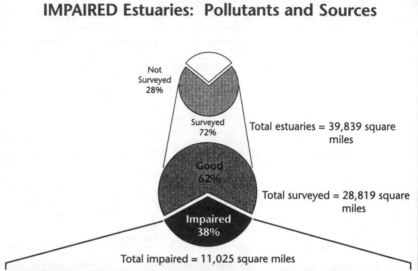

FIGURE 5.7

IMPAIRED Estuaries: Pollutants and Sources

Not Surveyed 28%
Surveyed 72%
Good 62%
Impaired 38%

Total estuaries = 39,839 square miles

Total surveyed = 28,819 square miles

Total impaired = 11,025 square miles

Leading Pollutants/Stressors	Impaired %
Nutrients	57
Bacteria	42
Priority Toxic Organic Chemicals	40
Oxygen-Depleting Substances	33
Oil and Grease	20
Salinity	18
Habitat Alterations	14

Major
Moderate/Minor
Not Specified

Percent of Impaired Estuarine Square Miles

Leading Sources	Impaired %
Industrial Discharges	56
Urban Runoff/Storm Sewers	46
Municipal Point Sources	44
Upstream Sources	30
Agriculture	27
Combined Sewer Overflows	20
Land Disposal of Wastes	19

Major
Moderate/Minor
Not Specified

Percent of Impaired Estuarine Square Miles

Note: Percentages do not add up to 100% because more than one pollutant or source may impair an estuary.

Source: *National Water Quality Inventory: 1996 Report to Congress*, Environmental Protection Agency, Washington, DC, 1998

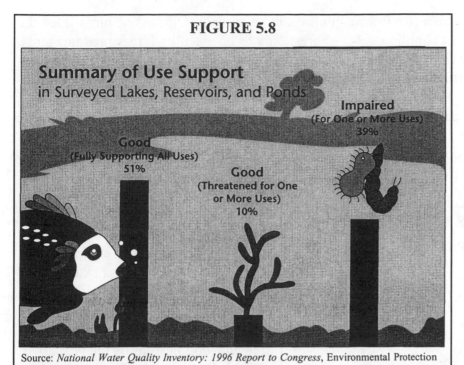

FIGURE 5.8

Summary of Use Support
in Surveyed Lakes, Reservoirs, and Ponds

Good
(Fully Supporting All Uses)
51%

Good
(Threatened for One or More Uses)
10%

Impaired
(For One or More Uses)
39%

Source: *National Water Quality Inventory: 1996 Report to Congress*, Environmental Protection Agency, Washington, DC, 1998

Coastal Development and Recreation

Almost three-fourths of the U.S. population lives within 50 miles of a coastline, and more people move to coastal regions each year. Millions more visit seaside areas, drawn by the mild climates, scenic beauty, and recreational activities. To accommodate an increasing number of residents and tourists, developers are building more houses, resorts, marinas, and boat yards. Commercial establishments to accommodate the influx of new residents add to the population density.

than 20 years ago but still used in other countries, is known to destroy eggshells, thus reducing bird populations. It is still found in ocean sediment and the tissue of many fish and marine mammals. Toxic pollutants travel up the food chain and eventually accumulate in the bodies of fish-eating land animals. Surface runoff is a serious problem because it is almost impossible to control and regulate.

Toxic Metals

Perhaps the most widely publicized case of a waterborne health hazard to humans occurred in Minamata, Japan, in 1956. More than 600 people died, and many others suffered severe neurological damage from eating shellfish contaminated with methyl mercury. Toxic metals and pesticides in seafood pose a possibly more serious health threat than viruses and bacteria because their effects can be permanent. Due to high concentrations of metals and pesticides, health officials have recommended limiting intake of a variety of fish and shellfish, especially by highly susceptible populations, such as pregnant women, children, and people with chronic health problems. (For more information on contamination found in fish, see below.)

Development often comes at the expense of ocean life. Destruction of marine habitats is common in populated areas. Many water organisms and animals have little tolerance for disturbances such as light and temperature changes. When one species is eliminated from an ecosystem, the food chain is broken, and other species will often be destroyed or leave the area in search of a more suitable habitat. Other marine animals are sometimes harmed by collisions with recreational and fishing boats, causing extensive injuries or death.

Oil Spills

Oil spills are a dramatic form of water pollution. They are highly visible, and their impact is sometimes immediate and severe. The sight of dead and dying otters and birds covered with black film arouses instant sympathy, and the bigger the spill, the more newsworthy. While it is true that oil can have a devastating effect on marine life, the size of the spill itself is often not the determining factor in the amount of damage it causes. Other factors include the amount and type of marine life in the area and weather conditions that would disperse the oil. Figure 5.5 shows the physical, chemical, and biological results of marine oil spills.

When the *Exxon Valdez* ran into a reef in Prince William Sound, Alaska, in 1989, 11 million gallons of oil spilled into one of the richest and most ecologically sensitive areas in North America. (Figure 5.6 shows the area affected.) A slick the size of Rhode Island threatened fish and wildlife. Otters, which cannot tolerate even a small amount of oil on their fur, died by the thousands, despite efforts by trained environmentalists and local volunteers to save them. Oil-soaked birds lined the shores, only to be eaten by larger predator birds, which then succumbed to dehydration and starvation because the ingested oil destroyed their metabolic systems.

In response to the *Exxon Valdez* disaster, Congress passed the Oil Pollution Act of 1990 (PL 101-380), which called for prompt reaction and a $1 billion cleanup-damage fund, early planning for response to spills, more strict crew standards, and double hulls on new tankers. (When equipped with two hulls, if the tanker's exterior hull is punctured, the interior hull holding the oil will still likely remain intact.) The law requires older tankers to be fitted with double hulls by the year 2010. The *Exxon Valdez* was not double-hulled. An Alaskan state commission estimated that if the *Valdez* had been equipped with a double-hull design, 20 to 60 percent of the spill might have been prevented.

Until recently, the only way to battle oil spills was intensive, manual cleanup. In 1990, an explosion occurred on the Norwegian tanker *Mega Borg* 57 miles off the Texas coast, spilling 4 million gallons of crude oil into the ocean. At the request of several Texas agencies, a new method of dispersing the spill was tried. The technology, **bioremediation**, uses billions of living microbes to consume the oil.

There are three types of bioremediation — nutrient enrichment, seeding, and the use of genetically engineered organisms. Once the tiny organisms begin eating, they multiply until their food source, the oil, is depleted. The microbes then die and are, in turn, eaten by other scavenger microbes. The resulting waste is a fatty acid that harmlessly re-enters the nor-

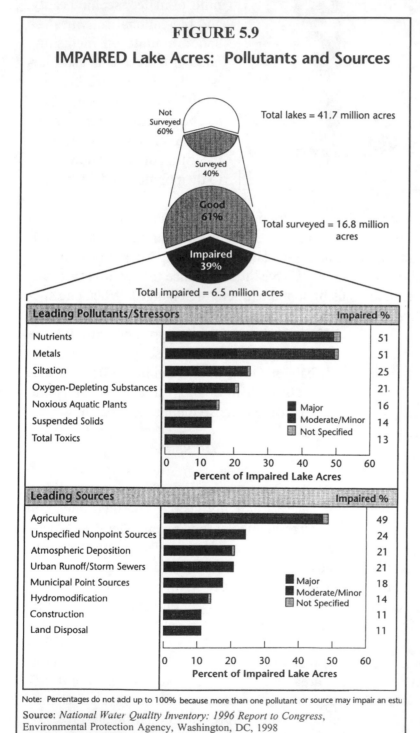

FIGURE 5.9

IMPAIRED Lake Acres: Pollutants and Sources

Not Surveyed 60%

Total lakes = 41.7 million acres

Surveyed 40%

Good 61%

Total surveyed = 16.8 million acres

Impaired 39%

Total impaired = 6.5 million acres

Leading Pollutants/Stressors	Impaired %
Nutrients	51
Metals	51
Siltation	25
Oxygen-Depleting Substances	21
Noxious Aquatic Plants	16
Suspended Solids	14
Total Toxics	13

Major
Moderate/Minor
Not Specified

Percent of Impaired Lake Acres (0 10 20 30 40 50 60)

Leading Sources	Impaired %
Agriculture	49
Unspecified Nonpoint Sources	24
Atmospheric Deposition	21
Urban Runoff/Storm Sewers	21
Municipal Point Sources	18
Hydromodification	14
Construction	11
Land Disposal	11

Major
Moderate/Minor
Not Specified

Percent of Impaired Lake Acres (0 10 20 30 40 50 60)

Note: Percentages do not add up to 100% because more than one pollutant or source may impair an estu

Source: *National Water Quality Inventory: 1996 Report to Congress*, Environmental Protection Agency, Washington, DC, 1998

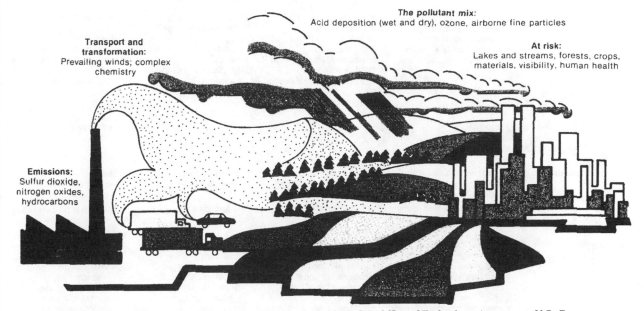

FIGURE 5.10

Transported Air Pollutants: Emissions to Effects

The transported pollutants considered in this study result from emissions of three pollutants: sulfur dioxide, nitrogen oxides, and hydrocarbons. As these pollutants are carried away from their sources, they form a complex "pollutant mix" leading to acid deposition, ozone, and airborne fine particles. These transported air pollutants pose risks to surface waters, forests, crops, materials, visibility, and human health.

The pollutant mix:
Acid deposition (wet and dry), ozone, airborne fine particles

Transport and transformation:
Prevailing winds; complex chemistry

At risk:
Lakes and streams, forests, crops, materials, visibility, human health

Emissions:
Sulfur dioxide, nitrogen oxides, hydrocarbons

Source: *Acid Rain and Transported Air Pollutants: Implications for Public Policy*, Office of Technology Assessment, U.S. Congress, Washington, DC, not dated

mal food chain. For the *Mega Borg* spill, 110 pounds of microbes were sprayed over the 40 acres of oil. (There are over a trillion microbes in each gram.) Within hours, the dark brown areas turned mottled, then yellow, and finally disappeared. Table 5.3 shows the advantages and disadvantages of using bioremediation.

The U.S. National Research Council estimates that approximately 8.4 billion gallons of oil enter marine waters each year, not from major oil spills, but from street runoff, industrial liquid wastes, and intentional discharge from ships flushing their oil tanks. The agency indicated concern for areas that are habitually exposed to oil pollution, since as little as one part of oil per million parts of water can be detrimental to the reproduction and growth of fish, crustaceans, and plankton.

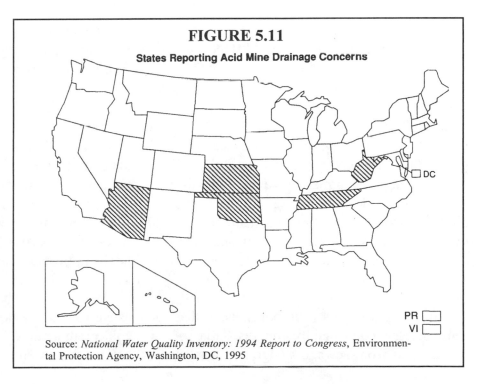

FIGURE 5.11

States Reporting Acid Mine Drainage Concerns

DC

PR

VI

Source: *National Water Quality Inventory: 1994 Report to Congress*, Environmental Protection Agency, Washington, DC, 1995

105

TABLE 5.6

Properties and Effects of Metals of Primary Concern in Marine Environments

	Arsenic	Cadmium	Lead	Mercury
Bioaccumulation	Low except in some fish species	Moderate	Low or none	Significant (methylated form)
Biomagnification	Low or none	Low or none	Low or none	Significant (methylated form)
Properties	Metallic form: insoluble Readily methylated by sediment bacteria to become highly soluble, but low in toxicity	Metallic form: relatively soluble Not subject to biomethylation Less bioavailable in marine than in fresh water Long biological residence time Synergistic effects with lead	Generally insoluble Adsorption rate age-dependent, 4 to 5 times higher in children than adults Synergistic effects with cadmium	Metallic form: relatively insoluble Readily methylated by sediment bacteria to become more soluble, bioavailable, persistent, and highly toxic
Major environmental sink	Sediments	Sediments	Sediments	Sediments
Major routes of human exposure:				
Marine environments	Seafood: very minor route, except for some fish species	Seafood contributes ≈10% of total for general population	Seafood comparable to other food sources	Seafood is primary source of human exposure
Other environments	Inhalation: the major route	Food, primarily grains	Diet and drinking water	Terrestrial pathways are minor sources in comparison
Health effects	Acute: gastrointestinal hemorrhage; loss of blood pressure; coma and death in extreme cases Chronic: liver and peripheral nerve damage; possibly skin and lung cancer	Emphysema and other lung damage; anemia; kidney, pancreatic, and liver impairment; bone damage; animal (and suspected human) carcinogen and mutagen	Acute: gastrointestinal disorders Chronic: anemia; neurological and blood disorders; kidney dysfunction; joint impairments; male/female reproductive effects; teratogenic	Kidney dysfunction; neurological disease; skin lesions; respiratory impairment; eye damage; animal teratogen and carcinogen
References	Doull, et al., 1980 Harrington, et al., 1978 O'Connor and Kneip, 1986 Woolson, 1983	Chapman, et al., 1968 Nriagu, 1981 O'Connor and Kneip, 1986 Wiedow, et al., 1982	Callahan, et al., 1979 Heltz, et al., 1975 Kneip, 1983 NAS, 1980 O'Connor and Kneip, 1986 O'Connor and Rachlin, 1982	Grieg, et al., 1979 Kay, 1984 Nriagu, 1979 Windom and Kendall, 1979

Source: *Wastes in Marine Environments*, Office of Technology Assessment, U.S. Congress, Washington, DC, 1987

THE HEALTH COST OF OCEAN POLLUTION

Eating contaminated seafood can cause viral, bacterial, chromosomal, and genetic diseases in man. Although some contaminants are naturally present in marine waters, human activity has greatly increased the types and quantities of hazardous organisms in marine waters. Over the past several years, dozens of people have contracted cholera after eating shellfish from the coastal marshlands of southwestern Louisiana, the first cases of cholera originating in this country since 1911.

Human pathogens (microorganisms that can cause disease) come mainly from discharges of raw sewage and from sewage sludge and wastewater outflow from sewage treatment plants, although they can enter marine waters directly through surface runoff. Viruses and bacteria can exist in marine environments for months or years. Concentrations of some intestinal viruses may be 10 to 10,000 times greater in coastal sediments than in other waters. Table 5.4 shows the pathogens and swimming-associated illnesses that may be contracted from polluted waters. Such illnesses cause dehydration, vomiting, and, in extreme cases, collapse. A swimmer who contracts a sewage-borne illness may also pass the disease on to family members, multiplying the effect of the polluted water.

While some pathogens survive better in warmer estuaries and coastal environments, for others the colder temperatures of the open ocean, particularly bottom waters, enhance survival, although growth may be retarded. For these reasons, U.S. health officials advise against eating raw or undercooked seafood, including oysters.

BEACH CLOSINGS

Thousands of times each year, American beaches are closed to protect the public from disease-carrying organisms. But there are many coastal states that do not regularly monitor surf pollution, and millions of tourists may be unaware of whether it is safe to swim, boat, or fish at any given time or place. Even heavily visited beaches such as those in Key West and Miami Beach in Florida, Myrtle Beach, South Carolina, the Outer Banks of North Carolina, and Santa Barbara, California, are inadequately protected. Currently, the federal government does not monitor beach water or require the states to do so.

Every summer since 1991, the Natural Resources Defense Council (NRDC), a not-for-profit environmental organization based in New York, has performed a nationwide survey of beach closings and beachwater monitoring programs in coastal states. Its latest report, *Testing the Waters — A Guide to Water Quality at Vacation Beaches* (1999), found that during 1998, U.S. ocean, bay, or Great Lakes beaches were closed or advisories were issued against swimming on more than 7,236 individual closings and advisories, up from 4,153 in 1997. There were 41 extended (6-12 weeks) closings and advisories, up from 17 in 1998, and 36 permanent closings and advisories, down from 55 in 1997. Since 1988, there have been more than 29,996 closings and advisories and 114 extended closings and advisories. (See Table 5.5.)

Among the major causes of beach closings and advisories in 1997,

- 69 percent were due to excessive bacteria levels.

- 13 percent were in response to a known pollution event, such as aquatic disease organisms or waste dumping by an industry.

- 18 percent were precautionary, due to rain known to carry pollution to swimming waters.

FIGURE 5.12
The Progression of Eutrophication

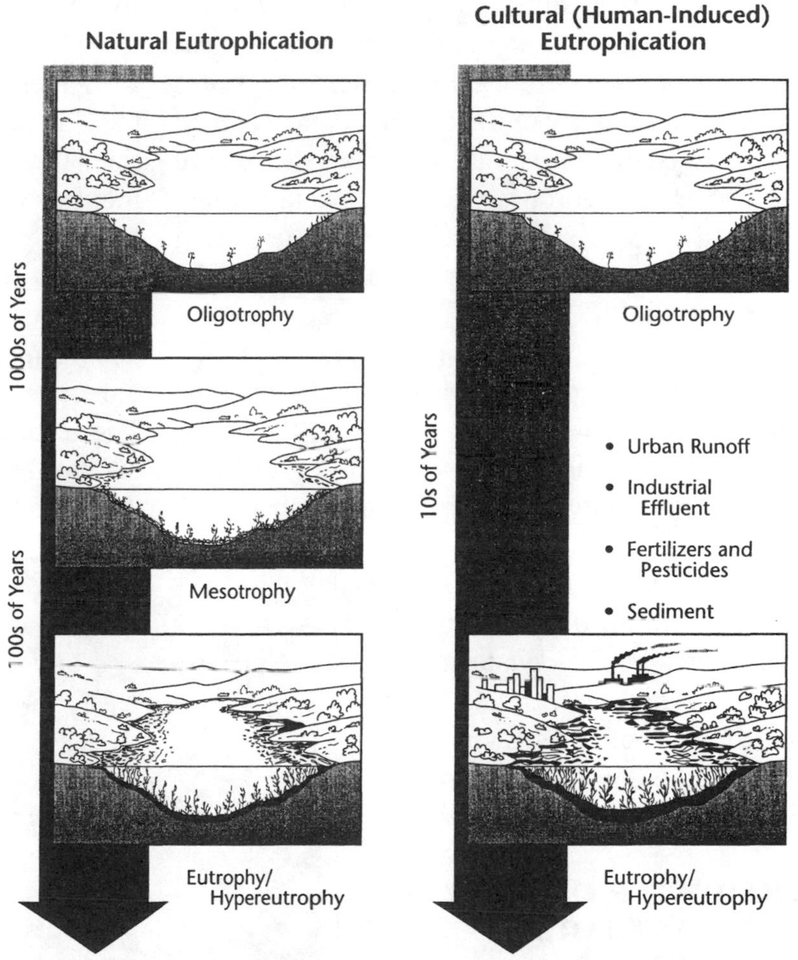

(left column) The progression of natural lake aging or eutrophication through nutrient-poor (oligotrophy) to nutrient-rich (eutrophy) sites. Hypereutrophy represents extreme productivity characterized by algal blooms or dense macrophyte populations (or both) plus a high level of sedimentation. The diagram depicts the natural process of gradual nutrient enrichment and basin filling over a long period of time (e.g., thousands of years).
(right column) Cultural eutrophication in which lake aging is greatly accelerated (e.g., tens of years) by increased inputs of nutrients and sediments into a lake, as a result of watershed disturbance by humans.

Source: *National Water Quality Inventory: 1996 Report to Congress*, Environmental Protection Agency, Washington, DC, 1998

The major pollution sources responsible for the closings and advisories included polluted runoff and storm water, sewage spills and overflows, and rain. Many cities tended to issue preemptive closings or advisories when rains exceeded certain levels. Almost every coastal state reported having at least one beach where stormwater drains onto or near bathing beaches. California, Connecticut, Massachusetts, and New Jersey reported having numerous beaches near stormwater outlets.

Despite the threat of pollution, many states with popular beach areas still do not have regular beach-monitoring programs. The NRDC found that only nine states — Connecticut, Delaware, Illinois, Indiana, New Hampshire, New Jersey, New York, North Carolina, and Ohio — comprehensively monitor beach waters and notify the public. Other states monitor infrequently or in certain locations. Some federal legislators are considering laws to require states to meet rigorous nationwide standards that would have to be set by the EPA for monitoring coastal waters and notifying the public when the water is unhealthy.

Coastal water pollution has a significant economic impact on coastal states. Failing to invest in clean waters costs states economic growth — jobs, job productivity, tourism, and property tax dollars. Beaches are the top vacation destinations in the United States, generating over $100 billion in revenues in 12 coastal states alone. Polluted waters cause economic losses both from swimming-related illnesses and the loss of beachgoers' use of beaches.

THE WATER QUALITY OF ESTUARIES

An **estuary** is an inlet, bay, or area where a river meets the ocean. Estuaries and the nearby coastal areas are among the richest and most useful areas in the world. Fish and shellfish lay their eggs and grow up

TABLE 5.7
Trophic States

Oligotrophic	Clear waters with little organic matter or sediment and minimum biological activity.
Mesotrophic	Waters with more nutrients and, therefore, more biological productivity.
Eutrophic	Waters extremely rich in nutrients, with high biological productivity. Some species may be choked out.
Hypereutrophic	Murky, highly productive waters, closest to the wetlands status. Many clearwater species cannot survive.
Dystrophic	Low in nutrients, highly colored with dissolved humic organic matter. (Not necessarily a part of the natural trophic progression.)

Source: *National Water Quality Inventory: 1994 Report to Congress*, Environmental Protection Agency, Washington, DC, 1995

in estuaries, and about two-thirds of all fish caught are hatched in estuaries. Birds and many animals live in the wetlands that border the estuaries.

An estimated 75 percent of the population of the United States lives within 50 miles of the coastline. That means major cities with sewage plants, industry with its industrial wastes, and millions of tourists pour their garbage into these estuaries. Because living near an estuary is so attractive, more and more people are moving to these areas and producing more and more garbage. The land along the estuaries is very rich, so farmers farm the land. The fertilizers and pesticides they use often run off the farmers' land into streams and rivers and then into the estuaries.

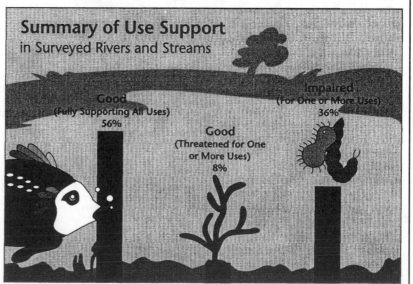

FIGURE 5.13

Summary of Use Support in Surveyed Rivers and Streams

Good (Fully Supporting All Uses) 56%

Good (Threatened for One or More Uses) 8%

Impaired (For One or More Uses) 36%

Source: *National Water Quality Inventory: 1996 Report to Congress*, Environmental Protection Agency, Washington, DC, 1998

Twenty-three of the 27 coastal states assessed 72 percent of the nation's estuaries. Of the 28,819 miles assessed, 58 percent were fully supporting their uses, 4 percent were threatened, and 38 percent were impaired. Figure 5.7 shows the major pollutants in U.S. estuaries. Nutrients were the most common pollutant, followed by bacteria and organic chemicals. This pollution came from industrial point sources, urban runoff/storm sewers, and municipal point sources.

The National Estuaries Program

As part of the Water Quality Act of 1987 (PL 100-4), the United States government is working to improve the condition of the nation's beaches and coastal waters through the National Estuary Program. The program concluded that the biggest problem faced by estuaries is development — the building of houses, roads, malls, factories, schools, etc. With more people, more businesses, and more industry comes added pollution. The second most important finding was that states and local governments, not the federal government, have to make the big decisions. Wise zoning decisions — what types of businesses, factories, and housing can be built and where they can be built — are very important for controlling pollution.

THE WATER QUALITY OF THE NATION'S LAKES

Water is found not only at the seashore, but also in almost 40 million acres of lakes and reservoirs (which store water) in the United States. These lakes and reservoirs provide water for drinking, swimming, fishing, and generating electric power. In the *National Water Quality Inventory: 1996 Report to Congress* (Washington, DC, 1998),

the states evaluated about 40 percent of the nation's 41 million acres of lakes, ponds, and reservoirs. Fifty-one percent were fully supporting their designated uses. However, 10 percent of these acres of lakes were threatened and might not be able to support uses in the future if immediate action is not taken to control pollution. Thirty-nine percent of assessed acres were impaired. (See Figure 5.8.)

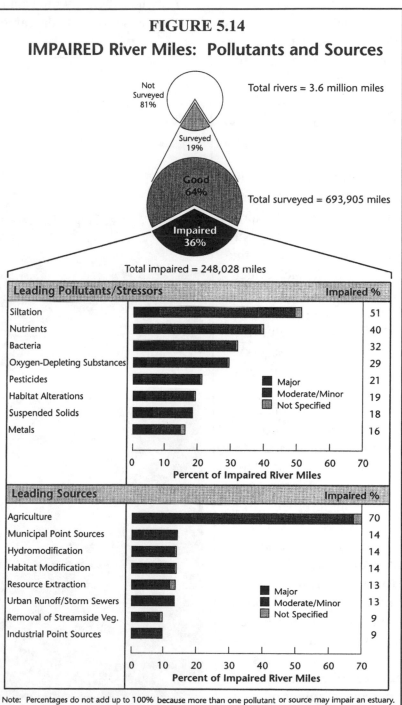

FIGURE 5.14

IMPAIRED River Miles: Pollutants and Sources

Not Surveyed 81%

Total rivers = 3.6 million miles

Surveyed 19%

Good 64%

Total surveyed = 693,905 miles

Impaired 36%

Total impaired = 248,028 miles

Leading Pollutants/Stressors	Impaired %
Siltation	51
Nutrients	40
Bacteria	32
Oxygen-Depleting Substances	29
Pesticides	21
Habitat Alterations	19
Suspended Solids	18
Metals	16

Major
Moderate/Minor
Not Specified

Percent of Impaired River Miles

Leading Sources	Impaired %
Agriculture	70
Municipal Point Sources	14
Hydromodification	14
Habitat Modification	14
Resource Extraction	13
Urban Runoff/Storm Sewers	13
Removal of Streamside Veg.	9
Industrial Point Sources	9

Major
Moderate/Minor
Not Specified

Percent of Impaired River Miles

Note: Percentages do not add up to 100% because more than one pollutant or source may impair an estuary.

Source: *National Water Quality Inventory: 1996 Report to Congress*, Environmental Protection Agency, Washington, DC, 1998

Causes and Sources of Lake Pollution

Lakes are products of their watershed (the area that drains into a lake); therefore, a lake's water quality reflects the condition and management of the lake's watershed. The states that reported pollution of their lakes in 1996 often cited multiple pollutants in any given lake acre. Because a single acre of a lake can be affected by several sources of pollution, the states were asked to include their acres of lakes under each of the various source categories that contribute to impairment. This means that a single lake acre could be counted several times if it is polluted by multiple sources.

Figure 5.9 shows the top pollutants and the percent of impaired lake acres affected by each type. Nutrients and metals were the most prevalent, each affecting 51 percent of lake acres. Siltation was reported to affect 25 percent of the impaired lake acreage. Oxygen-depleting substances, which can lead to organic enrichment and lowered levels of oxygen, hazardous to both plant and animal life, affected 21 percent. This process is called *eutrophication* (the aging process of a lake in which the water is choked by an overabundance of plant life — see below). Noxious aquatic plants and suspended solids were also found in affected lake acres. Agricultural runoff was the most extensive source of pollution, affecting 49 percent of impaired lake acres.

Acid in Lake Waters

Acid Rain

Acid pollutes many lakes in the United States. This acid comes from two sources — acid rain or wastes from mines. Acid rain (or acid snow or acid fog) is produced when the smoke or emissions from factories and coal-burning electric power plants, which contain sulfur dioxide, nitrogen oxides, and hydrocarbons, mix with the water in the air to form

FIGURE 5.15

Wetlands

Source: *National Water Quality Inventory: 1994 Report to Congress*, Environmental Protection Agency, Washington, DC, 1995

a mild acid. (Figure 5.10 shows how acid rain develops.) This rain may fall close to the factories or power plants, or it may be carried many hundreds of miles away by the winds high in the atmosphere. If there is no water in the air, the acid may fall to the earth as dust, which mixes with rainwater.

Acid rain falls everywhere — on cities, on forests, and into lakes. When it lands in the cities, it can damage stone statues and buildings. When it is in smog, it can harm people's lungs. When it lands on the forests, it can kill trees. When it lands in lakes, it acidifies the water. That, in turn, harms plants and animals living in lakes. Small increases in the acid level in a lake can make it harder for fish to reproduce, and higher levels of acid can kill all the fish in a lake.

Many states are very concerned about the effects of acid rain on their lakes. Many states add limestone or other alkaline materials to neutralize the acidic affect on the lakes, although this often works for only a short time. The problem of acid rain will not be solved until many of the clean-up programs passed under the Clean Air Act (see Chapter IV) are put into effect. Most major factories and coal-burning power plants have to put scrubbers on their smokestacks to clean up the smoke before it goes into the air. Others have to burn coal that produces less sulfur.

In 1999, EPA tests of the acidity in the Adirondack Mountains (New York) found acid levels about five times as acidic as clean water and too low for most fish to survive. The EPA reports that conditions are worsening in the lakes and forests of the Adirondacks. (For a full discussion of acid rain, see *Water — No Longer Taken for Granted*, Information Plus, Wylie, Texas, 1999.)

Acid from Mines

Mining companies have to separate the stone and dirt that they take from mines to get the mineral ore that they want. To do

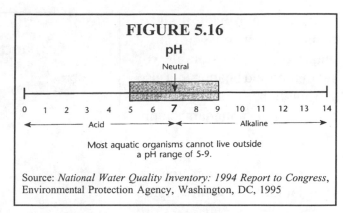

Source: *National Water Quality Inventory: 1994 Report to Congress*, Environmental Protection Agency, Washington, DC, 1995

this, they use chemicals, many of which are acidic. Sometimes the wastes from this method of extracting ore end up in rivers or lakes. When this happens, it can make the lake too acidic and kill the plants and fish in the lake. Figure 5.11 shows the states that are most concerned about the effects of mine waste on their lakes and rivers, and Table 5.6 shows the metals that threaten marine environments.

The Trophic Status of U.S. Lakes

Lakes naturally change over the years, filling with sediment and organic material that alter many of the basic characteristics such as lake depth, biological life, oxygen levels, and the inherent clearness of the water. This natural aging process is called **eutrophication**.

Human activities often speed up eutrophication by increasing the nutrients through agricultural runoff or sewage discharge. This can over-

TABLE 5.8

Effects of pH on Aquatic Life	
pH Range	**General Biological Effects**
6.5 to 6.0	Some adverse effects for highly acid-sensitive species
6.0 to 5.5	Loss of sensitive minnows and forage fish; decreased reproductive success for trout and walleye
5.5 to 5.0	Loss of many common sports fish and additional nongame species
5.0 to 4.5	Loss of most sports fish; very few fishes able to survive and reproduce where pH levels commonly below 4.5

Source: *National Water Quality Inventory: 1996 Report to Congress*, Environmental Protection Agency, Washington, DC, 1998

stimulate the growth of algae, plants, and weeds, not only making lakes unsuitable for swimming and boating, but also killing fish populations that depend on an abundant supply of oxygen to live.

The eutrophication progression includes several trophic stages. *Oligotrophic* lakes are clear waters with little organic matter or sediment; *mesotrophic* waters contain more organic material, and the oxygen level is being depleted; *eutrophic* waters are extremely high in nutrients, and the water is murky and shallow with lots of algae and a depleted oxygen level. Figure 5.12 illustrates the stages of lake eutrophication, and Table 5.7 lists the characteristics of each stage of lake trophication.

THE WATER QUALITY OF THE NATION'S RIVERS AND STREAMS

The United States has about 3.6 million miles of rivers and streams. The EPA's 1996 inventory showed that 56 percent of the state-evaluated rivers and streams were fully supporting their designated uses. Eight percent of those waters were identified as threatened waters that could soon become impaired if pollution control action was not taken. Thirty-six percent were impaired. (See Figure 5.13.)

Causes and Sources of Pollution in Rivers and Streams

Pollutants such as pesticides or raw sewage can affect any stream or river. But, according to the EPA's report, siltation, the smothering of river and stream beds by sediment (usually from soil ero-

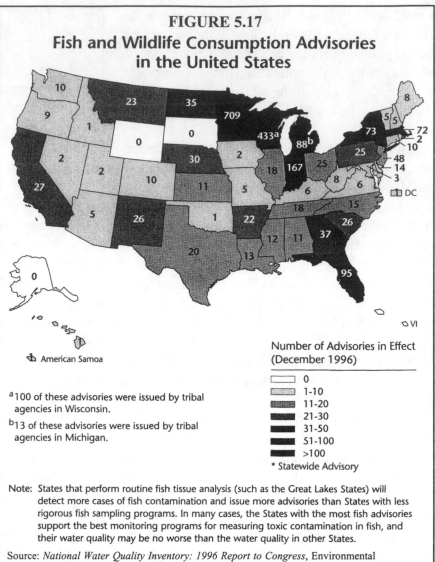

FIGURE 5.17
Fish and Wildlife Consumption Advisories in the United States

a 100 of these advisories were issued by tribal agencies in Wisconsin.

b 13 of these advisories were issued by tribal agencies in Michigan.

Number of Advisories in Effect (December 1996)

- 0
- 1-10
- 11-20
- 21-30
- 31-50
- 51-100
- >100

* Statewide Advisory

Note: States that perform routine fish tissue analysis (such as the Great Lakes States) will detect more cases of fish contamination and issue more advisories than States with less rigorous fish sampling programs. In many cases, the States with the most fish advisories support the best monitoring programs for measuring toxic contamination in fish, and their water quality may be no worse than the water quality in other States.

Source: *National Water Quality Inventory: 1996 Report to Congress*, Environmental Protection Agency, Washington, DC, 1998

sion), was the most common cause of pollution. Nutrients, which usually contain phosphorus and nitrogen compounds used in fertilizers, and bacteria, pathogens that cause serious health hazards, were the second and third most common causes of river impairment and pollution. (See Figure 5.14.) Both siltation and nutrients usually come from nonpoint sources.

Agriculture was, by far, the leading source of pollution, affecting 70 percent of impaired river miles. Other major sources of pollution included municipal discharges, waterway and habitat modification, resource extraction, urban runoff/storm sewers, vegetation removal, and industrial point sources. (See Figure 5.14.)

FIGURE 5.18

Pollutants Causing Fish and Wildlife Consumption Advisories

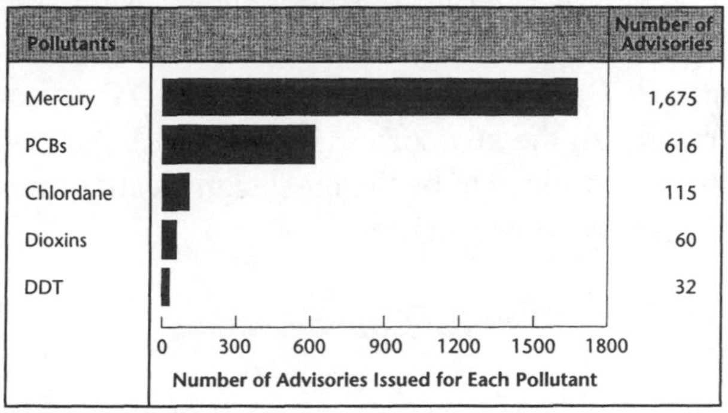

Pollutants	Number of Advisories
Mercury	1,675
PCBs	616
Chlordane	115
Dioxins	60
DDT	32

Number of Advisories Issued for Each Pollutant

Source: *National Water Quality Inventory: 1996 Report to Congress*, Environmental Protection Agency, Washington, DC, 1998

THE WATER QUALITY OF THE NATION'S WETLANDS

The EPA defines wetlands as areas inundated by water at a frequency or duration sufficient to support a prevalence of vegetation typically adapted for life in saturated soil conditions. Found throughout the United States, wetlands include swamps, marshes, bogs, and similar areas (Figure 5.15). They are recognized as some of the most unique and important areas of the earth. (For more information on wetlands, see *Water — No Longer Taken For Granted*, Information Plus, Wylie, Texas, 1999.)

The *National Water Quality Inventory* reported that in 1996, the states evaluated only 3 percent of U.S. wetlands including Alaska and 8 percent of wetlands excluding Alaska. Not only would drawing conclusions from that figure be misleading, but also two states, North Carolina and Louisiana, contain 91 percent of wetland acreage. Of the wetlands studied, sediment/siltation and nutrients were the most widespread causes of degradation, followed by filling and draining, pesticides, flow alteration, habitat modification, and metals. Agriculture topped the list of sources degrading wetlands.

TABLE 5.9

Shellfish Harvesting Restrictions Reported by the States

State	Number of Waterbodies with Restrictions	Area Affected (sq. miles)
Alabama	2	523.0
Alaska	—	—
California	—	—
Connecticut	—	—
Delaware	—	—
Delaware River Basin	1	96.0
District of Columbia[a]	—	—
Florida	9	2,756.8
Georgia	18	394.0
Hawaii	0	0
Louisiana	26	—
Maine	—	—
Maryland	37	172.6
Massachusetts	—	—
Mississippi	—	—
New Hampshire	11	18.0
New Jersey	—	—
New York	71	301.7
North Carolina	—	—
Oregon	—	—
Puerto Rico	—	—
Rhode Island[b]	18	66.7
South Carolina	95	324.0
Texas	—	—
Virginia	—	151.5
Virgin Islands	—	—
Washington	—	—
Totals	288	4,804.2

[a] The District of Columbia prohibits commercial harvest of shellfish in all of its waters.
[b] Rhode Island includes waterbodies where shellfishing is not a designated use and restriction is in accordance with NSSP regulations.
— Not reported in a numerical format.

Source: *National Water Quality Inventory: 1996 Report to Congress*, Environmental Protection Agency, Washington, DC, 1998

DO THE NATION'S WATERS MEET THE "FISHABLE/SWIMMABLE" GOALS?

Swimming

State reporting on recreational restrictions, such as beach closures, is often incomplete because agencies rely on local health departments to voluntarily monitor and report beach closures. The *National Water Quality Inventory* found eight states reporting no contact recreation restrictions. Thirteen states identified 342 sites where recreation was restricted at least once in 1996. Pathogens (bacteria) from sewage treatment malfunctions, pipeline breaks, runoff, livestock operations, and sewer overflows caused most of these restrictions.

The Natural Resources Defense Council (NRDC), an environmental advocacy group, reported that, in 1996, eight states — Alabama, Georgia, Louisiana, Mississippi, North Carolina, South Carolina, Oregon, and Washington — did not regularly monitor beachwater pollution for swimmer safety and public warnings. On the other hand, New Jersey's tough standards close beaches so often that annual losses to the tourist economy approach $1 billion.

Fishing

Fish make up a considerable portion of the diets of many people, especially in Asia and the Far East. Fish kills, in which large numbers of dead fish are found in lakes, reservoirs, rivers, and estuaries, are indicators of pollution problems. The statistics on fish kills are only educated guesses. Most reports on fish kills come from fishermen, hunters, boaters, and hikers who see a fish kill and report their sightings to game wardens and other state officials. The Environmental Protection Agency (EPA) believes the number of reported fish kills is only a small part of the real number, since most are found accidentally.

Acidity regulates many chemical reactions in living organisms. Most aquatic organisms cannot live outside the pH range of 5 to 9 (Figure 5.16). Even within that range, fish health may be affected (Table 5.8).

Meeting the fishable goal means providing a level of water quality that protects and promotes the population of fish, shellfish, and wildlife. Such incidences as fishing advisories, bans on eating certain fish, and tumors found on fish are all indications that the waters are not supporting healthy fish or the fishable goal.

Warnings About Eating Fish

Not all fish die from living in polluted waters. However, many fish take the pollution into their bodies. When states find dangerous pollutants in fish, they issue orders warning people not to eat the fish from certain lakes, rivers, or estuaries.

Overall, 76 percent of lake, reservoir, and pond acres, 94 percent of river and stream miles, and only 2 percent of the Great Lakes miles

surveyed were judged supportive of fish consumption. Figure 5.17 reports the number of advisories against eating fish in each of the states. In 1996, 47 states issued 2,196 advisories against eating fish in its water bodies, up from 1,531 in 1994. Mercury, PCBs, chlordane, dioxin, and DDT caused virtually all the advisories (Figure 5.18). Air pollution is believed to be the most significant source of mercury contamination.

Shellfish Contamination

Contaminated shellfish pose a public health risk, particularly to those who eat raw shellfish, such as oysters, clams, and mussels. In 1996, only 10 of the 27 coastal states reported the extent of their waters affected by shellfish harvesting restrictions — more than 4,804 square miles (Table 5.9).

FEDERAL ENFORCEMENT OF LAWS REGARDING SURFACE WATER

Numerous laws have been enacted to protect the environment. Many of those laws involve surface water protection.

- The Clean Water Act (PL 95-217; 1972) regulates water disposal.

- The Clean Air Act (PL 91-604; 1970) prevents the deterioration of air quality, which may introduce acidity into surface waters.

TABLE 5.10

Federal environmental enforcement actions initiated, by type of violation and enforcement action, 1997

Type of violation	Total	Type of enforcement action		
		Administrative	Civil[a]	Criminal[b]
Total	4,129	3,427	207	446
Environmental protection	3,842	3,427	204	211
Clean Air Act	457	391	35	31
Clean Water Act	1,812	1,642	62	108
RCRA	505	423	23	59
CERCLA	391	305	82	4
TSCA	191	185	0	6
Other	486	481	2	3
Wildlife	287	--	3	235

--Statistics not available.
[a]Represents filing by U.S. Attorneys in U.S. district court only. Statistics describing administrative actions for wildlife and conservation offenses were not available.
[b]Criminal actions include only those offenses classified as felonies or Class A misdemeanors.

Source: John Scalia, *Federal Enforcement of Environmental Laws, 1997*, Bureau of Justice Statistics, Washington, DC, 1999

- The Comprehensive Environmental Response, Compensation, and Liability Act (CERCLA; PL 96-510; 1980) addresses the problem of abandoned hazardous waste sites.

- The Resource Conservation and Recovery Act (RCRA; PL 95-510; 1976) protects human health and the environment from dangers associated with waste management.

- The Toxic Substances Control Act (PL 94-469; 1976) regulates chemical substances that may leach into soil and water supplies.

- The Act to Prevent Pollution by Ships (APPS; PL 96-478) addresses the discharge of harmful substances, such as refuse and sewage, into the oceans.

- The Federal Insecticide, Fungicide, and Rodenticide Act of 1988 (FIFRA; PL 100-532) controls dangerous chemicals used on farms.

- The Oil Pollution Act of 1990 (PL 101-380) deals with storing and transporting petroleum and was enacted to deal with oil spills on land or in water.

- The Marine Protection, Research, and Sanctuaries Act of 1972 (PL 92-532) regulates international ocean disposal of materials. (Title I of the act is known as the Ocean Dumping Act.)

Criminal Actions

According to the U.S. Department of Justice, the EPA initiated 3,842 enforcement actions in the United States in 1997. About half

TABLE 5.11

Fines imposed on defendants convicted of a criminal violation of Federal environmental law in U.S. district courts, by type of offense, 1997

Type of violation	Total	Mean	Median
Total*	225	$67,416	$1,000
Environmental protection	120	124,035	2,500
Clean Air Act	20	2,734	243
Clean Water Act	61	183,681	5,000
RCRA	29	123,849	3,000
Other	10	3,335	2,000
Wildlife	105	$2,710	$1,000
Bald and Golden Eagle Protection Act	11	928	500
Endangered Species Act	8	--	--
Lacey Act	66	2,773	1,000
Migratory Bird Treaty Act	18	1,155	625
Other	2	--	--

*Criminal actions include only those offenses classified as felonies or Class A misdemeanors.
--Not calculated, too few cases.

Source: John Scalia, *Federal Enforcement of Environmental Laws, 1997*, Bureau of Justice Statistics, Washington, DC, 1999

involved a violation of the Clean Water Act; 12 percent involved the Resource Conservation and Recovery Act (RCRA); 11 percent, the Clean Air Act; and 28 percent, violations of other statutes. (See Table 5.10.)

Eighty-five percent of defendants charged with an environmental offense during 1997 were convicted. Most of these (91 percent) pleaded guilty. Sixty-four percent of those convicted were ordered to pay a fine, either alone (14 percent) or with a sentence of imprisonment (9 percent) or probation (41 percent). The average fine imposed for an environmental offense was $124,035. The median

TABLE 5.12

Cases filed in U.S. district court charging a civil violation of Federal environmental law, 1994-97

Type of violation	1994	1995	1996	1997
Total	209	207	220	207
Environmental protection	199	200	211	204
Clean Air Act	45	35	56	35
Clean Water Act	80	74	72	62
CERCLA	60	66	61	82
RCRA	13	25	21	23
Other	1	--	1	2
Wildlife	10	7	6	3
National Environmental Policy	--	--	3	--

--Not calculated, too few cases.

Source: John Scalia, *Federal Enforcement of Environmental Laws, 1997*, Bureau of Justice Statistics, Washington, DC, 1999

115

(half were more and half were less) fine was $2,500. (See Table 5.11.)

Among those sentenced to prison in 1997 for environmental offenses (54), most (22) were for violations of the Clean Water Act. Half of those convicted received prison terms of a year or less. Sixty-two percent of those convicted were sentenced to probation.

Civil Lawsuits

In addition to criminal charges, U.S. attorneys filed 204 cases charging a civil violation of environmental law in 1997, approximately the same number of cases filed annually since 1994. Almost all (99 percent) involved the emission of environmental pollutants: 40 percent, a violation of the Comprehensive Environmental Response, Compensation, and Liability Act (CERCLA); 30 percent, a Clean Water Act violation; 17 percent, a Clean Air Act violation; and 12 percent, other violations. (See Table 5.12.) Most (77 percent) of the cases were decided in favor of the government. The defendant prevailed in less than 3 percent of cases, and in 20 percent, both were judged partially responsible.

A monetary settlement was ordered in 74 of the cases. The average monetary award was about $2.5 million; the median award was $287,500. Cases involving Resource Conservation and Recovery Act (RCRA) violations resulted in the largest monetary awards — $5.4 million, on average. (See Table 5.13.)

TABLE 5.13

Monetary award/settlement in cases concluded in U.S. district court charging a civil violation of Federal environmental law, 1997

	Cases with a monetary award/settlement		
Type of violation	Total	Mean	Median
Total	74	$2,454,447	$287,500
Environmental protection	74	2,454,447	287,500
Clean Air Act	15	520,039	275,000
Clean Water Act	24	2,877,190	98,927
CERCLA	22	1,815,722	440,000
RCRA	12	5,402,087	279,800
Other	1	--	--
Wildlife	0	--	--

--Not calculated, too few cases.

TABLE 5.14

Citizen suits filed in U.S. district court charging civil violations of environmental laws, 1994-97

Type of violation	1994	1995	1996	1997
Total	576	584	658	642
Environmental Protection	540	548	536	496
Clean Air Act	19	21	16	28
Clean Water Act	223	254	249	242
CERCLA	157	142	132	130
RCRA	133	127	136	94
Other	8	4	3	2
Wildlife	36	36	24	27
National Environmental Policy Act	--	--	98	119

--Not calculated, too few cases.

Source of both tables: John Scalia, *Federal Enforcement of Environmental Laws, 1997*, Bureau of Justice Statistics, Washington, DC, 1999

Citizen Suits

In about a third of the private suits filed in 1997, the U.S. government was named as the defendant. Private parties may also bring suits in U.S. district courts for violation of environmental laws. The number of private suits involving environmental protection decreased from 540 in 1994 to 496 cases in 1997. Forty-six percent of the environmental protection cases litigated between 1994 and 1997 involved the Clean Water Act; 27 percent, CERCLA; and 23 percent, RCRA. Only 4 percent involved the Clean Air Act. (See Table 5.14.)

CHAPTER VI

CONTAMINATION OF GROUND WATER

WHERE DOES GROUND WATER COME FROM?

Water lies under the earth's surface almost everywhere — beneath hills, mountains, plains, and even deserts. This water may be close to the surface, as in a marsh, or many hundreds of feet below the surface, as in some very dry areas of the American West. Approximately 96 percent of the planet's available fresh water reserve is stored in the ground as ground water. (Figure 6.1).

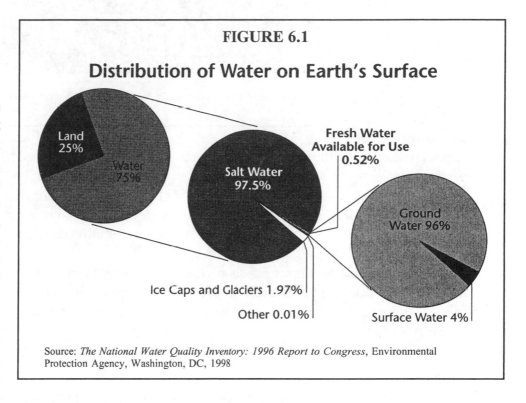

FIGURE 6.1

Distribution of Water on Earth's Surface

Land 25%

Water 75%

Salt Water 97.5%

Fresh Water Available for Use 0.52%

Ground Water 96%

Ice Caps and Glaciers 1.97%

Other 0.01%

Surface Water 4%

Source: *The National Water Quality Inventory: 1996 Report to Congress*, Environmental Protection Agency, Washington, DC, 1998

This water comes from rain. When rain falls or snow melts, plants and soil take up water. Some water evaporates into the atmosphere, some runs off into streams, and some seeps into the soil and openings and cracks in the rocks underneath the ground. (See Figure 6.2.)

Ground water is stored in and moves slowly through underground layers of rock called aquifers. This water fills the openings or cracks in underground rocks. Ground water may have been under the earth for months or hundreds or even thousands of years.

GROUND WATER USE

Slightly more than half the nation's population — and 95 percent of rural residents — depend on ground water as the primary source of drinking water. Ground water is used for agricultural, domestic, industrial, and commercial purposes. Irrigation (64 percent) for agriculture and public water supply (19 percent) are the largest users of ground water. (See Figure 6.3.)

The nation's reliance on ground water has grown dramatically over recent decades. If ground water is not overused, its rate of recharge and discharge balances out, as do other phases of the hydrologic (water) cycle (Figure 6.4). Ground water feeds rivers, streams, lakes, and other surface water bodies, maintaining flow during periods of drought conditions. With ground water playing such an important part in maintaining water flow in surface waters, the quality of the ground water can have an important effect on the condition of the surface waters. Surface waters can become contaminated if the ground water carries pollutants to the surface waters (and vice-versa).

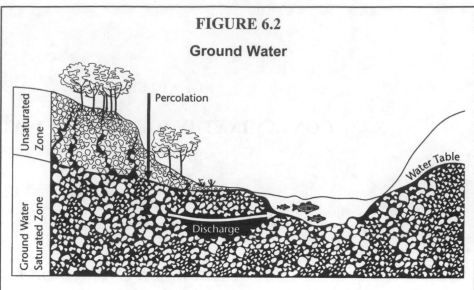

FIGURE 6.2

Ground Water

Unsaturated Zone
Ground Water Saturated Zone
Percolation
Water Table
Discharge

Source: *The National Water Quality Inventory: 1996 Report to Congress*, Environmental Protection Agency, Washington, DC, 1998

A VULNERABLE RESOURCE

There are few human activities that do not influence ground water quality. Figure 6.5 shows the different events that can lead to ground water contamination. It is impossible to determine the extent and severity of ground water pollution in the United States. For years, wastes were dumped into open pits or buried in containers that soon corroded. Cities sprayed icy roads with salts and chemicals. Pesticides and fertilizers were seen as miracles of modern science, and the stronger, the better.

While the threat to surface waters was evident, no one suspected that many of these materials would eventually work their way into the ground water, only to reappear in our drinking water, in the water used to raise our food crops, or in fish and shellfish. The Clean Water Act of 1970 (PL 92-500) was considered the answer to many water problems, but it did little to address ground water pollution problems.

Once it became apparent that ground water was being contaminated, the questions of which waters were being polluted, the severity of contami-

FIGURE 6.3

National Ground Water Withdrawals by Water Use Category

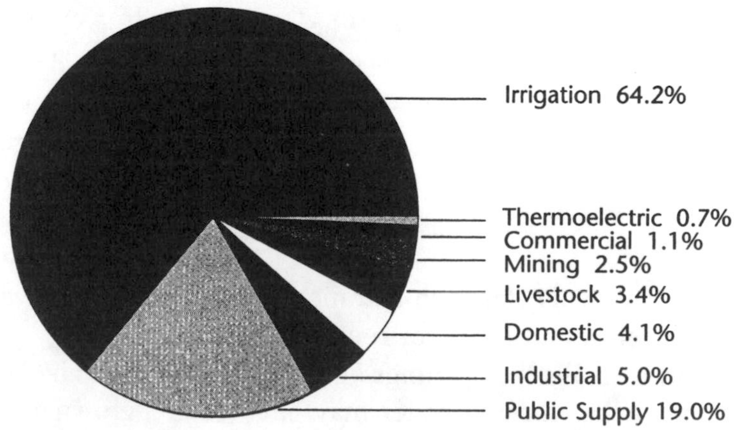

Irrigation 64.2%
Thermoelectric 0.7%
Commercial 1.1%
Mining 2.5%
Livestock 3.4%
Domestic 4.1%
Industrial 5.0%
Public Supply 19.0%

Source: *The National Water Quality Inventory: 1996 Report to Congress*, Environmental Protection Agency, Washington, DC, 1998

nation, and what should be done about it had to be addressed. Many government and private organizations are working to find the answers, but it is not an easy task. As with other types of pollution control, problems include lack of accurate data, inadequate reporting and measurement techniques, the determination of acceptable standards, illegal dumping, the designation of cleanup responsibilities, and, of course, funding.

It is generally believed that the quality of most available ground water in the United States is good. However, the worst damage is in the very areas where use is heaviest — towns and cities, industrial complexes, and agricultural regions such as California's Central Valley.

THE QUALITY OF THE NATION'S GROUND WATER

Ground water moves more slowly than surface waters, less than an inch to tens of feet per day. Consequently, contaminants introduced into the subsurface are less likely to be diluted than those introduced into more rapidly moving surface water. The slow movement of ground water often re-

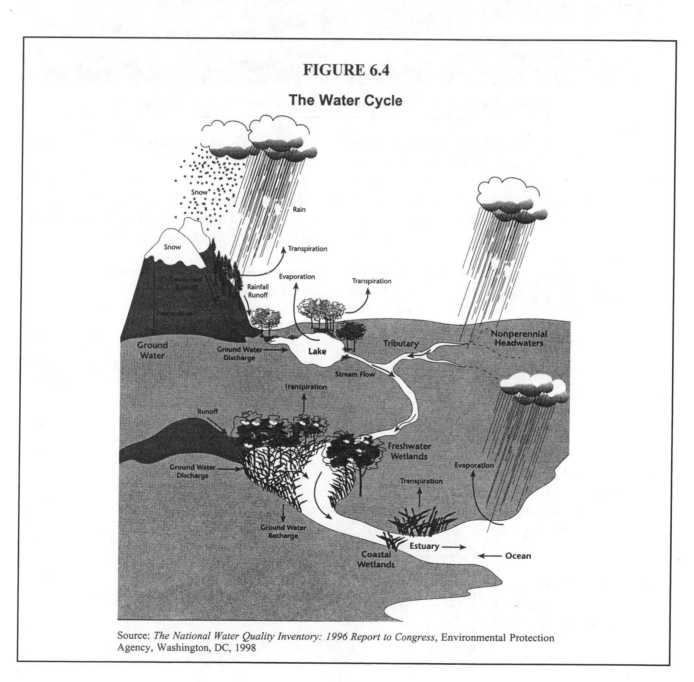

FIGURE 6.4

The Water Cycle

Source: *The National Water Quality Inventory: 1996 Report to Congress*, Environmental Protection Agency, Washington, DC, 1998

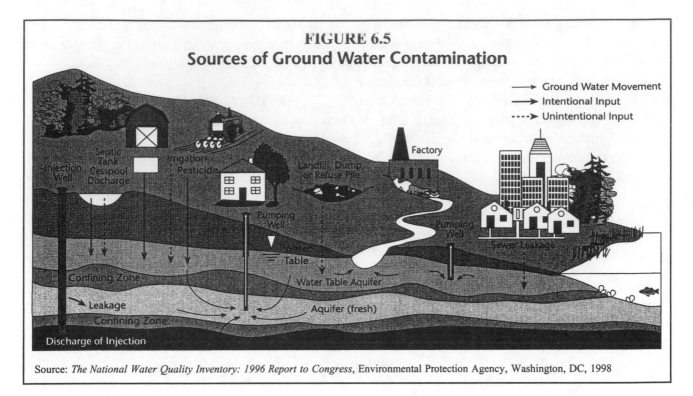

FIGURE 6.5
Sources of Ground Water Contamination

Source: *The National Water Quality Inventory: 1996 Report to Congress*, Environmental Protection Agency, Washington, DC, 1998

sults in a delay in the detection of ground water contaminants. In some cases, contaminants introduced into the subsurface more than 10 years ago are only now being detected. Contamination of ground water typically occurs in localized areas.

The Environmental Protection Agency (EPA) periodically compiles a nationwide assessment of aquifers in the 48 contiguous states. *National Water Quality Inventory: 1996 Report to Congress* (Washington, DC, 1998) reported that

- Forty-four percent of the aquifers are highly susceptible to contamination, and 60 percent have some degree of susceptibility.

- More than 85 percent of abandoned hazardous waste sites (Superfund

sites; see below) have some degree of ground water contamination.

- Of the contaminated aquifers at Superfund sites, 62 percent discharge into surface waters, 38 percent of which supply drinking water.

TABLE 6.1

Results of CDC's Survey of the Presence of Contaminants in Water from Private Wells in Nine Midwestern States

State and number of wells sampled	Percentage of wells with total coliform detections[a]	Percentage of wells with E. coli[b]	Percentage of wells with nitrate levels above EPA's standard
Illinois (540)	45.9	15.4	15.3
Nebraska (598)	37.3	2.5	14.7
Wisconsin (534)	22.8	2.6	6.6
Iowa (526)	58.6	20.5	20.6
Kansas (716)	48.7	16.3	24.3
Minnesota (718)	27.3	4.5	5.8
Missouri (632)	57.4	22.6	9.7
North Dakota (673)	35.5	8.2	13.5
South Dakota (583)	40.1	8.4	10.4
Total (5,520)	**41.3**	**11.2**	**13.4**

[a]CDC's survey procedure was to test one water sample per private well and note the presence or absence of any total coliform bacteria.

[b]Wells in CDC's survey were also tested for E. coli. EPA requires community water systems that detect total coliform bacteria in any water sample to test that sample for fecal coliform bacteria or E. coli.

Source: *Drinking Water: Information on the Quality of Water Found at Community Water Systems and Private Wells,* U.S. General Accounting Office, Washington, DC, 1997

- The EPA estimates that of 1.2 million underground storage tanks (USTs) nationwide, 139,000 USTs have leaked into ground water, and another 400,000 more will likely leak in the next several years.

- Nineteen states reported excesses of contaminant levels for at least one contaminant in water affecting a total of 1.4 million people.

- Fourteen states detected nitrate levels between 50 percent and 100 percent of the maximum contaminant level (MCL; see below).

TABLE 6.2

Principal geologic and hydrologic features that influence an aquifer's vulnerability to contamination

Feature determining aquifer vulnerability to contamination	Low vulnerability	High vulnerability
A. HYDROGEOLOGIC FRAMEWORK		
Unsaturated zone.	Thick unsaturated zone containing clay and organic materials.	Thin unsaturated zone in sand, gravel, limestone, and basalt.
Confining unit.	Thick confining unit of clay or shale above aquifer.	No confining unit.
Aquifer properties.	Silty sandstone or shaly limestone of low permeability.	Cavernous limestone, sand and gravel, gravel, or basalt of high permeability.
B. GROUND-WATER-FLOW SYSTEM		
Recharge rate.	Negligible recharge rate, as in arid regions.	Large recharge rate, as in humid regions.
Location within a flow system (proximity to recharge or discharge area or point).	Located in the deep, sluggish part of a regional flow system.	Located within a recharge area or within the cone of depression of a pumped well.

Source: *Water Pollution: More Emphasis Needed on Prevention in EPA's Efforts to Protect Groundwater*, U.S. Department of the Interior/Geological Survey, Washington, DC, 1988

Under the Safe Drinking Water Act of 1974 (PL 93-523), community water systems are required to monitor their water for 72 specific contaminants, including pesticides, bacteria, industrial solvents, and other radiological and chemical compounds. In 1997, the General Accounting Office (GAO), in *Information on the Quality of Water Found at Community Water Systems and Private Wells* (1997), studied the quality of drinking water in the United States and determined that the sources of drinking water are highly vulnerable to contamination. (For a complete discussion of drinking water, see *Water — No Longer Taken for Granted*, Information Plus, Wylie, Texas, 1999.)

Not surprisingly, land use has a significant impact on ground water. For example, in agricultural areas, long-term application of pesticides and fertilizers has contaminated underlying ground water. Near landfills and industrial facilities, improper waste disposal or chemical spills have also tainted ground water. Abandoned wells that were not sealed can introduce contamination from the surface. Geologic formations can seep naturally occurring substances, such as fluoride, arsenic, and radiological compounds.

The GAO found that coliform bacteria (microscopic organisms that live in the intestinal tracts of warm-blooded animals) were the most common contamination problem. Between 3 and 6 percent of community water systems exceeded the maximum contaminant level (MCL) for coliform bacteria. A sizable number of systems violated standards for radiological contaminants, nitrates, and the herbicide atrazine. Because private wells often use the same ground water in an area as the community systems, contaminants found in community systems are also likely to occur in private wells. Furthermore, because private wells are often not tested or treated, they may contain even more contamination than community systems.

Table 6.1 shows the presence of contaminants in water from wells in the Midwest found by a Centers for Disease Control and Prevention (CDC)

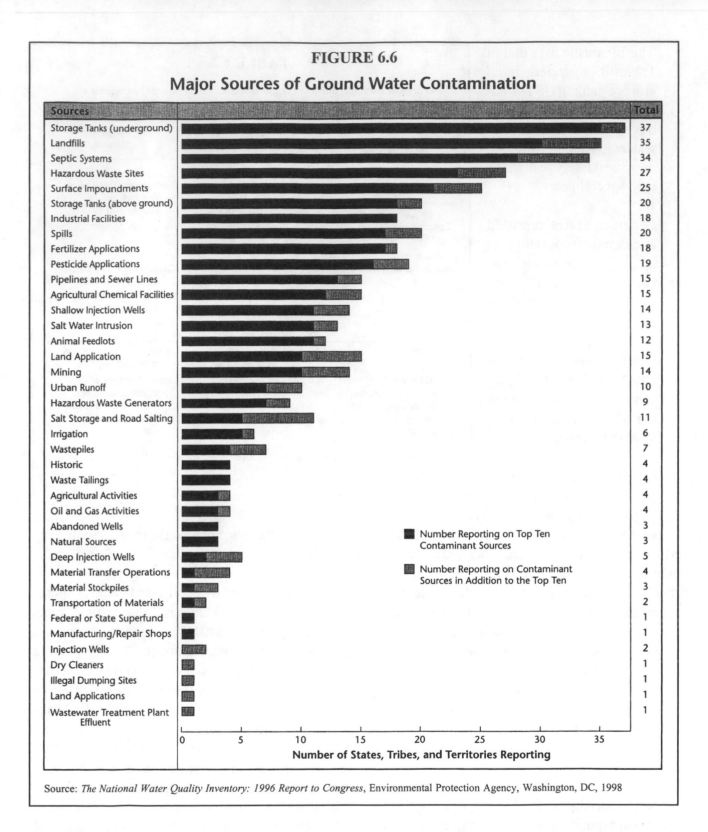

FIGURE 6.6

Major Sources of Ground Water Contamination

Sources		Total
Storage Tanks (underground)		37
Landfills		35
Septic Systems		34
Hazardous Waste Sites		27
Surface Impoundments		25
Storage Tanks (above ground)		20
Industrial Facilities		18
Spills		20
Fertilizer Applications		18
Pesticide Applications		19
Pipelines and Sewer Lines		15
Agricultural Chemical Facilities		15
Shallow Injection Wells		14
Salt Water Intrusion		13
Animal Feedlots		12
Land Application		15
Mining		14
Urban Runoff		10
Hazardous Waste Generators		9
Salt Storage and Road Salting		11
Irrigation		6
Wastepiles		7
Historic		4
Waste Tailings		4
Agricultural Activities		4
Oil and Gas Activities		4
Abandoned Wells		3
Natural Sources		3
Deep Injection Wells		5
Material Transfer Operations		4
Material Stockpiles		3
Transportation of Materials		2
Federal or State Superfund		1
Manufacturing/Repair Shops		1
Injection Wells		2
Dry Cleaners		1
Illegal Dumping Sites		1
Land Applications		1
Wastewater Treatment Plant Effluent		1

■ Number Reporting on Top Ten Contaminant Sources

▨ Number Reporting on Contaminant Sources in Addition to the Top Ten

Number of States, Tribes, and Territories Reporting

Source: *The National Water Quality Inventory: 1996 Report to Congress*, Environmental Protection Agency, Washington, DC, 1998

study. Forty-one percent of wells had coliform present, 13.4 percent had nitrate levels above EPA standards, and 11.2 percent were contaminated with *E. coli* bacteria.

FACTORS AFFECTING GROUND WATER CONTAMINATION

Ground water is affected by many of the following factors:

- The distance between the land surface where pollution occurs and the depth of the water table. The greater the distance, the greater the chance pollutants will biodegrade (be absorbed by) or react with soil minerals.

- The mineral composition of the soil and rocks in the unsaturated zone. Heavy soil and organic materials lessen the potential for contamination.

- The presence of biodegrading microbes in the soil.

- The amount of rainfall. Less rainfall results in less water entering the saturated zone and, therefore, lower quantities of contaminants.

- The evapotranspiration rate. (This is the rate at which water is discharged into the atmosphere through evaporation from the soil, surface water, and plants.) High rates reduce the amount of contaminated water reaching the saturated zone.

The characteristics of an individual aquifer also affect the degree of contamination. Table 6.2 indicates the geologic and hydrologic features that influence an aquifer's vulnerability to contamination.

MAJOR CONTAMINANTS IN GROUND WATER

In addition to identifying the sources of pollution, the EPA, in its *National Water Quality Inventory,* requested that each state identify the types of contaminants found in its ground water. Among the pollutants found in ground water were petroleum products, nitrates, metals, organic chemicals, pesticides, bacteria, brine, salt, and fluorides.

SOURCES OF POLLUTANTS

The states identified the major sources of ground water pollution in their specific areas. They rated underground storage tanks, landfills, septic systems, hazardous waste sites, surface impoundments, industrial facilities, oil spills, and fertilizer and pesticide applications as the most serious threats to ground water quality (Figure 6.6).

UNDERGROUND STORAGE TANKS

The EPA reported that leaking under-

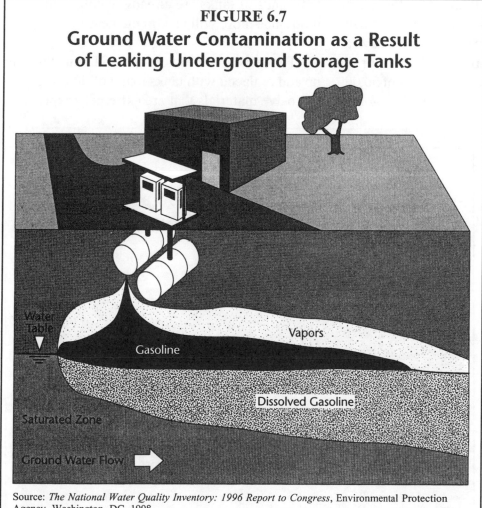

FIGURE 6.7

Ground Water Contamination as a Result of Leaking Underground Storage Tanks

Water Table

Gasoline

Vapors

Dissolved Gasoline

Saturated Zone

Ground Water Flow

Source: *The National Water Quality Inventory: 1996 Report to Congress*, Environmental Protection Agency, Washington, DC, 1998

ground storage tanks (USTs) were the leading source of contamination of ground water in 1996 (Figure 6.6.). While USTs are used to store hazardous and toxic chemicals and diluted wastes, the great majority (an estimated 1.5 to 2 million) are used to store gasoline. Most are located beneath the thousands of service stations throughout the country.

Most underground storage tanks are made of steel, which eventually rusts and disintegrates, releasing the contents of the tanks into the ground. A contaminant in the ground is likely to become a ground water contaminant. (See Figure 6.7.) One gallon of gasoline a day can contaminate one million gallons of water, or the amount of water needed for a community of 50,000 people. According to the EPA, "Leaking storage tanks may be causing the most serious risks to human health and the environment."

The average lifespan of a gasoline storage tank varies dramatically depending on where it is installed. In the Great Lakes region, a typical tank may begin to leak within seven years, while a tank may remain intact for well over 30 years in an arid region like Arizona. Of all the tanks currently in use, more than one million have been in place for more than 18 years. Some experts believe that many

thousands of tanks are already leaking and many thousands more will leak in the near future.

To resolve the problem, all USTs must be dug up and replaced with tanks made of durable, non-corrosive materials that are extremely expensive.

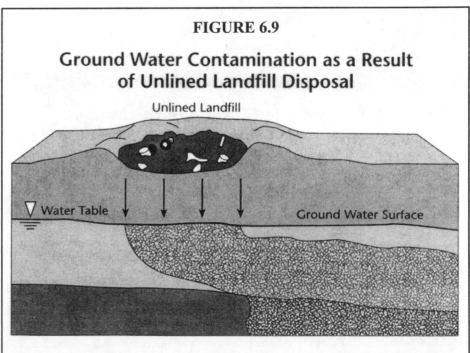

FIGURE 6.8

UNDERGROUND STORAGE TANK WITH MONITORING WELLS

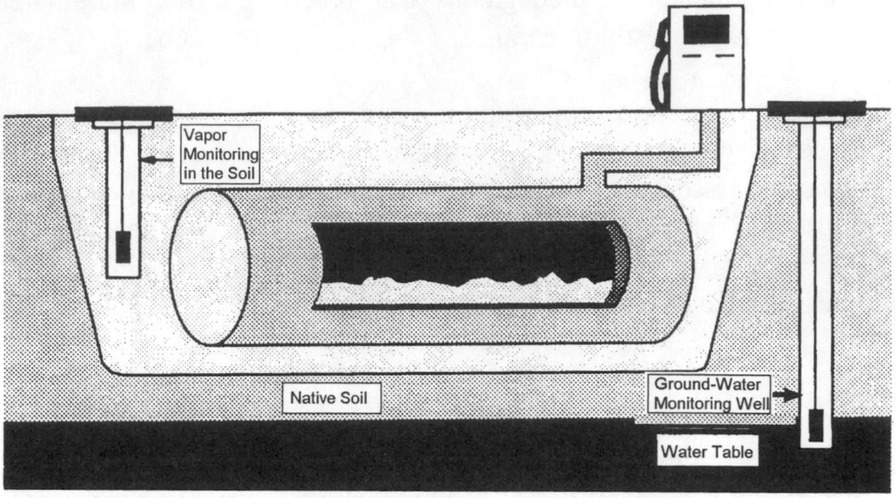

Vapor Monitoring in the Soil

Native Soil

Ground-Water Monitoring Well

Water Table

Source: *Progress in Ground-Water Protection and Restoration*, Environmental Protection Agency, Washington, DC, 1990

FIGURE 6.9

Ground Water Contamination as a Result of Unlined Landfill Disposal

Unlined Landfill

Water Table

Ground Water Surface

Source: *The National Water Quality Inventory: 1996 Report to Congress*, Environmental Protection Agency, Washington, DC, 1998

FIGURE 6.10

Generation, Treatment, and Disposal of Municipal Effluent and Sludge

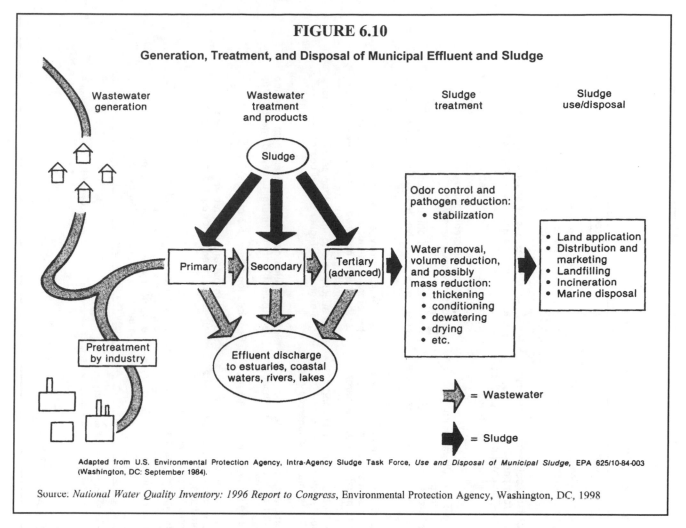

Adapted from U.S. Environmental Protection Agency, Intra-Agency Sludge Task Force, *Use and Disposal of Municipal Sludge*, EPA 625/10-84-003 (Washington, DC: September 1984).

Source: *National Water Quality Inventory: 1996 Report to Congress*, Environmental Protection Agency, Washington, DC, 1998

Buying and installing one new steel tank can cost more than $70,000. The major oil companies, which own thousands of tanks, know the chances of leakage are high and they can be held liable for cleanup procedures. They have developed programs to make more durable tanks and replace old ones. Owners of small gas stations who have only a few tanks sometimes take the gamble that their tanks will not leak and, if they do, the leaks will go undetected. Of course, if the gamble is lost, the costs can run into millions of dollars in fines, cleanup costs, and lawsuits.

Government regulations greatly reduced the options for most tank owners. In 1984, Congress amended the Resource Conservation and Recovery Act (PL 94-580) to deal with the construction, installation, and monitoring of underground tanks. Figure 6.8 shows an example of a tank with a monitoring system to protect against leakage.

In 1986, Congress established the Leaking Underground Storage Tank (LUST) program to enforce clean ups. It established a trust fund, derived primarily from a 0.1 cent-per-gallon motor fuel tax from 1987 to 1995. The tax generated approximately $150 million per year. In 1988, the EPA issued "comprehensive and stringent" rules requiring devices to detect leaks, modification of tanks to prevent corrosion, regular monitoring, and immediate cleanup of leaks and spills. Older tanks were required to be upgraded, replaced, or closed by December 22, 1998. Many small UST owner/operators, "Mom and Pop" gasoline stations, could not afford the cost of replacements and the liability insurance for storage tanks, resulting in the closing of many smaller, independently owned operations. Congress reinstated the LUST tax in the Taxpayer Relief Act of 1997 (PL 105-34) effective through March 2005.

TABLE 6.3

Advantages and Disadvantages of Selected Effluent Disinfection and Sludge Treatment Processes

Technique	Used for[a]	Advantages	Disadvantages
Effluent disinfection:			
Chlorination	DI	Commonly used; 98 to 99% destruction for bacteria; high removals of viruses and cysts	Low removal of bacterial spores; formation of chlorine residuals and chlorinated hydrocarbons; residual test not correlated with concentration of microorganisms
Ozonation	DI	99% removal of fecal coliform; high removal of viruses; destroys phenols, cyanides, trihalomethanes; no chlorinated byproducts	Toxic gas; requires onsite generation; expensive; removal of spores and cysts unknown
UV radiation	DI	Initially effective on all microorganisms	Only penetrates a few centimeters; microorganisms sometimes reactivated; potential microorganism mutagenesis; unpredictable
Gamma radiation	DI	Penetrates deeper than UV radiation	High costs; worker safety
Heat	DI	Destroys most pathogens	High energy costs
Chlorine dioxide	DI	98 to 99% bacteria removal; high virus removal; no chlorinated compounds; small measurable residual	Three times cost of chlorination; unstable, sometimes explosive; requires onsite generation
Sludge treatment:			
Aerobic digestion	ST,DI	Removes up to 85% of microorganisms and 40% of volatile solids; more rapid, simpler, less subject to metal upset than anaerobic digestion, PSRP[b]	Costly (requires oxygen); susceptible to upset by pH, organic chemicals, metals; slower at cold temperatures; not always easy to dewater; no commercial gas byproducts
Anaerobic digestion	ST,DI	Removes >85% of microorganisms and 40% of volatile solids; easier to dewater; preferred at larger plants; commercial gas byproducts; PSRP	More susceptible to upset than aerobic digestion; gas explosions; higher capital costs
Thermophilic aerobic digestion	ST,DI	Faster than aerobic; near complete destruction of bacteria and viruses; heat self-generated; PFRP[b]	Requires solids content >1.5% and heat retention equipment; only in emerging/development status
Air drying	DW,DI	Reduces some solids and microorganisms; PSRP	Requires long time (>3 months)
Heat drying	DW,DI	Significant reduction in volume; destroys most bacteria; useful for distribution and marketing products; PFRP	Subject to putrefaction; requires associated digestion; needs prior costly dewatering
Heat treatment (under pressure)	DW,DI	Sterilization; readily dewatered; PFRP	Expensive
Liming	ST,DI	Destroys bacteria; binds metals, so less leaching; PSRP	Sludge solids not destroyed, so microorganisms can regrow if pH falls prior to total drying
Chlorination	DI	Free of odors; dewaterable	No significant solids reduction; requires lime to neutralize pH; chlorinated byproducts
Composting	DI	PSRP and PFRP	Requires large space

[a]DI = disinfection; DW = dewatering, ST = stabilization.
[b]PSRP = Process to Significantly Reduce Pathogens; PFRP = Process to Further Reduce Pathogens (see text for details).
Office of Technology Assessment, 1987; after Science Applications International Corp., *Overview of Sewage Sludge and Effluent Management*, prepared for U.S. Congress, Office of Technology Assessment (McLean, VA: 1986).

Source: *Wastes in Marine Environments*, Office of Technology Assessment, Washington, DC, 1987

FIGURE 6.11

Cross Section of a Minimal Groundwater Monitoring System

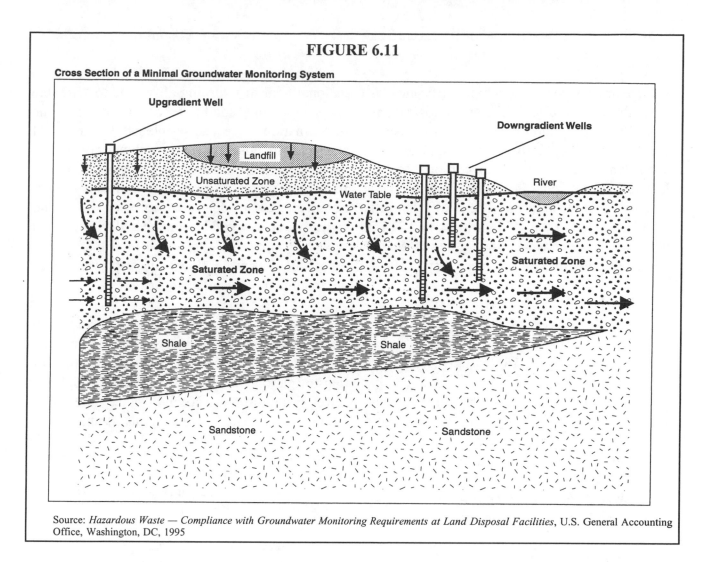

Source: *Hazardous Waste — Compliance with Groundwater Monitoring Requirements at Land Disposal Facilities*, U.S. General Accounting Office, Washington, DC, 1995

The EPA estimates that since the federal government UST program began, nearly 1.2 million of the 2.1 million tanks subject to regulation have been closed. From the program's beginning, 370,000 leaks of contaminants were identified, 302,000 cleanups were begun, and 192,000 cleanups were completed. In roughly 95 percent of the cases, the EPA or the states have been successful in getting the responsible party to perform the cleanup.

LANDFILLS

The EPA cited landfills as the second highest source of contaminants in 1996 (Figure 6.6). Materials that are commonly discarded in landfills include plastics, metals, sludges, low-level radioactive waste, wood, brick, cellulose (plant matter), petroleum compounds, ceramics, synthetics, polypropylene, and ash. Landfills were generally located on land considered to have no other use — abandoned sand and gravel pits, old strip mines, marshlands, and sinkholes. In many instances, the water table was at or very near the surface, and the potential for ground water contamination was high (Figure 6.9).

Early environmental regulation aimed at reducing air and surface-water pollution called for disposing of solid wastes underground. Many of the disposal sites were nothing more than large holes in the ground, and chemicals and bacteria of all sorts seeped through the earth into underground aquifers. The leachate (the liquid that percolates through the waste materials) from landfills contains contaminants that can easily pollute ground water. Although regulations have changed dramatically, past practices continue to cause a threat to ground water. Some studies estimate that 75 per-

127

cent of all active and inactive landfill sites are leaking contaminants into the ground water.

There have been attempts to identify and classify the thousands of landfills, or dumps, that are spread all over the country, but the lists are incomplete. It is the responsibility of each state to count its own dumps and report on its compliance with federal pollution standards. In 1993, new standards went into effect for landfills. The 20,000 landfills that had operated in the 1970s shrunk to 2,314 in 1998, at least in part because of the new rules. For more information on landfills, see Chapter II.

SEPTIC SYSTEMS AND SEWAGE DISPOSAL

Septic Tanks

Septic systems ranked as the third greatest source of contamination to ground water (Figure 6.6). Septic systems are designed to release fluids and waste waters into constructed leach beds and then into the soil. Waste waters are then expected to be attacked by biological organisms in the soil or degraded by other natural processes over time. Ground water may be contaminated when the systems are poorly constructed, improperly used or maintained, or abandoned. Typical contaminants from septic systems include bacteria, nitrates, viruses, phosphates from detergents, and chemicals from household cleaners.

Approximately 20 million Americans, living mostly in rural areas, use individual sewage-disposal systems, which are the main source of disease-causing bacteria and nitrates. Septic tanks discharge between 820 and 1,450 billion gallons of waste into the ground each year.

Sewage Disposal

Two decades after the Clean Water Act set a national goal of returning all waters to "fishable and swimmable" conditions, sewage remains one of the nation's greatest problems. Treatment of sewage is inconsistent, even within a given sewage system. While most sewage passes through a first stage, which skims off grit and heavy material, much sewage does not ever reach the second stage, where it would be aerated, chlorinated, and further decomposed. Worst of all, more than a quarter of all U.S. sewage flows into waterways without treatment by disinfectants or filters.

Most of this raw sewage is body waste, which mixes with industrial wastes and chemicals, curbside runoff, and storm-water drainage. Millions of gallons of raw sewage wash through the sewer system into the ocean or other waterways. Some of it is treated at sewage plants and turned

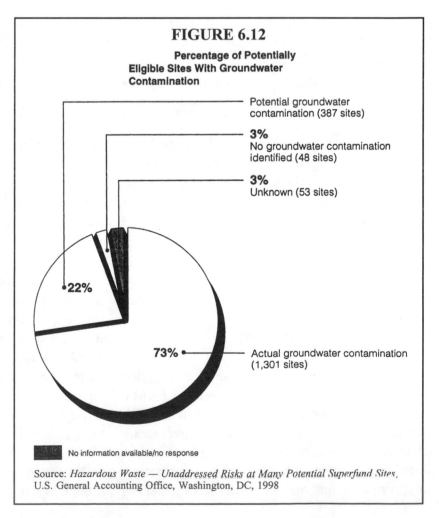

FIGURE 6.12

Percentage of Potentially Eligible Sites With Groundwater Contamination

Potential groundwater contamination (387 sites)

3%
No groundwater contamination identified (48 sites)

3%
Unknown (53 sites)

22%

73%
Actual groundwater contamination (1,301 sites)

No information available/no response

Source: *Hazardous Waste — Unaddressed Risks at Many Potential Superfund Sites*, U.S. General Accounting Office, Washington, DC, 1998

into what is called "sludge," a watery, black mud that is aerated, baked, and decomposed. This sludge must then be deposited in landfills, incinerated, dumped, or disposed of in some manner (Figure 6.10).

What can be done with this sewage? Any dumping ground — landfills, incinerators, or waterways — will become the repository of nutrient overload, toxic polluters, and non-degradable matter that will end up somewhere in the environment. Traditionally, the responsibility for dealing with waste water has fallen to the community, but growing populations and increasingly complex environmental problems have created the need for centralized regulation. The Clean Water Act of 1970 (PL 92-500) was legislated in an effort to resolve these problems.

Table 6.3 shows the advantages and disadvantages of traditional methods of sewage treatment. To provide national direction in resolving environmental problems, researchers are studying alter-

FIGURE 6.13

Surface Impoundment at Coal-Fired Electric Utility

Photo credit: Electric Power Research Institute

Source: *Managing Industrial Solid Wastes*, Office of Technology Assessment, Washington, DC, 1992

native methods of sewage disposal. Some possibilities include using bio-purification with micro-organisms and plants, recycling methane to heat greenhouses, and applying treated sludge as fertilizer on farmlands.

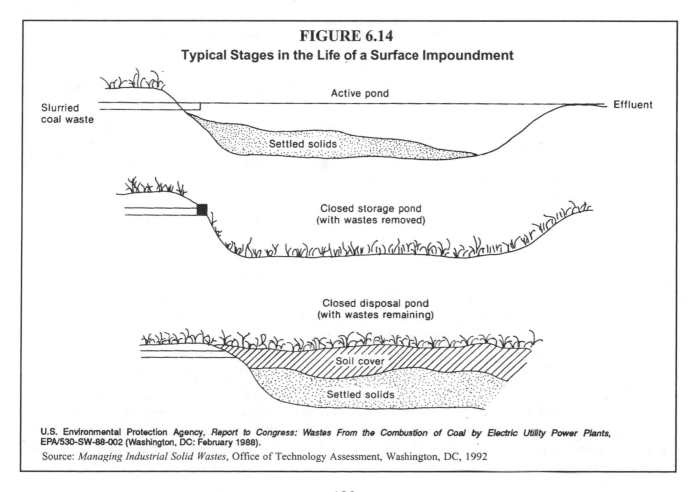

FIGURE 6.14

Typical Stages in the Life of a Surface Impoundment

U.S. Environmental Protection Agency, *Report to Congress: Wastes From the Combustion of Coal by Electric Utility Power Plants*, EPA/530-SW-88-002 (Washington, DC: February 1988).

Source: *Managing Industrial Solid Wastes*, Office of Technology Assessment, Washington, DC, 1992

129

HAZARDOUS WASTE SITES

Some materials that have been regularly deposited in landfills for many years are now known to be hazardous to human health. The majority of those sites considered dangerous contain industrial chemical wastes. Some are municipal dumps, where high concentrations of pesticides and hazardous household cleaning solvents are present. In many areas, the extent of the problem is only now becoming apparent. In remote areas, for example, dumping was often permitted.

<table>
<tr><th colspan="6">TABLE 6.4</th></tr>
<tr><th colspan="6" style="text-align:left">Symptoms and signs of pesticide intoxication among 34 farm workers — Fresno County, California, July 1998</th></tr>
<tr><th>Symptom/Sign</th><th>No.*</th><th>(%)</th><th>Symptom/Sign</th><th>No.*</th><th>(%)</th></tr>
<tr><td>SYMPTOMS</td><td></td><td></td><td></td><td></td><td></td></tr>
<tr><td>Respiratory</td><td>12</td><td>(35)</td><td>Skin</td><td>13</td><td>(38)</td></tr>
<tr><td>Runny nose</td><td>10</td><td>(29)</td><td>Itching</td><td>8</td><td>(24)</td></tr>
<tr><td>Odor detected</td><td>5</td><td>(15)</td><td>Irritation</td><td>6</td><td>(18)</td></tr>
<tr><td>Shortness of breath</td><td>1</td><td>(3)</td><td>Eye</td><td>29</td><td>(85)</td></tr>
<tr><td>Pleuritic chest pain</td><td>1</td><td>(3)</td><td>Irritation</td><td>29</td><td>(85)</td></tr>
<tr><td>Gastrointestinal</td><td>33</td><td>(97)</td><td>Tearing</td><td>23</td><td>(68)</td></tr>
<tr><td>Nausea</td><td>33</td><td>(97)</td><td>Blurred vision</td><td>5</td><td>(15)</td></tr>
<tr><td>Vomiting</td><td>27</td><td>(79)</td><td></td><td></td><td></td></tr>
<tr><td>Abdominal pain/ Cramping</td><td>15</td><td>(44)</td><td>SIGNS</td><td></td><td></td></tr>
<tr><td>Diarrhea</td><td>4</td><td>(12)</td><td>Cardiovascular</td><td>7</td><td>(21)</td></tr>
<tr><td>Genitourinary</td><td>6</td><td>(18)</td><td>Bradycardia (HR† <60)</td><td>7</td><td>(21)</td></tr>
<tr><td>Urgency/Incontinence</td><td>6</td><td>(18)</td><td>Tachycardia (HR >100)</td><td>1</td><td>(3)</td></tr>
<tr><td>Nervous system</td><td>34</td><td>(100)</td><td>Irregular rhythm</td><td>1</td><td>(3)</td></tr>
<tr><td>Headache</td><td>32</td><td>(94)</td><td>Gastointestinal</td><td>6</td><td>(18)</td></tr>
<tr><td>Dizziness</td><td>29</td><td>(85)</td><td>Vomiting</td><td>6</td><td>(18)</td></tr>
<tr><td>Muscle weakness</td><td>28</td><td>(82)</td><td>Nervous system</td><td>6</td><td>(18)</td></tr>
<tr><td>Salivation</td><td>19</td><td>(56)</td><td>Diaphoresis</td><td>5</td><td>(15)</td></tr>
<tr><td>Muscle shaking</td><td>11</td><td>(32)</td><td>Muscle weakness</td><td>1</td><td>(3)</td></tr>
<tr><td>Sweating</td><td>3</td><td>(9)</td><td>Eye</td><td>4</td><td>(12)</td></tr>
<tr><td>Confusion</td><td>1</td><td>(3)</td><td>Miosis</td><td>4</td><td>(12)</td></tr>
<tr><td>Anxiety</td><td>1</td><td>(3)</td><td>Respiratory</td><td>3</td><td>(9)</td></tr>
<tr><td>Loss of balance</td><td>1</td><td>(3)</td><td>Tachypnea (RR§ >20)</td><td>3</td><td>(9)</td></tr>
</table>

*Because more than one symptom or sign may have been reported for any person, the sum of specific symptoms and signs may not total the number reported for the organ system as a whole.
†Heart rate.
§Respiratory rate.

Source: "Farm Worker Illness Following Exposure to Carbofuran and Other Pesticides — Fresno County, California, 1998," *Morbidity and Mortality Weekly Report*, February 19, 1999

Today, as new suburban communities spread out from the cities, these sites have become serious contamination problems since people now live so close by. In some communities, such as Dallas, Texas, hazardous wastes were dumped in low-income areas of the city for years. In addition, industries known to produce large amounts of pollutants have often been located in such areas.

When a site is found to be so badly contaminated with hazardous waste that it represents a serious threat to human health (for example, contamination of ground water used for drinking), it is placed on the National Priorities List (commonly known as "Superfund"), making it eligible for federal intervention and cleanup assistance. For more information on hazardous waste, see Chapter VII.

The EPA reported in 1995 that approximately 73 million people live fewer than four miles from at least one Superfund site, and much debate has occurred about the extent to which these sites pose health risks to those residents. The EPA found that one-third of the sites studied posed serious health risks to nearby residents, primarily through ground water (*Superfund — Information on Current Health Risks*, 1995).

Ground water monitoring is the primary method of detecting contamination at hazardous waste sites. Monitoring systems consist of a number of wells placed around a waste facility. Data taken from those wells can indicate whether contamination is occurring at the site. (See Figure 6.11.)

Of the 1,200 hazardous waste sites on the National Priorities List (see Chapter VII), about 73 percent have already contaminated ground water, and another 22 percent could contaminate in the future (Figure 6.12). In addition, about 32 percent of the sites have already tainted drinking water sources, with another 56 percent being potentially capable of contaminating drinking water.

SURFACE IMPOUNDMENTS

Surface impoundments are pits, lagoons, and ponds, usually man-made, that receive treated or untreated wastes directly from the discharge point or are used to store chemicals for later use, to wash or treat ores, or to treat water for further use. Most are small, less than one acre, but some industrial and mining impoundments may be as large as 1,000 acres. (See Figure 6.13.)

Most impoundments were not lined with a synthetic or impermeable natural material, such as clay, to prevent liquids from leaching into the ground. (See Figure 6.14 for the stages in a surface impoundment.) This is particularly important, since about 87 percent of the impoundments are located over aquifers currently used as sources of

drinking water. Only 2 percent are located in areas where there is no ground water or it is too saline (salty) for use. About 70 percent of the sites are located over very permeable aquifers that can allow contaminants entering its waters to spread rapidly. Ground water protection has rarely, if ever, been considered during the site selection of impoundments.

PESTICIDE AND FERTILIZER USE BY AGRICULTURE

Irrigation can increase the salinity of ground water by leaching salts from the soil as the water seeps down into the aquifer. The pesticides applied to cropland spread into underground water supplies. In addition, fertilizers can raise nitrate levels in ground water so high that it becomes unsafe to drink.

Pesticides — An Ancient Remedy

If we are going to live so intimately with these chemicals — eating and drinking them, taking them into the very marrow of our bones — we had better know something about their nature and power. — Rachel Carson, *Silent Spring* (1962)

The ancient Greeks were the first documented users of pesticides. Pliny the Elder (C.E. 23-79) reported using common compounds such as arsenic, sulfur, caustic soda, and olive oil to protect crops. The Chinese later used similar substances to retard insect and fungi growth. In the 1800s, Europeans used heavy metal salts such as copper sulfate and iron sulfate as weed killers.

The invention of DDT (dichloro-diphenyl-trichloroethane, a powerful insecticide) in 1939 marked a revolution in the war against pests. DDT was effective, relatively inexpensive, and apparently safe — a miracle chemical that promised a world without insects and with unprecedented crop yields. Its discoverer, Paul Muller, received a Nobel Prize for its discovery. Convinced that chemicals were the modern wave of the future, farmers be-

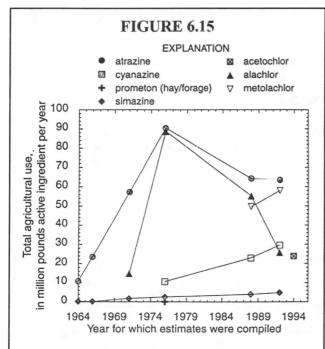

FIGURE 6.15

EXPLANATION

- ● atrazine
- ⊠ acetochlor
- ▨ cyanazine
- ▲ alachlor
- ✛ prometon (hay/forage)
- ▽ metolachlor
- ◆ simazine

Total nationwide agricultural use of the seven herbicides of interest from 1964 to 1994. Use of prometon for hay and forage in 1976 was 20,000 pounds active ingredient per year.

Source: Jack E. Barbash et al., *Distribution of Major Herbicides in Ground Water of the United States*, U.S. Geological Survey, prepared in cooperation with U.S. Environmental Protection Agency, Sacramento, CA, 1999

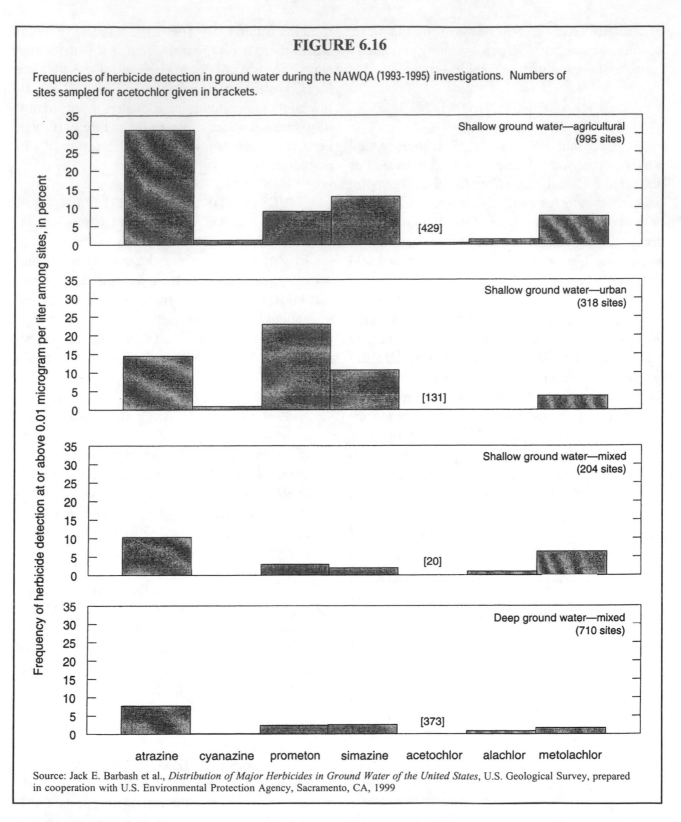

FIGURE 6.16

Frequencies of herbicide detection in ground water during the NAWQA (1993-1995) investigations. Numbers of sites sampled for acetochlor given in brackets.

Frequency of herbicide detection at or above 0.01 microgram per liter among sites, in percent

Shallow ground water—agricultural (995 sites) [429]

Shallow ground water—urban (318 sites) [131]

Shallow ground water—mixed (204 sites) [20]

Deep ground water—mixed (710 sites) [373]

atrazine   cyanazine   prometon   simazine   acetochlor   alachlor   metolachlor

Source: Jack E. Barbash et al., *Distribution of Major Herbicides in Ground Water of the United States*, U.S. Geological Survey, prepared in cooperation with U.S. Environmental Protection Agency, Sacramento, CA, 1999

gan using pesticides, herbicides, and fungicides intensively and began to accept chemicals as essential to agriculture.

Today, farmers apply about one pound of pesticide per year for every person on the earth, 75 percent of it in industrial countries. In the United States, pesticide use in agriculture has approximately tripled since 1965. Pesticide use is particularly high in California, Mississippi, Wisconsin, New York, Massachusetts, and Maine, but use is considerable throughout the United States.

Despite problems associated with chemicals and a growing number of farmers who are using fewer pesticides, pesticide use continues to grow. Unlike most chemicals, pesticides are designed to kill or alter living organisms. According to the United Nations World Health Organization (WHO), pesticide poisonings affect about 1 million people per year. Of these, three-quarters suffer health problems such as dermatitis, nervous system disorders, and cancer. WHO estimates that 4,000 to 19,000 people die annually as a result of pesticides.

The discovery of certain pesticides in underground drinking water many years after being banned challenged long-held notions about agricultural chemicals. Farmers had thought pesticides either evaporated or degraded into harmless substances. Now farmers are confronted with the possibility they may have poisoned their own drinking water. Many experts believe this is the tip of the iceberg, and evidence of pesticides in the air, water, and food chains is being found. The EPA currently lists 55 possible carcinogens (cancer-causing substances) being used on U.S. food crops. At one time, drinking water in Des Moines, Iowa, was so contaminated by agricultural chemicals that the local nightly news announced tap-water nitrate levels.

In recent years, improved safety testing has prompted tougher standards for a new generation of pesticides. The best of the new pesticides can be used in minute quantities and cause few health problems. They are, however, more expensive. Many farmers continue to use the older pesticides, especially in developing countries. DDT is now banned in most industrialized countries, but it is still used in developing nations, where many farmers see it as an inexpensive way to control pests. Nonetheless, even the new formulations are not entirely safe, especially for wildlife. The U.S. Fish and Wildlife Service reports that pesticides are the cause of deterioration in at least one-fifth of endangered and threatened animal and plant species.

A major problem with the use of pesticides is that they create the need for more and different chemicals. The development of a resistant strain of insect to a pesticide is virtually automatic, because those insects that survive are unaffected by that chemical and will breed offspring that are also immune — "superbugs." In the United States, overall crop losses due to insects have actually gone up since DDT's discovery. At first, insecticides cause crop losses to fall, but over time, the pests become immune, their numbers rebound, and a new pesticide must be found to destroy immune insects. Worldwide, the number of pests resistant to chemicals continues to climb. In 1938, scientists knew of only seven insect species resistant to pesticides. Today, hundreds of species are resistant, including most of the world's major pests.

As an alternative to pesticide use and abuse, many scientists and the federal government encourage the practice of Integrated Pest Management (IPM). This method combines biological controls (like natural predators of pests), cultural practices (planting rotation and diversification), and genetic manipulation (pest-resistant crop varieties) with a modest use of chemicals. Rather than attempting the impossible task of eliminating pests, the goal is to strike a sustainable, profitable balance with nature.

Many farmers have been slow to adopt the new methods for a variety of reasons:

- Some banks require farmers to use pesticides to qualify for crop loans.

- Pesticide companies spend heavily on advertising and political lobbying. Their lobbies are among the strongest in the nation.

- In underdeveloped countries, funds and expertise are lacking.

- IPM is new and different, and old habits and beliefs are hard to break.

- Government subsidies and pricing policies encourage pesticide use.

Nonetheless, sustainable agriculture is gaining ground, and researchers estimate that U.S. farmers could cut their pesticide use by up to 50 percent and still not lower harvests or significantly raise costs. Organic pesticides and fertilizers, which come from biological sources rather than chemical factories, are beginning to compete successfully in the marketplace. These products include pyrethrum and neem, extracts of flower and tree seeds, which cause no contamination from handling or from leaching into the water supply or food chain.

Some critics of organic pesticides and fertilizers contend that low levels of chemicals in ground water should be acceptable. They also argue that some areas should be designated for agribusiness and allowed to become polluted. They emphasize the uncertainty of health-risk calculations, especially since tests have been done not on humans, but on animals. Pesticide supporters wield a great deal of influence in Congress and have, in the past, generally impeded ground water legislation.

Circle of Poison

Benlate, a fungicide once considered the farmer's best friend, has become his or her worst enemy, causing plants to wither and die. For two decades, benlate was the farmer's secret to growing unblemished fruits and ornamental plants. Some farmers in Florida now find their land has become unusable for farming. Researchers think the once-helpful chemical, when combined with humidity, heat, and other chemicals, has become poisonous over time, destroying the land.

A group of chemicals called organophosphates have been widely linked to death and illness. In 1991, deaths and illnesses occurred among California farm workers working around one such chemical, parathion. In 1999, Congress banned most uses of that chemical. Wildlife experts in California reported that a pesticide spill from a train derailment killed "every living thing" in the Sacramento River and Lake Shasta and that it would be years before fisheries were restored.

In California, suspected pesticide-related illnesses are reportable conditions. In 1999, the Centers for Disease Control and Prevention reported that 34 farm workers were exposed to carbofuran, a pesticide applied to a cotton crop. The workers became ill and were treated for a variety of symptoms after decontamination. Their symptoms included nausea (97 percent), headache (94 percent), eye irritation (85 percent), muscle weakness (82 percent), and vomiting (79 percent). (See Table 6.4.)

Dioxin

In 1982, the chemical dioxin became "Toxic Enemy Number One." In Times Beach, Missouri, the soil was declared contaminated with dioxin after a hazardous-waste trucking company sprayed roads and parking lots (for dust control) with waste oil containing dioxin in the early 1970s. The government permanently evacuated all 2,240 residents, and the state and federal governments bought the property of residents for $37 million. About 100,000 cubic yards of contaminated soil were removed, awaiting the construction of an incinerator at Times Beach.

Dioxin comes in 75 varieties, including the defoliant Agent Orange, which some Vietnam veterans blame for their cancers and nervous system disorders and for genetic defects in their children. Many of those soldiers have been granted disability benefits by the federal government, although the connection between their problems and dioxin has not been scientifically proven.

Most recently, environmentalists have expressed concern over the emission of dioxin from incinerators. Incineration (combustion) is identified by the EPA as the primary cause of known dioxin emissions. For more information on incineration, see Chapter II.

Fertilizers

For more than three decades, fertilizer contributed to the increase in the world's food production. Fertilizer use and food production both increased at the rate of 7 percent per year from 1950 to 1984. Since 1984, however, these increases have dropped to less than 2 percent annually. As the world adds another 90 million people per year, the need for food supplies expands, yet the growth in world fertilizer use has actually slowed.

In the United States, the high cost of fertilizer, coupled with new methods to more precisely measure the fertilizer needs of various crops, is discouraging excessive use of chemical fertilizers. Farmers have found that the "little bit" extra that they might once have used is lost in nutrient run-off and adds to stream pollution in agricultural areas. The major factor, however, is the decreasing response of crops to fertilizer. During the 1960s, an additional ton of fertilizer applied on a farm in the U.S. cornbelt boosted output by 20 tons. Today, another ton may boost output by only a few tons. Crops are apparently approaching the limits of photosynthetic efficiency (maximum possible yield).

Nitrates

Nitrate (a nitrogen compound used as a fertilizer) is the second most widespread agricultural contaminant after petroleum compounds. It is a human health concern. The 1996 *National Water Quality Inventory* reported that approximately half the states indicated elevated levels of nitrate in ground water.

At exposures greater than 10 milligrams per liter, it can cause "blue baby" syndrome in infants. It also causes nutrient enrichment of coastal waters. Most ground water studies use nitrate as an indicator of ground water quality because of its stability and solubility in water. High levels of nitrate in well water typically indicate that pollution is seeping from septic tanks, animal wastes, fertilizers, municipal landfills, or other nonpoint sources. The EPA has established 10 milligrams per liter (mg/L) as the allowable level of nitrate nitrogen in water (MCL — maximum contaminant level), although 3 mg/L is typically held as the threshold for human impacts.

Attempts to Measure Contamination by Herbicides

In 1995, the U.S. Geological Service (USGS) reported that 50 percent of wells sampled had elevated levels of nitrate nitrogen (over 3 mg/L), and 21 percent exceeded 10 mg/L, the EPA Maximum Contaminant Level (MCL). Agricultural areas had significantly higher concentrations than other land-use settings. Nitrate concentrations were typically higher in the Northeastern, Northern Plains, and Pacific states. The EPA reported that 4.5 million people were potentially exposed to high levels of nitrate from drinking water (*Guidelines for Preparation of the Comprehensive State Water Quality Assessments [305b Reports] and Electronic Updates*, 1997).

During the early 1990s, the USGS performed a major study of ground water contamination. In its *Distribution of Major Herbicides in Ground Water of the United States* (1999), the USGS measured the presence of seven herbicides in ground water samples throughout the United States. The herbicides studied included seven high-use herbicides: atrazine, alachlor, cyanazine, simazine, prometon, acetochlor, and metachlor. Figure 6.15 shows the use of the seven agricultural herbicides from 1964 to 1994. Six of those chemicals (all except acetochlor) were found in samples taken from shallow ground water (ground water "recharged" within the past 10 years). The study re-

TABLE 6.5

Per Capita Annual Consumption of Meat, By Major Type (in pounds)

Category	1975	1997
Beef	88.9	63.8
Pork	50.9	45.6
Chicken	40.3	50.9
Turkey	8.6	13.9

USDA, Economic Research Service, *National Food Situation*, March 1977, and *Agricultural Outlook*, March 1999.

Source: *Animal Waste Management and the Environment: Background for Current Issues*, Congressional Research Service, Washington, DC, 1999

FIGURE 6.17
Cemented and Curbed Barnyards

Source: *Animal Agriculture — Waste Management Practices*, U.S. General Accounting Office, Washington, DC, 1999

ported that some pesticides were detected in shallow ground water within one year following application. Samples found atrazine, metolachlor, prometon, and simazine most frequently (Figure 6.16), with atrazine the most commonly reported chemical, especially in agricultural areas.

The study found, however, that more than 98 percent of the detections were of concentrations of less than one microgram per liter. Consequently, water quality criteria for drinking water were exceeded at fewer than 0.1 percent of the sites sampled. This does not fully reflect the overall health risks because the measurements were of only seven herbicides. Also, they do not account for the additive effects of mixtures of chemicals, long-term additive concentrations are unknown, and the impacts on human and aquatic health are largely unknown.

Attacking Pesticide Use Through Food Monitoring

Legislation has been introduced recently designed to control pollution of food by a large number of elements, including pesticides. In 1996, Congress enacted the Food Quality Protection Act (FQPA; PL 104-170), which established new standards for food safety and required that "tolerances" be established for many hundreds of chemicals. In the years since the law was enacted, EPA implementation of the law has been criticized, for conflicting reasons, by farmers, chemical manufacturers, environmentalists, other stakeholders, and the Clinton administration. Politically active stakeholders, such as multinational pesticide producers, and farmers and food industry groups contend the law is unduly alarmist. Environmentalists and consumer advocacy groups complain that the regulations do not go far enough; for example, the rules do not refer to pesticides as poisons.

ANIMAL WASTE AND GROUND WATER

Animal agriculture, the production of livestock and poultry, is important to the economic well-being of the United States, producing $98.8 billion per year in farm revenue. In addition to providing food for Americans, the industry also contributes to the stability of many rural communities.

Livestock includes cattle (beef, dairy, and veal), swine, poultry (chickens and turkeys), and sheep and lambs. The USDA reports that markets for these have changed in recent decades, with Americans eating less beef and pork and more poultry (Table 6.5). Overall, livestock consumption has grown because of the growing population and in-

FIGURE 6.18

Mechanized Scraping System for Collecting Dairy Cow Waste

Source: *Animal Agriculture — Waste Management Practices*, U.S. General Accounting Office, Washington, DC, 1999

Concern over pollution resulting from intensive livestock and poultry production has increased in recent years. Nationwide, about 130 times more animal waste* is produced than human waste — roughly five tons per U.S. citizen — and some operations with hundreds of thousands of animals produce as much waste as a town or city. This huge volume of waste threatens surface and ground water quality. As animal production is increasingly concentrated in larger operations and in certain areas of the country, traditional animal management practices may not be adequate to prevent water contamination. Figures 6.17-6.19 show some of the animal waste management practices currently available.

creasing affordability in many parts of the world. The United States has become the largest exporter of meat in the world.

* Animal waste generally refers to manure but also includes wastewater, urine, bedding, poultry litter, and animal carcasses.

FIGURE 6.19

Open-Air Manure Composting

Source: *Animal Agriculture — Waste Management Practices*, U.S. General Accounting Office, Washington, DC, 1999

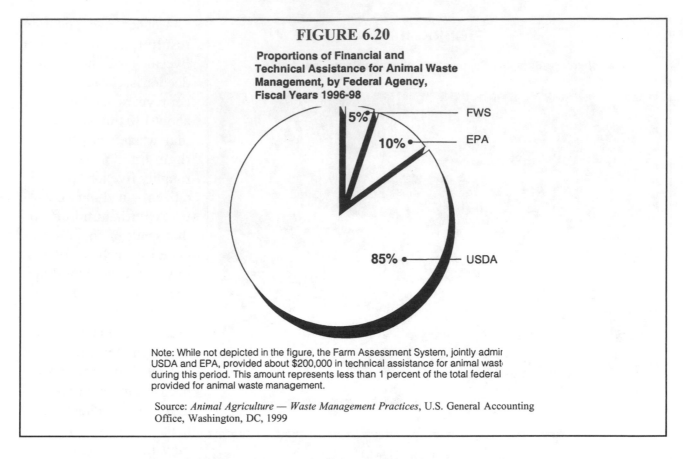

FIGURE 6.20

Proportions of Financial and Technical Assistance for Animal Waste Management, by Federal Agency, Fiscal Years 1996-98

5% — FWS

10% — EPA

85% — USDA

Note: While not depicted in the figure, the Farm Assessment System, jointly admir USDA and EPA, provided about $200,000 in technical assistance for animal wast during this period. This amount represents less than 1 percent of the total federal provided for animal waste management.

Source: *Animal Agriculture — Waste Management Practices*, U.S. General Accounting Office, Washington, DC, 1999

Today's large livestock operations look more like animal factories than farms. Typically, animals are tightly confined, often indoors on slatted metal floors, beneath which their feces are flushed. Animal waste can introduce pollutants such as nutrients, organic matter, sediments, pathogens, heavy metals, hormones, antibiotics, and ammonia. These pollutants are transported by rainwater, snowmelt, or irrigation water through the soil or into rivers, lakes, and coastal waters. They can affect water quality and public health, such as contaminating drinking water supplies and killing fish. Other potential problems include odors, loss of wildlife habitat, and the depletion of ground water.

According to the EPA, agricultural activity is the leading source of impairment to the nation's rivers, lakes, and estuaries. From 1996 through 1998, the federal government provided more than $384 million in assistance to producers for animal waste management. (Figure 6.20 shows the share of assistance provided by the various agencies.) The U.S. Department of Agriculture (USDA) administers several major programs to provide finan-

cial and technical assistance to producers for managing animal wastes. The nation's federal and state regulatory systems for protecting environmental health have, however, largely been unable to keep pace with the rapid growth of factory farms.

CLEANUP AND PROTECTION

Cleaning up the nation's ground water is expensive. The costs for cleaning up typical ground water contamination from a chemical landfill are estimated at $5 to $10 million per site.

In allocating limited resources, cleanup decisions are based on a cost/benefit analysis that considers such factors as the extent of the problem, the potential health effects, and the alternatives, if any. If the pollution is localized, it may be more practical to simply shut down the contaminated wells and find water elsewhere. Cleanup options range from "capping" a section of an aquifer with a layer of clay that prevents more pollution to more complex (and expensive) methods such as pumping out and treating the water and then returning it

FIGURE 6.21

Treatment Facility for Removal of Strontium from Ground Water near the Columbia River at Hanford

Source: *Nuclear Waste: Greater Use of Removal Actions Could Cut Time and Cost for Cleanups,* U.S. General Accounting Office, Washington, DC, 1996

to the aquifer. Where radioactive or hazardous materials have permeated the soil and contaminated ground water, water and soil may need to be treated (Figure 6.21).

The States' Role — Three Basic Approaches

In 1984, the EPA established a national Ground Water Protection Strategy that gives states the lead role in setting and implementing ground water policies. The types of principal state programs that address ground water protection are depicted in Figure 6.22. The states use three basic approaches to protect ground water and address the problems of contaminants and sources of contamination:

- *Nondegradation* policies are designed to protect ground water quality at its existing level.

- *Limited degradation* policies involve setting up water-quality standards to protect ground water. These standards set maximum contamination levels for chemicals and bacteria and for taste, odor, and color of the water.

- *Ground water classification systems* are similar to the classification systems for surface waters established under the Clean Water Act and its amendments. These classification systems are used by state officials to determine which aquifers should receive higher or lower priorities for protection and cleanup. High-priority areas include recharge areas, which affect large quantities of water, and public water supplies where pollution affects drinking water.

139

FIGURE 6.22
Types of State Ground Water Protection Programs

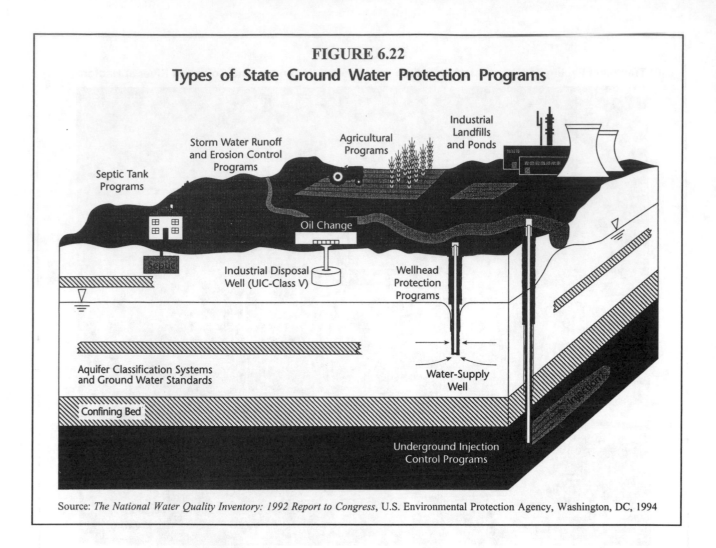

Source: *The National Water Quality Inventory: 1992 Report to Congress*, U.S. Environmental Protection Agency, Washington, DC, 1994

The Federal Role

Parts of several federal laws help to protect the ground water. (See Table 6.6.) The Clean Water Act provides guidance and money to the states to help develop ground water programs. The Safe Drinking Water Act of 1986 (PL 93-523) requires communities to test their water to make sure it is safe. The Resource Conservation and Recovery Act of 1976 (RCRA; PL 91-512) includes many programs designed to clean up hazardous waste sites, landfills, and underground storage tanks. New storage tanks will have to be made of strong plastics that will not rust and leak.

The Comprehensive Environmental Response, Compensation, and Liability Act of 1980 (CERCLA; PL 96-510) and the Superfund Amendments and Reauthorization Act of 1986 (PL 99-499, PL 99-563, PL 100-202) require the cleanup of hazardous wastes that can seep into the ground water. The two laws also require that cities and industry build better managed and constructed garbage dumps and landfills for hazardous materials so that the ground water will not be polluted in the future.

The Federal Insecticide, Fungicide, and Rodenticide Act of 1988 (FIFRA; PL 100-532) was written to control dangerous chemicals used on farms. The law requires the EPA to register the pesticides farmers use against insects, rats, mice, etc. If the EPA thinks pesticides might be dangerous to the ground water, they can refuse to register them. The EPA has proposed a rule under FIFRA to cancel the use of pesticides in certain areas if samples taken exceed certain levels. To do so, each state would be required to prepare a Pesticide Management Plan (PMP). The USGS would assist the states in studying the water quality in their boundaries.

TABLE 6.6

EPA Statutory Authorities With Groundwater Protection Provisions

Resource Conservation and Recovery Act	• Provides the authority to prevent hazardous wastes from leaching into groundwater from hazardous waste facilities and sources such as municipal landfills, impoundments, and underground storage tanks.
Comprehensive Environmental Response, Compensation, and Liability Act, or Superfund	• Provides the authority to clean up abandoned hazardous waste sites that present a major threat to human health or the environment.
Federal Insecticide, Fungicide, and Rodenticide Act	• Provides the authority to control the availability and use of harmful pesticides, including those with a potential to leach into groundwater.
Toxic Substances Control Act	• Provides the authority to control the availability and use of harmful toxic substances, including those with a potential to contaminate groundwater.
Safe Drinking Water Act	• Provides the authority for (1) setting and enforcing drinking water standards for surface and groundwater public drinking water supplies, (2) controlling underground injection practices, and (3) establishing state wellhead protection programs.
Clean Water Act	• Provides authority for federal grant programs to assist states in developing groundwater protection strategies and nonpoint source pollution programs.

Source: *Water Pollution: More Emphasis Needed on Prevention in EPA's Efforts to Protect Groundwater*, U.S. General Accounting Office, Washington, DC, 1991

In August 1993, the Oil Pollution Act of 1990 (PL 101-380) went into effect. The law, which was passed in response to the 1989 *Exxon Valdez* oil spill in Alaska, requires companies involved in storing and transporting petroleum to have standby plans for cleaning up spills on land or in water. A result of the law has been a resurgence of interest in and a new market for innovative methods for oil-spill cleanup.

CHAPTER VII

HAZARDOUS WASTE

WHAT IS HAZARDOUS WASTE?

Solid, liquid, or gas waste can be harmful to human beings or the environment when not handled properly. This waste material may be the by-product of manufacturing or the accidental spill or release of a chemical product. It can be toxic, corrosive, flammable, explosive, or radioactive. Because of these potential dangers, hazardous waste requires special care when being stored, transported, or discarded.

Hazardous waste is the inevitable by-product of industrialization. Manufacturers use many chemicals to create their products. Hazardous waste is generated by big industries like automobile and computer manufacturers and by small businesses like neighborhood photo shops or dry cleaners. Studies show that, although people can reduce quantities of hazardous waste through careful management, it is not possible to eliminate hazardous residues entirely because of the continual demand for goods.

Waste falls primarily into two categories: hazardous waste and nonhazardous waste. Between 2 and 4 percent of all waste generated in the United States is hazardous. Ninety percent of all hazardous waste in the United States is produced by about 14,000 large waste generators (facilities each producing over 1,000 kilograms of hazardous waste a month). The chemical industry is by far the largest producer, followed by petroleum refiners, then by the metal processing industry. The remaining 10 percent comes from more than 100,000 small-quantity generators — businesses that each produce less than 1,000 kg of hazardous waste per month. These include photo labs, service stations, dry cleaners, body shops, printers, laboratories, and private homes. (See Figure 7.1.)

Industrial wastes are usually a combination of compounds, one or more of which may be hazardous; for example, used pickling solution from a metal processor can also contain residual acids and metal salts. A mixture of waste produced regularly as a result of the industrial process is called a waste stream, and it generally consists of diluted rather than full-strength compounds. Often the hazardous components are diluted in a mixture of dirt, oil, or water.

Contamination of the air, water, and soil with hazardous wastes can frequently lead to serious health problems. The Environmental Protection Agency (EPA) estimates that roughly 1,000 cases of cancer annually can be linked to public exposure to hazardous waste, as well as degenerative diseases, mental retardation, birth defects, and chromosomal changes. While most scientists agree that exposure to high doses of hazardous waste is dangerous, there is less agreement on the danger of exposure to low doses.

METHODS OF DEALING WITH HAZARDOUS WASTE

In North America, 96 percent of all hazardous waste is treated and disposed of on the site at which it is produced. Four percent is treated and disposed of by commercial waste service companies. A variety of techniques exist for safely managing hazardous wastes, including

FIGURE 7.1
Hazardous Waste

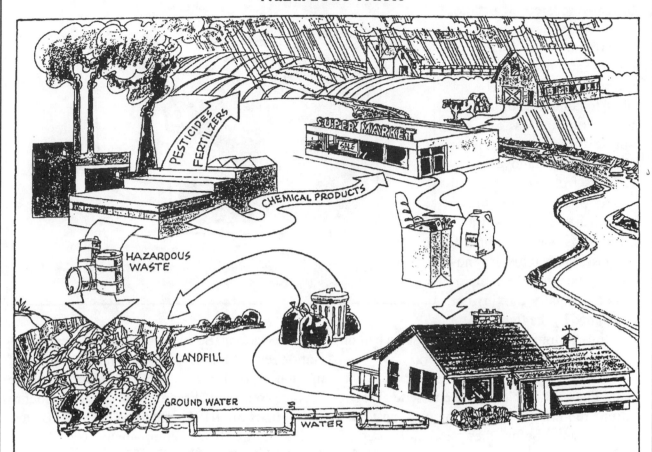

Of the 80,000 chemicals on the market, only a small percentage have been tested for their effects on man and nature. A good many have not even been named. Worldwide, 1,500 new chemicals are invented each year. Monitoring them all is necessary in order to predict their potential harms.

Incineration is one way to dispose of hazardous waste, but this produces more dioxins, pollutants, and toxic residue. Alternatives are being explored—some microbes (microscopic organisms) have been found that can eat toxics and convert them into harmless compounds.

These new methods are costly and experimental. The most efficient way to cut down on hazardous waste is by substituting benign for toxic chemicals. Simply using nontoxic cleaning agents at home is one way each individual can help.

• Reduction — This approach reduces the waste stream at the outset. Waste generators change their manufacturing processes and materials in order to produce less waste. For example, a food packaging plant might replace solvent-based adhesives used to seal packages with water-based adhesives.

143

- Recycling — Some waste materials become raw material for another process or can be recovered, reused, or sold.

- Treatment — A variety of chemical, biological, and thermal processes can be applied to neutralize or destroy toxic compounds. For example, microorganisms or chemicals can remove hydrocarbons from contaminated water. Unfortunately, incineration has a serious drawback — as waste is burned, hot gases spew into the atmosphere, carrying toxic materials (especially dioxin) not consumed by the flames. The Clinton Administration has imposed a ban on new hazardous waste incinerators.

- Land disposal — New state and federal regulations require the pre-treatment of most hazardous wastes before they can be disposed of in landfills. These treated materials can be placed only in specially designed land disposal facilities. Figure 7.2 shows the design of a landfill for hazardous materials.

- Injection wells — Hazardous waste may be injected under high pressure deep underground in wells thousands of feet deep.

HOUSEHOLD HAZARDOUS WASTE

Household hazardous waste (HHW) consists of the residue of many common consumer products that can result in the release of potentially toxic substances. Because of the relatively low amount of hazardous substances in individual products, HHW is not regulated as a hazardous waste. Examples of HHW include nail polish remover, toilet and drain cleaners, chlorine bleach, pesticides, small batteries, automotive oil and batteries, and oil-based paints and thinners.

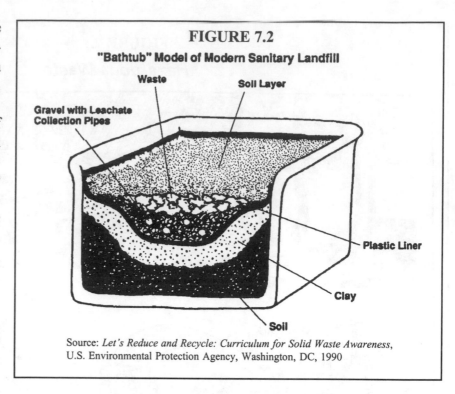

FIGURE 7.2

"Bathtub" Model of Modern Sanitary Landfill

Source: *Let's Reduce and Recycle: Curriculum for Solid Waste Awareness*, U.S. Environmental Protection Agency, Washington, DC, 1990

The National Solid Waste Management Association reports that HHW is less than 1 percent of municipal solid waste. The EPA reports that the average household discards approximately four to five pounds of HHW per person per year. Batteries outnumber all other components of HHW, with "selected cosmetics" in second place. By weight, however, paint, stain, and varnish are the greatest components, followed by batteries and automotive products.

Most HHW products have a low to negligible recycling rate. The exception is lead-acid (car) batteries, which have a 96.6 percent recycling rate due to the value of the lead in them. Since 1980, some 4,600 HHW collection programs have been organized. Most of these were one-day programs in which residents brought all household products containing hazardous materials to a collection point to be discarded. Every state has at least one such program. In addition, many municipalities now maintain permanent locations for drop-off of HHW. A small number of residential curbside recycling programs collect certain HHW items, such as oil and batteries.

FIGURE 7.3

Types of Environmental and Public Health Risks Addressed at Superfund Sites

Contaminated Air

Direct Contact With Hazardous Waste

Contaminated Drinking Water

Ecological Damage

Fire and Explosion Hazard

Exposure Through Food Chain

Contaminated Groundwater

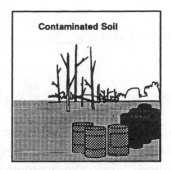

Contaminated Soil

Contaiminated Surface Water

Source: *Superfund Program Management*, U.S. General Accounting Office, Washington, DC, 1992

INDUSTRIAL WASTE MANAGEMENT

U.S. industry generates the bulk of hazardous waste. This waste can, if not properly managed, pose severe environmental and health risks. It can contain lead, arsenic, and mercury, which can cause cancer and birth defects in humans and animals.

In some instances, industry can reduce the dangers posed by hazardous waste by generating less or none of it. In other instances, industry can recycle the waste, and recently many companies have been developing ways to turn wastes into sources of income. Nonetheless, generally, once hazard-ous waste is created, industry has few plans for managing it. Historically, burying waste has been the least expensive, and thus preferred, means of disposal. However, over the past two decades, Congress has shown increased concern over the adverse effects of hazardous waste land disposal facilities.

The Berkeley Pit mine near Butte, Montana, is the nation's largest federally designated hazardous waste site. More than a mile across and 1,800 feet deep, the hole contains millions of cubic yards of mine tailings and feeds into a 125-mile stretch of river that has become contaminated with mining metals.

Where to Bury the Waste?

Many states have refused to accept toxic trash from states that have not developed their own disposal programs. Their position has been undermined, however, by the U.S. Supreme Court's determination in *Chemical Waste Management, Inc., v. Hunt* (504 U.S. 334, 1992) that waste is a commodity in interstate commerce and could be subject to federal, but not state, regulation.

Because of the problems in finding disposal sites for toxic wastes, the United States is sending larger and larger amounts of toxic waste out of the country. Mexico and Central and South America have become preferred spots for sludge and incinerator ash. Occasionally, toxic waste is mislabeled nontoxic when it arrives in South American countries. Africa had been a favorite location until 1988, when African countries signed agreements that restricted importation of dangerous materials.

GOVERNMENT REGULATION

The Resource Conservation and Recovery Act (RCRA)

The Resource Conservation and Recovery Act of 1976 (RCRA; PL 94-580) regulates the production and disposal of hazardous waste and improves waste disposal practices. The RCRA was designed to manage disposal, incineration, treatment, and storage of waste in landfills, surface impoundments, waste piles, tanks, and container storage areas. Facilities in operation after November 1980 are regulated under the act and subject to closure and cleanup requirements. Owners of facilities that ceased operation prior to November 1980 are required to clean up any hazardous waste threats posed by the units.

The RCRA imposed design and maintenance standards for waste disposal facilities, such as the installation of liners to prevent waste from migrating into ground water. Abandoned sites and those that owners cannot afford to clean up under the RCRA are usually referred to the national Superfund program (see below).

TABLE 7.1
EPA's 16 Site Types

Contaminant-based Categories
Asbestos
Dioxin
Metals
Metals/organic compounds
Organic compounds
Polychlorinated biphenyls (PCBs)
Pesticides
Radioactive/mixed waste
Solvents
Former Use Categories
Battery recycling/lead
Metal-plating
Industrial landfill
Mining waste
Municipal landfill
Munitions
Wood-preserving

Source: EPA.

Source: *Superfund: Problems with the Completeness and Consistency of Site Cleanup Plans*, U.S. General Accounting Office, Washington, DC, 1992

In 1985, under the RCRA, 837 of the nation's 1,538 land disposal facilities for hazardous waste were required to close because they failed to meet RCRA requirements. Those units then came under mandate for cleanup although, because of lack of funds, follow-up inspections and enforcement actions have lagged considerably.

The EPA has the authority under the RCRA to require businesses with hazardous waste operations to take corrective action to clean up the waste they have released into the environment. An estimated 3,400 facilities out of about 4,300 under the RCRA authority are suspected of contaminating the environment. Corrective action, however, has been a slow process.

The National Priorities List — The Superfund

The Comprehensive Environmental Response, Compensation, and Liability Act of 1980

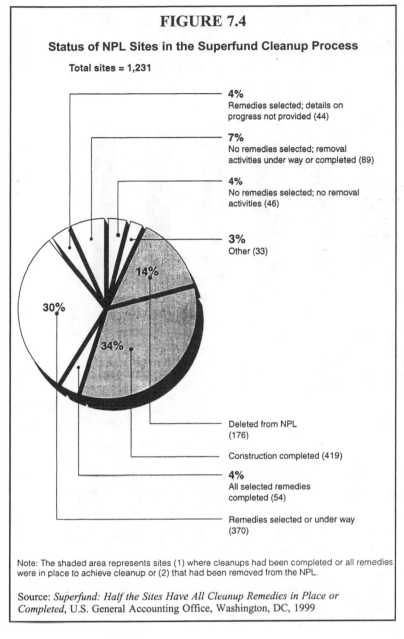

FIGURE 7.4

Status of NPL Sites in the Superfund Cleanup Process

Total sites = 1,231

4%
Remedies selected; details on progress not provided (44)

7%
No remedies selected; removal activities under way or completed (89)

4%
No remedies selected; no removal activities (46)

3%
Other (33)

14%

30%

34%

Deleted from NPL (176)

Construction completed (419)

4%
All selected remedies completed (54)

Remedies selected or under way (370)

Note: The shaded area represents sites (1) where cleanups had been completed or all remedies were in place to achieve cleanup or (2) that had been removed from the NPL.

Source: *Superfund: Half the Sites Have All Cleanup Remedies in Place or Completed*, U.S. General Accounting Office, Washington, DC, 1999

The Superfund was designed primarily to correct the mistakes in hazardous waste management made in the past at sites that have been abandoned or where a sole responsible party cannot be identified. (Facilities that seek a permit to store, treat, or dispose of hazardous waste — with viable operators and ongoing operations — are governed under the RCRA Corrective Action Program.)

A Huge Project

CERCLA requires the government to maintain a National Priorities List (NPL) of sites that pose the highest potential threat to human health and the environment. As of July 1999, the NPL included 1,231 sites. Most were general sites, such as landfills used by manufacturers and municipal landfills. About one-fifth of the sites slated for cleanup by the Superfund were municipal landfills. Some were federal sites, including those for the disposal of nuclear materials from bombs or U.S. Air Force bases that did not properly dispose of fuels and other dangerous materials. Figure 7.3 shows the types of environmental risks addressed at Superfund sites. Table 7.1 shows the categories of contaminants.

(CERCLA; PL 96-510) established the Superfund to pay for cleaning up abandoned sites. The Superfund, a $1.6 billion, five-year program, was intended to clean up leaking dumps that jeopardized ground water. During its original mandate, only six sites were cleaned up, and when the program expired in 1985, many observers viewed it as a billion-dollar fiasco rampant with scandal and mismanagement. Nonetheless, the negative publicity surrounding the program increased public awareness of the magnitude of the cleanup job in America. Consequently, in 1986 and 1990, the Superfund was reauthorized.

Many of the sites are still years away from being cleaned up. Current estimates indicate that cleanups are expected to cost the federal government about $300 billion and the private sector hundreds of billions more. As of 1999, 34 percent of sites were classified as cleanup-completed. Thirty percent have remedies pending, while 14 percent have been deleted because they have been satisfactorily completed. (See Figure 7.4.) Figure 7.5 shows the anticipated completion dates for the remaining cleanups.

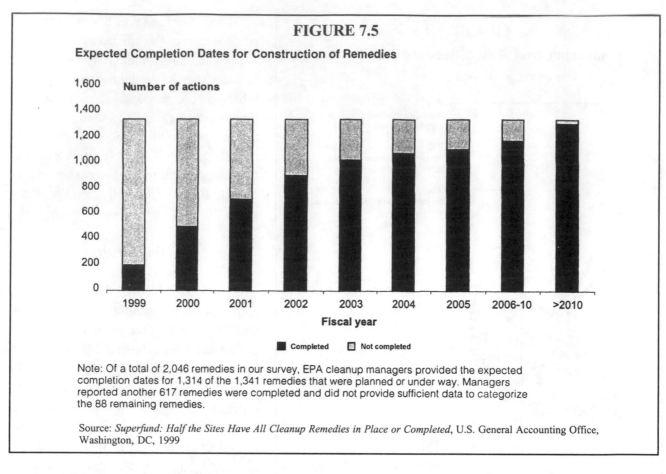

FIGURE 7.5

Expected Completion Dates for Construction of Remedies

Note: Of a total of 2,046 remedies in our survey, EPA cleanup managers provided the expected completion dates for 1,314 of the 1,341 remedies that were planned or under way. Managers reported another 617 remedies were completed and did not provide sufficient data to categorize the 88 remaining remedies.

Source: *Superfund: Half the Sites Have All Cleanup Remedies in Place or Completed*, U.S. General Accounting Office, Washington, DC, 1999

In addition to the sites that have been officially listed on the NPL, another 1,789 sites have been preliminarily judged as potentially eligible for the NPL. Most of those sites have already contaminated ground or drinking water. Metals are the principal contaminant at these sites. Additional contaminants include pesticides, volatile organic compounds (VOCs), dioxins, and polychlorinated biphenyls (PCBs). Table 7.2 shows the conditions present at the sites. The states vary in their ability to clean up the potentially eligible sites. Officials in more than half the states responding to a telephone survey reported their state's ability to fund cleanups was poor or very poor, while about a quarter claimed their state's ability to fund cleanup was excellent or good. (See Table 7.3.)

When the Superfund was created, the program was expected to deal with a limited number of sites over a relatively short time. It is now clear that the number of sites needing attention is much larger than originally believed and that the program could run several more decades. Since 1980, almost 37,000 sites have been reported to the EPA's inventory. The number of sites reported has declined steadily since 1985. The percentage of sites that the EPA believes warrant further consideration after initial investigation has remained relatively constant since 1984, with about 40 percent of the recommended sites needing further action. The average cleanup takes 12 years to complete.

Bills to reauthorize the Superfund law have languished in four successive Congresses. Currently, there are many unresolved issues in bills before Congress, and another impasse seems likely.

Who Pays the Bill for Superfund?

The EPA requested $7.2 billion for fiscal year (FY) 2000, 5 percent less than 1999 funding. (Figure 7.6 shows funding from 1983 through 2000.) The Superfund program represents about 20.8 percent of the EPA's budget, about $1.5 billion (Figure 7.7).

TABLE 7.2

Percentage of Potentially Eligible Sites Contributing to Specified Adverse Conditions and Percentage of Sites for Which Conditions' Presence Is Uncertain

Conditions resulting from contamination at 1,789 potentially eligible sites	Number of potentially eligible sites with condition	Percentage of potentially eligible sites with condition	Percentage of potentially eligible sites for which presence of condition is uncertain
Workers/visitors may have direct contact with contaminants	981	55	21
Trespassers may come into direct contact with contaminants	969	54	20
Fences/barriers/signs are erected to keep residents or others out of contaminated areas	618	35	19
Residents/community have concerns about contamination or potential health effects caused by this site	548	31	35
Fish could be unsafe to eat	486	27	29
Institutional restrictions[a] are necessary because of site's contamination	410	23	46
Residents/others should avoid exposure to contaminated dust on some days	355	20	23
Sources of drinking water permanently changed[b]	215	12	20
Obnoxious odors are present	194	11	24
Residents advised not to use wells	150	8	20
Fish, plants, or animals are sick/dying	143	8	33
Residents, workers, etc. use water (for bathing, landscaping, etc.) that fails to meet water quality standards	102	6	29
Recreation (e.g., fishing, swimming) is stopped or restricted	85	5	23
Residents advised to use filtered water	75	4	21
Residents advised to use bottled water	72	4	20
Residents advised not to let children play/dig in their yards	55	3	20
Crops are irrigated with contaminated water	52	3	29
Livestock drink contaminated water	44	3	28

[a]Institutional restrictions include limitations on uses of a property such as deed restrictions that limit a property to industrial use or legal limits placed on the depth of a well at a site.

[b]For example, by connecting residents to municipal water supplies in place of well water.

Source: *Hazardous Waste: Unaddressed Risks at Many Potential Superfund Sites*, U.S. General Accounting Office, Washington, DC, 1999

In addition to federal funding, the EPA is authorized to compel parties responsible for creating hazardous pollution, such as waste generators or haulers or site owners or operators, to clean up the sites. If these parties cannot be found or if a settlement cannot be reached, the EPA can conduct a cleanup, using funds from a trust fund established by CERCLA to perform such cleanups. This trust fund is financed primarily by a tax on crude oil and certain chemicals and by environmental taxes on corporations.

After completing a cleanup, the EPA can take action against the responsible parties to recover costs and replenish the fund. The average cost of cleanup is about $30 million, large enough to make it worthwhile for parties to pursue legal means to spread the costs among large numbers of responsible parties. Many cleanups involve dozens of parties.

Disputes have arisen between industries and cities over who is responsible for a cleanup, and numerous lawsuits have been filed by industries against cities over responsibility for what could be a huge expense. Many businesses and municipalities may be unable to assume such expense. The EPA reports that the government currently collects only one-fifth of the cleanup costs that could be recovered from polluters under the Superfund law.

According to the EPA, in many cases, the polluters have disappeared or are unable to pay. In other cases, the agency lacks the manpower or evidence to proceed with lawsuits.

BROWNFIELDS

Many former industrial sites have become eyesores of urban scenery. These trash-strewn plots, called *brownfields*, number nearly 450,000 sites in the United States, concentrated mostly in the Northeast and Midwest. The EPA defines brownfields as abandoned, idled, or underused industrial or commercial sites where expansion or redevelopment is complicated by real or perceived environmental contamination.

Many of the properties are polluted. They are shunned by developers, often stalling efforts to revive inner-city, mostly poor, neighborhoods. Until 1995, developers and buyers had avoided some 38,000 sites listed as possible targets under the Superfund Law, which says that anyone involved in the management of a property can be held liable for the entire cost of cleanup. Many of those sites had, in fact, been passed over by the EPA as not contaminated enough for Superfund action. Nonetheless, many of those properties were deemed untouchable by the real estate industry. A 1995 survey of the

TABLE 7.3

State Officials' Assessments of States' Financial Capabilities to Clean Up Potentially Eligible Sites

State[a]	State officials' assessment of state's financial capability to clean up potentially eligible sites
Alabama	Very poor
Alaska	Excellent
Arizona	Excellent
Arkansas	Good
California	Fair
Colorado	Very poor
Connecticut	Poor
Delaware	Excellent
Florida	Fair
Georgia	Poor
Hawaii	Fair
Illinois	Fair
Indiana	Very poor
Iowa	Very poor
Kansas	Very poor
Kentucky	Good
Louisiana	Poor
Maine	Poor
Maryland	Other[b]
Massachusetts	Fair
Michigan	Excellent
Minnesota	Good
Mississippi	Very poor
Montana	Very poor
Nebraska	Very poor
Nevada	Poor
New Hampshire	Poor
New Jersey	Good
New Mexico	Very poor
North Carolina	Poor
North Dakota	Poor
Ohio	Very poor
Oklahoma	Very poor
Oregon	Fair
Pennsylvania	Excellent
Rhode Island	Poor
South Carolina	Good
South Dakota	Other[b]
Tennessee	Poor
Texas	Poor
Vermont	Poor
Washington	Fair
West Virginia	Other[b]
Wisconsin	Excellent

[a]State officials in Idaho, New York, Missouri, Utah, Virginia, and Wyoming declined to participate in our telephone survey.

[b]"Other" indicates that the respondent was uncertain about the state's financial capability.

Source: *Hazardous Waste: Unaddressed Risks at Many Potential Superfund Sites*, U.S. General Accounting Office, Washington, DC, 1999

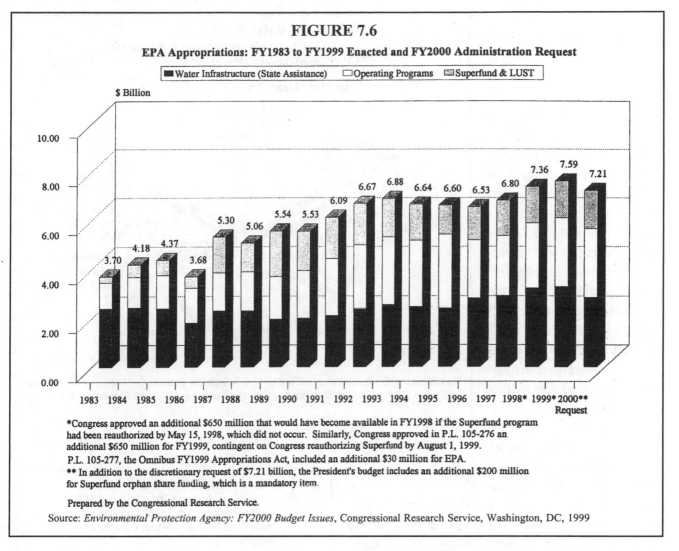

FIGURE 7.6

EPA Appropriations: FY1983 to FY1999 Enacted and FY2000 Administration Request

■ Water Infrastructure (State Assistance) ☐ Operating Programs ▨ Superfund & LUST

$ Billion

Values shown above bars by year:
- 1983: 3.70
- 1984: 4.18
- 1985: 4.37
- 1986: 3.68
- 1987: 5.30
- 1988: 5.06
- 1989: 5.54
- 1990: 5.53
- 1991: 6.09
- 1992: 6.67
- 1993: 6.88
- 1994: 6.64
- 1995: 6.60
- 1996: 6.53
- 1997: 6.80
- 1998*: 7.36
- 1999*: 7.59
- 2000** Request: 7.21

*Congress approved an additional $650 million that would have become available in FY1998 if the Superfund program had been reauthorized by May 15, 1998, which did not occur. Similarly, Congress approved in P.L. 105-276 an additional $650 million for FY1999, contingent on Congress reauthorizing Superfund by August 1, 1999.

P.L. 105-277, the Omnibus FY1999 Appropriations Act, included an additional $30 million for EPA.

** In addition to the discretionary request of $7.21 billion, the President's budget includes an additional $200 million for Superfund orphan share funding, which is a mandatory item.

Prepared by the Congressional Research Service.

Source: *Environmental Protection Agency: FY2000 Budget Issues*, Congressional Research Service, Washington, DC, 1999

American Bankers Association showed that 83 percent of smaller banks had refused to make loans to projects because of concerns about cnvironmental liability.

To help the reclamation effort, the EPA, in 1995, removed 25,000 of the least-polluted sites from the list. The sites will require some type of cleanup but will not be subjected to the tougher Superfund standards. In addition to restoring the environment, the purpose of reclamation programs is to encourage the reuse of abandoned sites, revitalize cities, create jobs, and generate municipal tax revenues. Redevelopment of polluted sites is becoming a thriving business. Experts estimate that about one-third of real estate sales involve sifting data bases of environmental agencies for records of spills before a real estate transaction can take place. Sensing a new business possibility, several insurance companies have created divisions offering policies that protect developers of polluted real estate against unforeseen cleanup costs or lawsuits.

The brownfields program has been popular in Congress. Congress has appropriated increasing amounts for it — $36.8 million in FY1997, $85 million in FY1998, $91.3 million for FY 1999, and $91.7 million for FY2000.

ENVIRONMENTAL JUSTICE — AN EVOLVING ISSUE

Environmental justice concerns stem from the claim that racial minorities are disproportionately subject to pollution hazards. The environmental justice movement gained national attention in 1982 when a demonstration took place against the building of a hazardous waste landfill in Warren County,

North Carolina, a county with a predominantly Black population. A resulting 1983 congressional study found that in 3 out of 4 landfills surveyed, Blacks made up the majority of the population living nearby. In addition, at least 26 percent of the population in those communities was below the poverty level. In 1987, the United Church of Christ published a nationwide study, *Toxic Waste and Race in the United States*, reporting that race was the most significant factor among the variables tested in determining locations of hazardous waste facilities.

In 1990, an EPA report (*Environmental Equity: Reducing Risk for All Communities*) concluded that racial minorities and low-income people bear a disproportionate burden of environmental risk. These groups were exposed to lead, air pollutants, hazardous waste facilities, contaminated fish, and agricultural pesticides in far greater frequencies than the general population. In 1994, President Clinton issued Executive Order 12898 (*Federal Actions to Address Environmental Justice in Minority Populations and Low-Income Populations*), requiring federal agencies to develop a comprehensive strategy for including environmental justice in their decision-making.

Unlike earlier findings, however, a 1995 U.S. General Accounting Office report (*Hazardous and Nonhazardous Wastes: Demographics of People Living Near Waste Facilities*, Washington, DC) found that minorities and low-income people were not disproportionately represented near the majority of nonhazardous landfills. People living near municipal landfills were likely to have poverty rates simi-

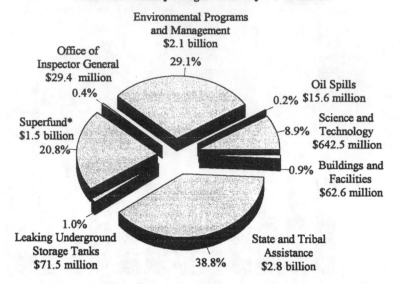

FIGURE 7.7
EPA Major Appropriations Accounts:
FY2000 Administration Request

Total Discretionary Budget Authority = $7.2 Billion

Environmental Programs and Management $2.1 billion 29.1%

Office of Inspector General $29.4 million 0.4%

Oil Spills 0.2% $15.6 million

Science and Technology 8.9% $642.5 million

Buildings and Facilities 0.9% $62.6 million

Superfund* $1.5 billion 20.8%

State and Tribal Assistance $2.8 billion 38.8%

1.0% Leaking Underground Storage Tanks $71.5 million

*In addition to the discretionary request of $7.2 billion, the President's budget also includes an additional $200 million for Superfund orphan share funding, which is a mandatory item.

Prepared by the Congressional Research Service.

Source: *Environmental Protection Agency: FY2000 Budget Issues*, Congressional Research Service, Washington, DC, 1999

FIGURE 7.8
Poverty Rate Within 1 Mile of Metropolitan Landfills Compared With Rate in Rest of Host County or Nation

Percentage of Landfills

	Compared With Host County		Compared With National Average[a]	
	Percent Where Poverty Rate Is Higher	Percent Where Poverty Rate Is Lower	Percent Where Poverty Rate Is Higher	Percent Where Poverty Rate Is Lower
	31	69	23	77

Source: *Hazardous and Nonhazardous Wastes: Demographics of People Living Near Waste Facilities*, U.S. General Accounting Office, Washington, DC, 1995

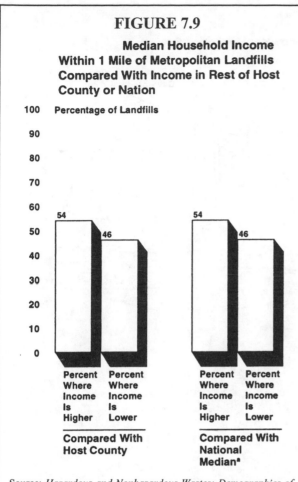

FIGURE 7.9

Median Household Income Within 1 Mile of Metropolitan Landfills Compared With Income in Rest of Host County or Nation

Source: *Hazardous and Nonhazardous Wastes: Demographics of People Living Near Waste Facilities*, U.S. General Accounting Office, Washington, DC, 1995

lar to or lower than the rate in the rest of the country (Figure 7.8). In fact, median household income was as likely to be higher than the national average as to be lower than the average (Figure 7.9). The study suggested that the results differed from prior studies because of different methodologies.

In Harm's Way

In 1997, residents of Kennedy Heights, a Houston, Texas, neighborhood of about 1,400, complained about a variety of illnesses such as cancer, tumors, lupus (an autoimmune disease), and rashes. Their homes were built three decades ago atop abandoned oil pits, and residents believed oil sludge from the pits had seeped into the water supply. Some tests of the municipal water found traces of crude oil. Kennedy Heights attracted ever-wider attention because of the accusations of environ-

mental racism. Homeowners, who were predominantly Black, were not told the property sat on an oil dump abandoned in the 1920s. Chevron Oil Company, which acquired the property from Gulf Oil, denied that contamination could have caused any illness. The homes lost virtually all their resale value because of the claims.

State Actions

Some states and communities have stepped in to ensure that racial minorities do not suffer disproportionately from environmental problems. Table 7.4 shows the states that have enacted or introduced legislation. Furthermore, lawsuits have occurred where discrimination is suspected. For example, in *James M. Seif v. Chester Residents Concerned Citizens et al.,* residents of Chester, Pennsylvania, argued that the Pennsylvania Department of Environmental Protection violated Title

TABLE 7.4

State Action on Environmental Justice

	Enacted Legislation	Introduced Legislation
Alabama		✔
Arizona		✔
Arkansas	✔	✔
California		✔
Colorado		✔
Connecticut		✔
Florida	✔	✔
Georgia		✔
Illinois		✔
Louisiana	✔	
Maryland	✔	
Massachusetts		✔
Michigan	✔	
Minnesota		✔
Mississippi		✔
Missouri		✔
New Mexico		✔
New York	✔	
North Carolina	✔	
Rhode Island	✔	
South Carolina		✔
Tennessee	✔	
Texas		✔
Virginia	✔	
Washington		✔

Source: "New Developments in Environmental Justice," *NCSL Legisbrief*, August/September 1999, National Conference of State Legislatures, Denver, CO. Copyright National Conference of State Legislatures.

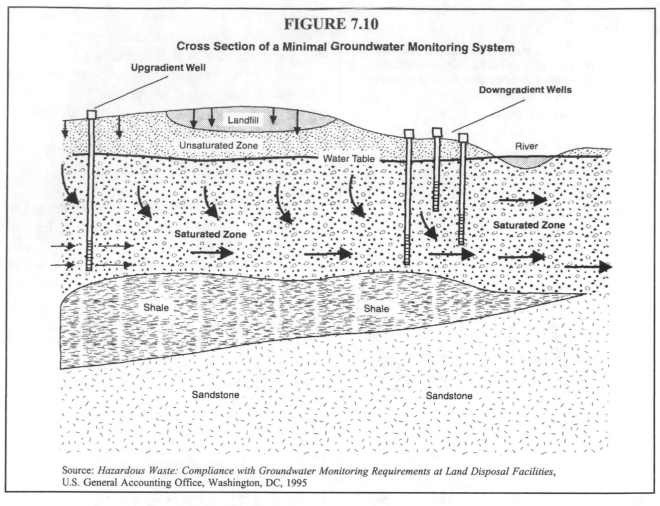

FIGURE 7.10

Cross Section of a Minimal Groundwater Monitoring System

Source: *Hazardous Waste: Compliance with Groundwater Monitoring Requirements at Land Disposal Facilities*, U.S. General Accounting Office, Washington, DC, 1995

IV of the Civil Rights Act of 1964 (PL 88-352) by issuing a solid waste permit for a facility in the minority community. Although the case was dismissed when the treatment facility withdrew its application, the action demonstrated the possibility of claiming discrimination under Title IV.

LAND DISPOSAL AND GROUND WATER CONTAMINATION

Ground water is a major source of drinking water for many parts of the nation. If not properly constructed, land disposal facilities for hazardous waste may leak contaminants into the underlying ground water. The RCRA imposes control over such facilities to minimize their adverse environmental impacts. The EPA, to implement the act, requires that owners/operators of hazardous waste sites install wells to monitor the ground water under their facilities. Figure 7.10 shows a cross-section of a ground water monitoring system.

By 1995, 1,209 hazardous waste land disposal facilities nationwide were subject to ground water monitoring requirements. Texas and Ohio had the greatest number of facilities subject to requirements (130 and 76, respectively). About 77 percent of the facilities require only one monitoring system; due to hydro-geological conditions, some facilities require from two to 17 systems.

Most land disposal facilities have released contaminants into the ground water since they began receiving hazardous waste. Of the 1,209 facilities, 74 percent have had a release (Figure 7.11). Of the monitored facilities, 54 percent were cited for ground water violations. The most common violations were sampling and analysis violations, followed by inadequate number of monitoring wells (Figure 7.12). The reasons why facilities have not complied with regulations vary. The most frequently cited reason was disagreement over the technical/administrative requirements. Recalcitrance (resistance to authority) was the second most common explanation.

NUCLEAR WASTE

In 1942, humanity's relationship with nature changed forever. In a Chicago laboratory, Italian physicist Enrico Fermi assembled enough uranium to cause a nuclear fission reaction. His discovery transformed warfare and energy production. But his experiment also produced a small packet of radioactive waste materials that will remain dangerous for hundreds of thousands of years. That original waste lies buried under a foot of concrete and two feet of dirt on a hillside in Illinois. Scientists and governments have yet to find a way to dispose of this deadly residue or the hundreds of thousands of tons that have been generated since.

A History of Secrecy

Nuclear waste management received little attention from government policymakers during the three decades after the atomic bomb's development in 1945. The nation spent billions of dollars to produce nuclear weapons and to commercialize nuclear power in the 1950s and 1960s, but spent only a few hundred million dol-

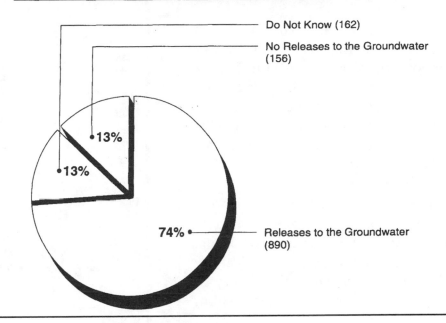

FIGURE 7.11

Releases to the Groundwater at Hazardous Waste Facilities

Do Not Know (162)

No Releases to the Groundwater (156)

13%

13%

74% — Releases to the Groundwater (890)

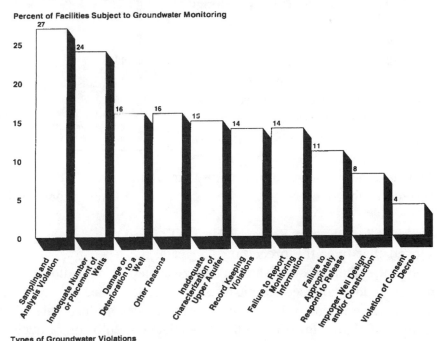

FIGURE 7.12

Frequency of Monitoring Violations Cited Since October 1, 1989

Percent of Facilities Subject to Groundwater Monitoring

Types of Groundwater Violations

Source of both figures: *Hazardous Waste: Compliance with Groundwater Monitoring Requirements at Land Disposal Facilities*, U.S. General Accounting Office, Washington, DC, 1995

155

lars to research storage and disposal processes. Since the 1970s, however, considerably more attention has focused on nuclear waste as a national and worldwide problem.

As scientists raced to develop an atomic bomb during World War II, wartime concern for national security led to a "culture of secrecy" that became characteristic of agencies dealing with nuclear power. Nuclear weapons moved from the experimental stage to full-scale industrial production in less than four years. On July 16, 1945, the first bomb, "Trinity," was exploded above ground in Alamogordo, New Mexico. A few weeks later, two nuclear bombs were dropped on Japan, and World War II ended. The nuclear age began. Table 7.5 shows the history of weapons production and early environmental legislation.

In 1948, the Atomic Energy Commission warned that then-existing disposal practices would result in contamination. The commission's advice was dismissed, in part because of the expense of improving disposal methods. By the 1950s, there was already evidence that the commission's advice should have been heeded. Officials at the Hanford, Washington (see below), nuclear facility discovered that high-level waste had corroded the tanks and was leaking into the soil and ground water. A number of similar events occurred in subsequent years.

In 1993, U.S. Energy Secretary Hazel O'Leary disclosed that over the preceding 45 years, the United States nuclear establishment had conducted hundreds of unannounced atomic tests (from 1948 to 1952), experimented with human subjects on the effects of plutonium, often without their knowledge or approval, and dumped tons of toxic waste across the United States. Secretary O'Leary revealed that of 925 nuclear tests, 204 were secret,

TABLE 7.5

Timeline of Nuclear Weapons Production and Environmental Legislation

► 1939	1939	Einstein's letter to Roosevelt
► 1941	1941	Pearl Harbor, World War II
► 1942	1942	Los Alamos and bomb production began Oak Ridge - Production of fuel U-235 Hanford - Production of plutonium fuel
► 1945		Los Alamos - Bomb production and assembly
► 1949	1945	July 16 - Fat Man test "Trinity" - 17,000 tons TNT
► 1950		August 6 - Hiroshima
► 1952	1946	Atomic Energy Act
► 1953	1949	Klaus Fuchs, Los Alamos physicist, discovered and captured as a spy Idaho National Engineering Lab built USSR explodes first atomic bomb
► 1958	1950	Truman decides to go ahead with H-Bomb Beginning of Cold War/arms race
	1952	Rocky Flats plant built in Colorado
	1953	China bomb? Stalin dies
	1958	America detonates H-Bomb "Mike"
	1969	National Environmental Policy Act
► 1969	1970s	Congress creates Environmental Protection Agency
► 1970s	1974	Energy Reorganization Act
► 1974	1976	Resource Conservation and Recovery Act
► 1976	1977	Department of Energy formed
► 1977	1980	Comprehensive Environmental Response Compensation and Liability Act (CERCLA; Superfund)
► 1980		Low-level Radioactive Waste Policy Act
► 1982	1982	Nuclear Waste Policy Act
► 1984	1984	NRDC case established federal hazardous waste laws apply to the weapons complex

National Conference of State Legislatures, 1993

Source: Katherine A. Mahoney and Linda K. Murakam, *Farewell to Arms: Cleaning Up Nuclear Weapons Facilities*, National Conference of State Legislatures, Denver, CO, 1993

and that the government continues to store 33.5 metric tons of plutonium in six U.S. locations.

What Is Radioactivity?

Radioactivity occurs when there is an imbalance of protons and neutrons in the nucleus of an atom, a state of instability. The production and explosion of nuclear weapons involves splitting the atoms by bombarding them with neutrons or fusing atoms together. (Figure 7.13 shows this chain reaction.) The transformation to stability is called radioactive decay, a process during which radiation is emitted. All radioactive elements eventually decay into the stable element lead.

Some radioactivity occurs naturally. This natural radiation makes up the majority of the radiation to which people are exposed. It occurs from elements within the earth and from cosmic rays that filter into Earth's atmosphere from outer space. Certain areas experience higher levels of radiation than others; residents of higher elevations, such as Denver, Colorado, receive roughly twice as much radiation as people who live in Amsterdam, which is below sea level.

Other radiation is created by humans. The largest doses of radiation from non-natural sources come from radiation used for medical diagnosis and treatment. Color televisions and video games also account for a considerable amount of man-made radiation. Figure 7.14 shows the sources of radiation.

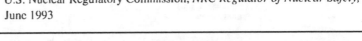

FIGURE 7.13

Nuclear Chain Reaction

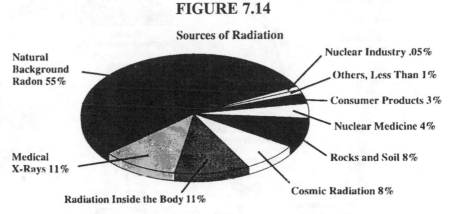

U.S. Nuclear Regulatory Commission, *NRC Regulator of Nuclear Safety,* June 1993

FIGURE 7.14

Sources of Radiation

Natural Background Radon 55%
Nuclear Industry .05%
Others, Less Than 1%
Consumer Products 3%
Nuclear Medicine 4%
Medical X-Rays 11%
Rocks and Soil 8%
Radiation Inside the Body 11%
Cosmic Radiation 8%

U.S. Department of Energy, *Environmental Restoration and Waste Management Five-Year Plan,* 1992

Source: Katherine A. Mahoney and Linda K. Murakam, *Farewell to Arms: Cleaning Up Nuclear Weapons Facilities*, National Conference of State Legislatures, Denver, CO, 1993

NUCLEAR ENERGY WASTE DISPOSAL

The nuclear energy process produces five basic types of radioactive waste.

- Uranium mill tailings are the sand-like wastes that are produced in uranium refining operations and that emit low levels of radiation.

- Low-level waste contains varying lesser levels of radioactivity, including trash, contaminated clothing, and hardware.

- Spent fuel is "used" reactor fuel that will be classified as waste if not reprocessed to recover the usable uranium and plutonium. In reprocessing, the used uranium and plutonium in spent reactor fuel can be removed for use again as nuclear reactor fuel.

- High-level waste is the by-product of a reprocessing plant. These wastes contain highly toxic and extremely dangerous fission products that require great care in disposal.

FIGURE 7.15
U.S. DEPARTMENT OF ENERGY FACILITIES INVOLVED IN NUCLEAR WEAPONS DISMANTLEMENT

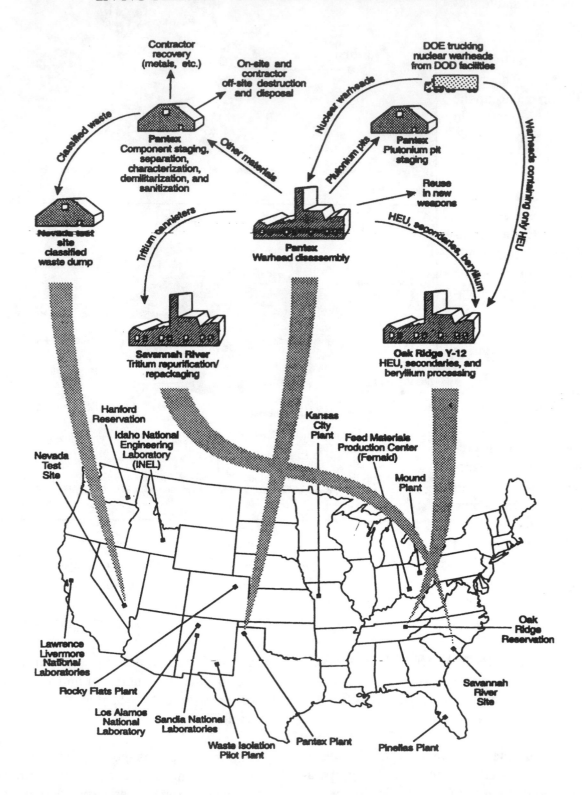

Source: "Dismantling the Bomb and Managing the Nuclear Materials," *Report Brief*, Office of Technology Assessment, Washington, DC, 1993

- Transuranic wastes are 11 man-made radioactive elements with an atomic number greater than that of uranium (92) and half-lives of thousands of years. They are found in trash produced mainly by nuclear weapons plants and are, therefore, a part of the nuclear waste problem that must be directly resolved by the government.

The end of the cold war has brought the problem of military nuclear waste to the forefront. Both the United States and Russia have agreed to begin to destroy many of their nuclear weapons. This is a very involved and lengthy process that will likely take many decades to complete. The highly toxic and extremely dangerous fission wastes produced by this process will likely have to be stored for extended periods of time and will then eventually have to be moved for permanent storage. Many facilities scattered across the United States will play a role in dismantling the American nuclear arsenal. Figure 7.15 shows the U.S. Department of Energy facilities involved in the nuclear weapons dismantlement.

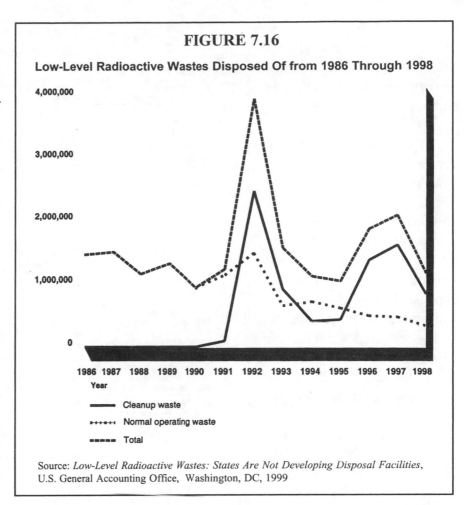

FIGURE 7.16

Low-Level Radioactive Wastes Disposed Of from 1986 Through 1998

Cleanup waste

Normal operating waste

Total

Source: *Low-Level Radioactive Wastes: States Are Not Developing Disposal Facilities*, U.S. General Accounting Office, Washington, DC, 1999

Uranium Mill Tailings

Uranium mill tailings are the earthen residues, usually in the form of fine sand, that remain after mining and extracting uranium from ores. These wastes emit low levels of radiation, mostly radon, which can contaminate water and air. Most tailing sites are west of the Mississippi River, primarily in Utah, Colorado, New Mexico, and Arizona.

Prior to the early 1970s, the tailings were believed to have such low levels of radiation that they were not harmful to humans. Miners, many of whom were Native Americans, received little protection from the radiation. Now, many of these workers are reporting very high rates of cancer. Tailings were also left in scattered piles without posted warnings or safeguards, exposing anyone who came near. Some tailings were deposited in landfills, and homes were built on top of them. Authorities now recognize that mill tailing handling and disposal must be properly managed to control radiation exposure.

Proper management of uranium mill tailings is particularly important because they are generated in relatively large volumes — about 10 to 15 million tons annually. About 15 percent of the radioactivity is removed during the milling process, while the remainder (85 percent) stays in the tailings. Radium-226, the major radioactive waste product, retains its radioactivity for thousands of years and produces two potentially hazardous radiation conditions — gamma radiation and the

159

emission of gaseous radon. There is a proven causal relationship between these radioactive elements and leukemia and lung cancer.

In response to growing concern, Congress passed the Uranium Mill Tailing Radiation Control Act of 1978 (PL 95-604) to regulate mill tailing operations. The law called for the cleanup of abandoned mill sites, primarily at federal expense, although owners of still-active mines were financially responsible for their own cleanup.

Low-Level Wastes

Low-level radioactive waste decays in 10 to 100 years. Until the 1960s, the United States dumped low-level wastes into the ocean. The first commercial site to house such waste was opened in 1962, and by 1971, six sites were licensed for disposal. The volume of low-level waste increased during the initial years (1963-1980) of commercially generated waste disposal, until the Low-Level Radioactive Waste Policy Act of 1980 (PL 96-573; see below), amended in 1985. At that time, approximately 3.25 million cubic feet of radioactive wastes were disposed. Since then, volume has declined to under 1 million cubic feet per year (Figure 7.16).

By 1979, only three commercial low-level waste sites were still operating — Richland (Hanford), Washington; Beatty, Nevada; and Barnwell, South Carolina. The facility at Beatty, Nevada, closed permanently in 1982. In response to the threatened closing of the South Carolina site, Congress passed the Low-Level Radioactive Waste Policy Act of 1980, calling for the establishment of a national system of such facilities. Every state was to be responsible for finding a low-level disposal site for wastes generated within its borders by 1986. It also gave states the right to bar low-level

TABLE 7.6

Status of Compacts and Unaffiliated States

Dollars in millions

State compacts (Host state and state members)	Status of disposal siting efforts	Development costs
Appalachian compact (Pennsylvania, Delaware, Maryland, West Virginia)	Halted.	$37.0
Central compact (Nebraska, Arkansas, Kansas, Louisiana, Oklahoma)	License application denied by Nebraska. Nebraska to withdraw from compact.	95.6
Central Midwest compact (Illinois, Kentucky)	Halted.	95.8
Midwest compact (No host state, Indiana, Iowa, Minnesota, Missouri, Ohio, Wisconsin)	Halted.	Not available
Northeast compact (Dual hosts: Connecticut, New Jersey)	Connecticut: halted disposal facility siting, considering storage for 100 years or longer. New Jersey: halted siting effort.	15.2 9.7
Northwest compact (Washington, Alaska, Hawaii, Idaho, Montana, Oregon, Utah, Wyoming)	Uses existing Richland disposal facility located on DOE's Hanford site.	Not applicable
Rocky Mountain compact (No host state, Colorado, Nevada, New Mexico)	Contracted with Northwest compact to use the Richland facility.	Not applicable
Southeast compact (North Carolina, Alabama, Florida, Georgia, Mississippi, Tennessee, Virginia	North Carolina halted licensing process for disposal facility, shut down its siting agency, and, on July 26, 1999, enacted legislation withdrawing from the compact.	112.0
Southwestern compact (California, Arizona, North Dakota, South Dakota)	Halted.	92.6
Texas compact (Texas, Maine, Vermont)	Halted, initial license application for original site denied by state's licensing authority.	52.0
Unaffiliated states		
District of Columbia	No plans to site a facility.	Not applicable
Massachusetts	Halted.	Not available
Michigan	No efforts under way.	12.6
New Hampshire	No plans to site a facility.	Not applicable
New York	Halted.	62.7
Puerto Rico	No plans to site a facility.	Not applicable
Rhode Island	No plans to site a facility.	Not applicable
South Carolina	Host state for Barnwell facility.	Not applicable
Totals		**$585.2**

Source: *Low-Level Radioactive Wastes: States Are Not Developing Disposal Facilities*, U.S. General Accounting Office, Washington, DC, 1999

FIGURE 7.17

States' Memberships in Compacts

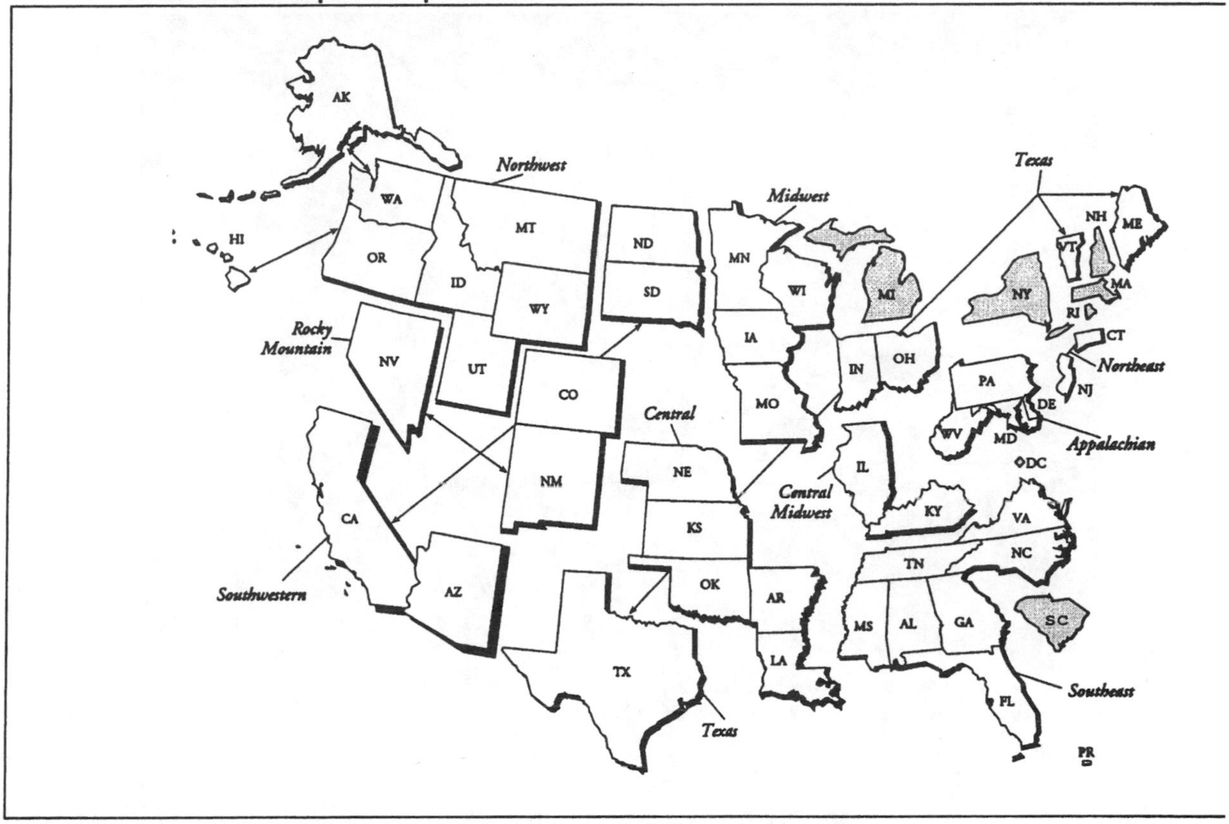

Note: Shaded states are not affiliated with a compact.

Source: *Low-Level Radioactive Wastes: States Are Not Developing Disposal Facilities*, U.S. General Accounting Office, Washington, DC, 1999

wastes if they were engaged in regional compacts for waste disposal. The disposal of high-level wastes, however, remained a federal responsibility.

Compacts

The 1980 law encouraged states to organize themselves into compacts to develop new dumps. As of 1999, 10 such compacts serving 44 states have been approved by Congress. Table 7.6 and Figure 7.17 show the organization of states into compacts and the six unaffiliated states, Puerto Rico, and the District of Columbia.

No compact or state has, however, successfully developed a new disposal facility for low-level wastes. California had planned a facility, but the land could not be obtained. Texas has received federal approval for a site at Sierra Blanca, which would receive waste from Maine and Vermont. The Texas Natural Resource Conservation Commission may reject the plan, however. Certain conditions have led some states to remain uncommitted to disposal development and to consider other options. The reopening of the Barnwell, South Carolina, facility in 1995 eased some of the pressure on the states. The entrance of the private sector — Envirocare of Utah, Inc.* — in 1995 has increased interest in the possibility of privately operated waste disposal facilities.

Compacts and unaffiliated states have confronted significant barriers to developing disposal

---

* Envirocare of Utah, Inc., a private company, accepts only Class A waste, the least-contaminated waste.

Source: *Low-Level Radioactive Wastes: States Are Not Developing Disposal Facilities*,
U.S. General Accounting Office, Washington, DC, 1999

sites, including public health and environmental concerns, antinuclear sentiment, substantial financial requirements, political issues, and "not in my backyard" campaigns by some citizen activists. State legislatures must approve regional compact agreements and, to date, no new disposal site has opened. Some policymakers, however, believe that safe disposal of radioactive materials is an operation that should be conducted by government institutions, not private companies.

Collectively, the Barnwell (Figure 7.18), Richland, and Envirocare facilities currently provide disposal capacity for almost all types of low-level wastes. Table 7.7 shows the volume of low-level waste disposed of at each of the three facilities by compact and state.

Storage and Transport Problems

Developing storage areas for hazardous waste is difficult because regulatory requirements mandate a buffer zone of land surrounding each site. The acreage will require constant monitoring and limited land-use applications for at least a century. Although larger sites would collectively reduce the total number of acres required, some state officials believe that having more numerous local facilities would be safer since it would reduce the number of transportation accidents.

As Congress considers legislation to put a temporary storage facility for nuclear fuel in Nevada, concern over the safety of transporting that nuclear waste to the repository is under debate again. The safe transport of spent fuel is primarily a federal responsibility. The U.S. Department of Transportation (DOT) and the Nuclear Regulatory Commission (NRC) are responsible for packaging regulations, container safety, regulations regarding sabotage, escorts, routing, and employee training.

In addition, officials are concerned about degradation of the packages that contain stored waste. Depending on the environment, degradation can occur from temperature fluctuations, corrosion, and containers becoming brittle. Figure 7.19 shows degradation of low-level waste containers.

TABLE 7.7

Volume and Radioactivity of Low-Level Wastes Disposed of in 1998 by Compact, State, and Disposal Site

Volume in cubic feet

Compact/State	Envirocare Volume	Envirocare Curies	Barnwell Volume	Barnwell Curies	Richland Volume	Richland Curies	Total Volume	Total Curies
Appalachian	**32,448**	**0**	**18,064**	**44,260**			**50,512**	**44,260**
Delaware			174	0			174	0
Maryland	5,600	0	2,004	531			7,605	532
Pennsylvania[a]	26,848	0	15,838	43,691			42,686	43,691
West Virginia			48	37			48	37
Central	**795**	**0**	**5,537**	**8,400**			**6,332**	**8,400**
Arkansas			366	7			366	7
Kansas			1,014	354			1,014	354
Louisiana			1,235	292			1,235	292
Nebraska[a]			2,922	7,747			2,922	7,747
Oklahoma	795	0	1	0			796	0
Central Midwest	**38,875**	**9**	**29,079**	**112,658**			**67,954**	**112,667**
Illinois[a]	35,995	8	28,952	112,654			64,947	112,662
Kentucky	2,880	1	126	4			3,006	5
Midwest	**144,582**	**2**	**6,024**	**1,543**			**150,605**	**1,545**
Indiana			74	45			74	45
Iowa			1,036	267			1,036	267
Minnesota			1,317	314			1,317	314
Missouri	15,629	0	499	811			16,128	812
Ohio	128,953	2	1,554	98			130,507	100
Wisconsin			1,544	8			1,544	8
Northwest			**16**	**725**	**142,569**	**692**	**142,586**	**1,417**
Alaska								
Hawaii			11	645	1,798	48	1,809	692
Idaho			2	22	4	0	6	22
Montana					9	0	9	0
Oregon			1	57	92,742	495	92,743	551
Utah					17,204	2	17,204	2
Washington[a]			2	2	30,808	148	30,810	150
Wyoming					4	0	4	0
Rocky Mountain			**3**	**23**	**2,199**	**964**	**2,202**	**987**
Colorado			2	11	1,747	964	1,749	975

(continued)

Some state officials worry that as the amounts of waste accumulate, illegal dumping will increase. Others worry that waste accumulation may result in the reduction of nuclear health care and medical research out of concern for how to dispose of the waste.

Spent Fuel and High-Level Waste

Spent fuel, the used uranium fuel that has been removed from a nuclear reactor, is far from being completely "spent." It contains highly penetrating and toxic radioactivity and requires isolation from living things for thousands of years. It still contains significant amounts of uranium, as well as plutonium created during the nuclear fission process. Spent fuel is a problem for nuclear power plants that will be decommissioned before the projected availability of a long-term, high-level waste disposal repository. (See Figure 7.20 for the locations of high-level and spent nuclear fuel accumulations.) Unless a temporary site becomes available, utilities have the following options:

- Leave the fuel on site.

TABLE 7.7 (Continued)

Volume in cubic feet

Compact/State	Envirocare Volume	Envirocare Curies	Barnwell Volume	Barnwell Curies	Richland Volume	Richland Curies	Total Volume	Total Curies
Nevada					56	0	56	0
New Mexico			1	12	395	0	396	12
Northeast	**5,173**	**0**	**12,034**	**21,406**			**17,206**	**21,406**
Connecticut[a]	5,173	0	3,480	223			8,653	223
New Jersey[a]			8,553	21,183			8,553	21,183
Southeast	**451,993**	**40**	**73,202**	**27,506**			**525,196**	**27,546**
Alabama	558	0	6,994	3,583			7,552	3,583
Florida	14,889	5	24,642	2,084			39,531	2,089
Georgia			9,916	1,233			9,916	1,233
Mississippi			777	17,376			777	17,376
North Carolina[a]	7,390	4					7,390	4
Tennessee	413,034	28	22,242	695			435,271	723
Virginia	16,122	2	8,631	2,536			24,753	2,538
Southwestern	**8,826**	**0**	**7,313**	**837**			**16,139**	**838**
Arizona			3,886	246			3,886	246
California[a]	8,826	0	3,376	570			12,202	571
North Dakota			49	2			49	2
South Dakota			2	19			2	19
Texas	**10,583**	**8**	**6,636**	**2,946**			**17,218**	**2,954**
Maine			4,125	1,067			4,125	1,067
Texas[a]	10,583	8	2,485	1,880			13,067	1,887
Vermont			26	0			26	0
Unaffiliated	**386,476**	**68**	**36,608**	**112,474**			**423,084**	**112,542**
District of Columbia			245	26			245	26
Massachusetts	152,109	25	3,545	18,974			155,654	18,998
Michigan	71,495	0	10,206	37,423			81,701	37,424
New Hampshire			262	86			262	86
New York	2,313	0	11,521	54,757			13,834	54,757
Puerto Rico			11	0			11	0
Rhode Island			53	22			53	22
South Carolina	3,371	2	10,765	1,187			14,135	1,189
Unknown	157,188	40					157,188	40
Total	**1,079,750**	**127**	**194,516**	**332,779**	**144,768**	**1,656**	**1,419,034**	**334,563**
Percent	**76**	**0**	**14**	**99**	**10**	**0**	**100**	**100**

[a]Host state for compact.

Source: DOE's National low-level radioactive waste manifest information management system and Envirocare data from monthly reports submitted to the Northwest compact.

Source: *Low-Level Radioactive Wastes: States Are Not Developing Disposal Facilities*, U.S. General Accounting Office, Washington, DC, 1999

- Use on-site casks. This is not an option for hot fuel (fuel that is less than five years out of the core).

- Ship the spent fuel to France for reprocessing. France, which is heavily dependent on nuclear power, has developed the technology to repro- cess spent fuel, something not available in the United States. In a controversial action, as of 1993, spent nuclear fuel from the defunct Shoreham plant has been shipped to France for reprocessing at a cost of $74 million to utility customers. Nuclear watchgroups, including the Friends of the Earth and the Union of Concerned Scientists, oppose the program because they fear the possibility of theft or accidental spread of nuclear materials.

- Continue to operate the unit.

- Ship the fuel to a monitored retrievable storage facility, if one is available.

ATTEMPTS TO DISPOSE OF RADIOACTIVE WASTE

There is currently no agreed-upon safe way to dispose of nuclear waste. None of the current options guarantee to protect the environment from radiation, which remains dangerous for many thousands of years.

Russia

In April 1986, the world's worst nuclear power accident occurred — an explosion and fire at the former Soviet Union's Chernobyl plant in Ukraine. In the months that followed, at least 250 persons died. Release of radioactive materials continued for 10 days, scattering fallout over the former U.S.S.R., many European countries, and the rest of the Northern Hemisphere. Long-term health effects are being studied and will continue for years to come.

Russian authorities acknowledge that, for three decades, the Arctic fishing grounds near Norway were illegal dumping grounds for radioactive wastes that likely include 18 nuclear reactors and several nuclear submarines. As recently as 1993, Russia also dumped hundreds of tons of nuclear waste into the Sea of Japan.

Russian scientists have also disclosed that, for the past three decades, the former U.S.S.R. secretly pumped billions of gallons of atomic waste directly into the earth. They claim the practice of injecting the waste, which violates generally accepted global standards for waste disposal and is contrary to what they previously claimed they were doing, continues today. The Russians report that about

FIGURE 7.19

Degradation of Low-Level Waste Containers

Source: *Radioactive Waste: Status of Low-Level Waste Facilities*, U.S. General Accounting Office, Washington, DC, 1995

half of all nuclear waste they ever generated has been pumped into the ground at three sites near several major rivers — the Volga, the Ob, and the Yenisei. Russian scientists contend the practice is safe because the wastes are pumped under layers of clay and shale to cut them off from the earth's surface; nonetheless, the wastes at one site have already leaked beyond the expected range.

Before its dissolution, the U.S.S.R. had an estimated inventory of 45,000 nuclear warheads. Inadequate inventory control over the warheads during the chaotic collapse resulted in the successor states not knowing how much nuclear material they inherited. In 1996, Central Intelligence Agency Director John Deutch reported, "The chilling reality is that nuclear materials are more accessible now than at any other time in history — due primarily to the dissolution of the former Soviet Union and the region's worsening economic conditions."

Radioactive nuclear materials have been smuggled from the former Soviet Union into Western Europe. Recent arrests of suspected smugglers have alarmed governments about the apparent failure of the Russian government to protect their radioactive materials. There have also been hundreds

165

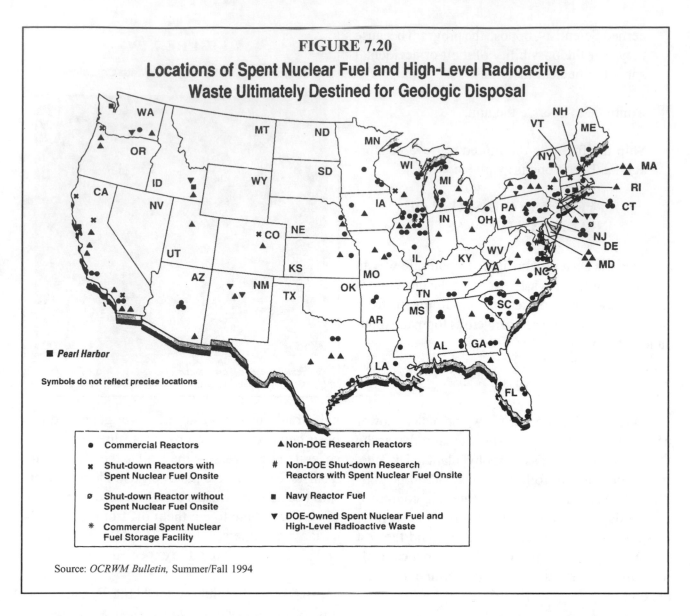

FIGURE 7.20

Locations of Spent Nuclear Fuel and High-Level Radioactive Waste Ultimately Destined for Geologic Disposal

■ *Pearl Harbor*

Symbols do not reflect precise locations

● Commercial Reactors	▲ Non-DOE Research Reactors
✕ Shut-down Reactors with Spent Nuclear Fuel Onsite	# Non-DOE Shut-down Research Reactors with Spent Nuclear Fuel Onsite
ø Shut-down Reactor without Spent Nuclear Fuel Onsite	■ Navy Reactor Fuel
✳ Commercial Spent Nuclear Fuel Storage Facility	▼ DOE-Owned Spent Nuclear Fuel and High-Level Radioactive Waste

Source: *OCRWM Bulletin*, Summer/Fall 1994

of reports of thefts of nuclear materials in the former U.S.S.R., mostly low-level materials suitable for power generation. However, several thefts of weapons-grade material have also been reported. Experts believe that once fissile (atoms capable of being split) materials escape the former U.S.S.R., smuggling the materials or bombs made from them into the United States and other countries would not be difficult. Officials in the United States have been trying to help the former Soviet states get control of these dangers.

In 1993, the United States agreed to purchase from Russia, over a 20-year period, 500 metric tons of highly enriched uranium (HEU) extracted from dismantled Russian nuclear weapons. Russia

agreed to dilute the material into low enriched uranium (LEU) before shipping it to the United States. From 1995 through December 1998, 1,487 metric tons of uranium were delivered to the United States. By 1999, Russia had received almost $940 million of an expected $12 billion from the agreement. Currently, four Russian facilities process the HEU, and six U.S. facilities process the LEU (Figure 7.21).

In accordance with the agreement, Russia agreed to allow the United States to monitor, through "transparency measures," nuclear processing facilities. Although some of those actions have been implemented, several measures have not yet been put into place.

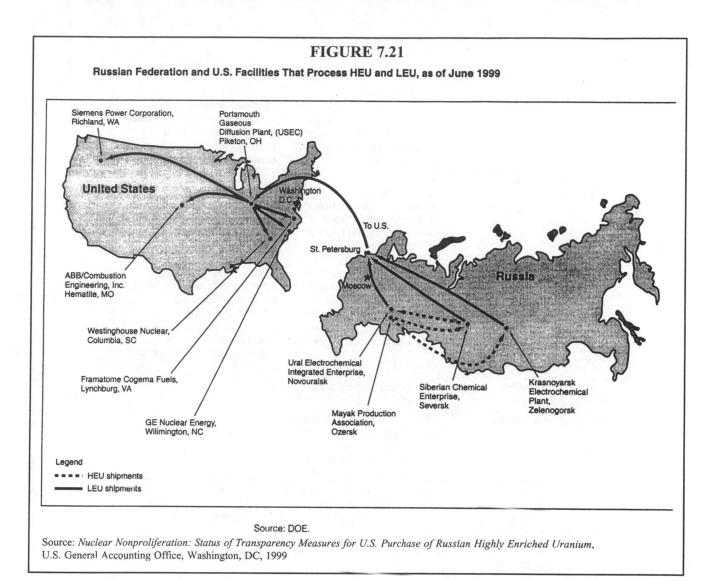

FIGURE 7.21

Russian Federation and U.S. Facilities That Process HEU and LEU, as of June 1999

Siemens Power Corporation, Richland, WA

Portsmouth Gaseous Diffusion Plant, (USEC) Piketon, OH

United States

Washington D.C.

To U.S.

St. Petersburg

Russia

Moscow

ABB/Combustion Engineering, Inc. Hematite, MO

Westinghouse Nuclear, Columbia, SC

Framatome Cogema Fuels, Lynchburg, VA

GE Nuclear Energy, Wilimington, NC

Ural Electrochemical Integrated Enterprise, Novouralsk

Mayak Production Association, Ozersk

Siberian Chemical Enterprise, Seversk

Krasnoyarsk Electrochemical Plant, Zelenogorsk

Legend
- - - - HEU shipments
——— LEU shipments

Source: DOE.

Source: *Nuclear Nonproliferation: Status of Transparency Measures for U.S. Purchase of Russian Highly Enriched Uranium*, U.S. General Accounting Office, Washington, DC, 1999

NO SOLUTION IN SIGHT

Only the natural decaying process, which can take hundreds of thousands of years, diminishes the radioactivity of nuclear waste. The original "solution" was to bury the waste deep in the earth, but scientists no longer believe they can guarantee the deadly debris will remain sealed off from the biosphere for hundreds of centuries. None of the options guarantee protection of Earth from radiation. Due to the scientific and political difficulties with geologic burial and other methods, aboveground "temporary" storage, despite the dangers, will likely remain the preferred option well into the twenty-first century. The most dangerous radioactive waste is irradiated uranium from commercial nuclear power plants.

According to the NRC, which licenses power plants, almost all nuclear plants will reach their capacity for storage before the end of the decade for several reasons.

- There is a backlog of nuclear waste — at least 35,000 metric tons of nuclear waste sitting in what are called "spent fuel pools" at 70 nuclear energy plants around the country. (There are 104 nuclear reactors in the United States, down from 112 in 1990.) By 2010, the earliest feasible date for opening the Yucca Mountain repository, the total waste is expected to reach 60,000 metric tons.

- Many nuclear plants are shutting down well ahead of schedule because of premature aging and skyrocketing maintenance and repair costs.

167

TABLE 7.8

Selected Provisions of RCRA and CERCLA

	Resource Conservation and Recovery Act of 1976, as amended (RCRA)	Comprehensive Environmental Response, Compensation, and Liability Act of 1980, as amended (CERCLA)
Purpose and selected features	RCRA regulates the management of hazardous waste treatment, storage, and disposal facilities through a permit program. In 1984, amendments required corrective action (cleanup) for releases of hazardous wastes from any active or inactive site within such facilities. Corrective actions are incorporated into a facility's RCRA permit.	CERCLA provides authority for the cleanup of the nation's inactive or abandoned waste sites. The most hazardous sites, including federal facilities, are listed on the National Priorities List. In 1986, amendments required that federal facilities be addressed under interagency agreements between the agency responsible for a waste site and EPA.
Agency responsible for administration	EPA or authorized state agency	EPA
Substances addressed	Hazardous wastes and the hazardous constituents of mixed waste—waste that contains both radioactive and hazardous material[a]	Hazardous substances, including radioactive wastes

[a]The Federal Facility Compliance Act of 1992 established additional requirements with respect to the storage and treatment of mixed waste at federal facilities. These requirements are discussed in our report Nuclear Waste: Much Effort Needed to Meet Federal Facility Compliance Act's Requirements (GAO/RCED-94-179, May 17, 1994).

Source: *Nuclear Cleanup: Difficulties in Coordinating Activities Under Two Environmental Laws*, U.S. General Accounting Office, Washington, DC, 1994

Although the NRC licenses power plants to operate for 40 years, they do not last that long. The average life of the more than 20 reactors that have been shut down has been around 13 years.

• The economic restructuring of the nation's power system from a regulated industry to one driven by competition — as many as 26 of U.S. nuclear power plants are vulnerable to shutdown because production costs are higher than the projected market prices of electricity.

What happens when a nuclear plant closes down? Right now, the nuclear waste and the radioactive equipment stay on the premises. There is no place to put it. As a result, every nuclear power plant in the United States has become a temporary nuclear waste disposal site. Those plants that close become mausoleums, largely untouched while they wait to be decommissioned or dismantled when a repository eventually opens. The states are under federal mandate to find storage for the radioactive waste they generate, which is currently shipped to storage sites in South Carolina, Washington, and Utah.

HIGH-LEVEL RADIOACTIVE WASTE CLEANUP

As with other hazardous waste, in cleaning up waste sites within its nuclear weapons facilities, the DOE must comply with the Resource Conservation and Recovery Act (RCRA, see above) and the Comprehensive Environmental Response, Compensation, and Liability Act of 1980

FIGURE 7.22

Waste Migration Through the Vadose Zone at the Hanford Site

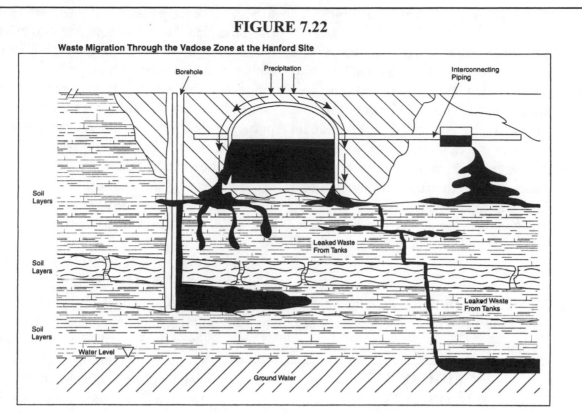

Source: *Nuclear Waste: Understanding of Waste Migration at Hanford Is Inadequate for Key Decisions*, U.S. General Accounting Office, Washington, DC, 1998

(CERCLA or Superfund; Table 7.8). The DOE is responsible for cleanup and waste management at major contaminated facilities and more than 100 smaller locations in 34 states and territories. Cleaning up these sites is an enormous task. The DOE estimates that the cleanup will cost at least $300 billion (perhaps as much as $1 trillion) and take more than 30 years to complete.

Nuclear Waste Policy Act — 1982

A major step toward shifting the responsibility for disposal of high-level nuclear wastes from the nuclear power industry to the federal government was taken in 1982. Congress passed the Nuclear Waste Policy Act (PL 97-425), which provided the first national, comprehensive policy and detailed timetable for the management and disposal of high-level nuclear waste. The major provisions of the act were to

- Authorize construction of the first waste repository.

- Provide a schedule for the site selection and operation.

- Define the means of achieving cooperation with the host state.

- Assure funding for the program by charging 1 mill (0.1 cent) per kilowatt-hour of electricity generated by nuclear energy. (This measure has been in effect since 1983, adding between 2 and 6 percent to the consumer's cost of electricity.)

- Provide for the President to decide if civilian repositories may accept nuclear waste from military activities.

- Establish an interim storage program to ease the backlog of spent nuclear fuel at power plants.

- Direct the DOE to design a monitored retrievable storage program for long-term storage of spent fuel (see Yucca Mountain, below).

169

1987 Congressional Amendments

In 1987, Congress passed the Nuclear Waste Policy Act, amended, as part of the Omnibus Budget Reconciliation Act (PL 100-203). As costs escalated from $23 to $30 billion, Congress directed the DOE to investigate only the Yucca Mountain Site in Nevada as the first repository for civilian waste. Congress limited the amount of waste that could be disposed of in the repository until a second repository was made ready. The DOE was also authorized to develop a facility to receive and temporarily store waste until the second repository was built.

In 1987, the DOE proposed developing a facility in Tennessee for temporary waste storage, to begin accepting waste in 1998. Congress authorized the plan, but it has not gone into effect. The Nuclear Regulatory Commission (NRC) must first authorize the construction of the Yucca Mountain repository (see below). Environmentalist groups contend that interim storage would result in transport of nuclear waste to the interim site and that it would be safer to leave the waste until a permanent solution can be found.

The Vestiges of Nuclear Disarmament

Nuclear disarmament resulted in the dismantling of much of the U.S. nuclear arsenal and the resulting need to store tons of plutonium. The federal government has proceeded to take apart as many as 15,000 warheads and store them at one of two former nuclear weapons-making plants — Pantex, near Amarillo, Texas, and Savannah River, South Carolina. Energy Department officials predict that dismantling will continue through the year 2003. The government must then decontaminate buildings used at those facilities, dispose of millions of gallons of boiling radioactive water, and decontaminate hundreds of square miles of desert at the Nevada nuclear test site. Congressional politics will likely play a role in choosing the site, since the economic future of both areas greatly depends on the plants.

Radioactive metals will be disposed of in one of two ways — immobilization in glass or ceramic containers or burning as a mixed oxide fuel (MOX). Immobilization is the preferred method among nuclear watchdogs, who fear increased nuclear waste. MOX fuel could be used in existing reactors, a process used in Europe but never tried in the United States. The Clinton Administration prefers the dual-track approach, using both options.

FIGURE 7.23
WASTE ISOLATION PILOT PLANT

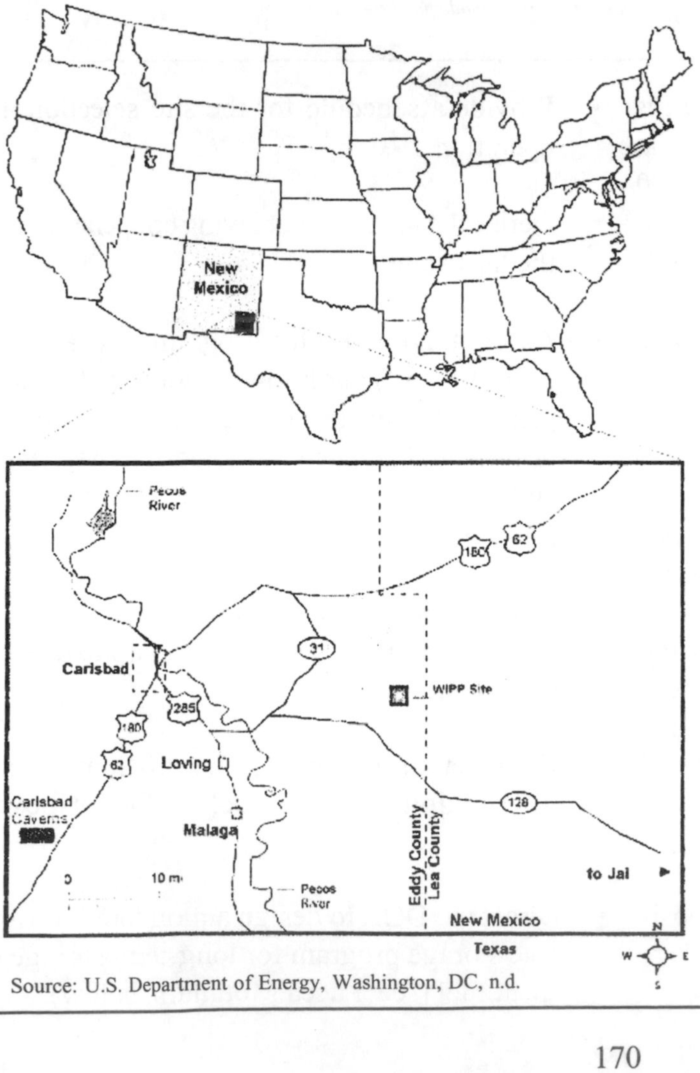

Source: U.S. Department of Energy, Washington, DC, n.d.

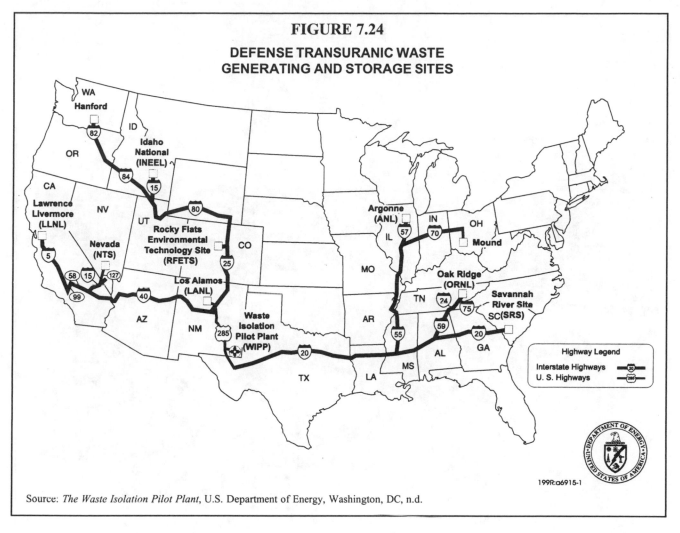

FIGURE 7.24

DEFENSE TRANSURANIC WASTE GENERATING AND STORAGE SITES

Source: *The Waste Isolation Pilot Plant*, U.S. Department of Energy, Washington, DC, n.d.

The Convention on Nuclear Safety

In the aftermath of the Chernobyl accident, representatives of over 50 nations participated in the Convention on Nuclear Safety, a multilateral treaty that seeks to increase the safety of civil nuclear power reactors. The convention has been signed by 65 countries, including the United States. Only 49 countries, however, have ratified it. For the United States to become legally bound by the convention, the U.S. Senate must ratify it. France, with 56 operating nuclear reactors, and Canada, with 21 reactors, have signed and ratified the convention. Japan (51 reactors), Korea (11), Russia (29), Sweden (12), and the United Kingdom (35) have signed and ratified the treaty.

The convention does not impose sanctions but seeks to encourage compliance through peer pressure. To determine compliance, countries are required to meet periodically to review one another's safety programs. The first meeting occurred April 1999, with subsequent meetings planned every three years. It is expected that countries with the most severe safety problems will use the convention to secure financial assistance to correct deficiencies.

A Serious Leak of Radioactive Waste — Hanford

In 1997, scientists discovered that about 900,000 gallons of radioactive waste had leaked into the soil from 68 of the 149 tanks at the nuclear weapons plant in Hanford, Washington. Eventually all the tanks are expected to leak. The leak has contaminated underground water moving toward the nearby Columbia River. Managers at the plant

FIGURE 7.25

Source: *The Waste Isolation Pilot Plant*, U.S. Department of Energy, Washington, DC, n.d.

had maintained that the leaks were insignificant because the radioactive materials would be trapped by the area above the water table, the "vadose zone." Furthermore, officials had been saying for decades that no waste from the tanks would reach the ground water in the next 10,000 years.

Nonetheless, the ground water under more than 85 square miles of the site is already contaminated. Washington's governor Gary Locke called it a "Chernobyl waiting to happen." (Figure 7.22 shows the migration of nuclear waste through the vadose zone at Hanford.) A threatened suit by the State of Washington against the U.S. Department of Energy to clean up the Hanford site resulted in an agreement to clean up the two indoor pools near the Columbia River by 2007.

NUCLEAR WASTE REPOSITORIES — WASTE ISOLATION PILOT PLANT AND YUCCA MOUNTAIN

In the United States, the government is focusing on two locations as geologic repositories: the Waste Isolation Pilot Plant (WIPP) in southeastern New Mexico for defense (transuranic) waste and Nevada's Yucca Mountain for civilian waste.

The Waste Isolation Pilot Plant (WIPP)

The Waste Isolation Pilot Plant (WIPP) became the world's first deep depository for nuclear waste when it received its first shipment of waste on March 26, 1999. The large facility near Carlsbad, New Mexico, is restricted to defense or transuranic waste. WIPP is 655 meters below the surface, in

FIGURE 7.26

Yucca Mountain, Nevada: Candidate site for the first U.S. geologic repository.

the salt beds of the Salado Formation, and is intended to house up to 6.25 million cubic feet of transuranic waste for more than 10,000 years. (See Figure 7.23.)

More than 99 percent of transuranic waste is temporarily stored in drums at nuclear defense sites in California, Colorado, Idaho, Illinois, Nevada, New Mexico, Ohio, Tennessee, South Carolina, and Washington. Under Congressional mandate, the WIPP facility will not allow commercial or high-level waste; only transuranic waste will be accepted. So far, the Energy Department has authorized the plant to receive waste from the Los Alamos National Laboratory, from the Idaho National Engineering and Environmental Laboratory, and from Rocky Flats, a former nuclear trigger factory near Denver. The waste is tracked by satellite and is moved only at night when traffic is lighter. It can be transported only in good weather and must be routed around major cities. Figure 7.24 shows transport routes, and Figure 7.25 shows a tractor-trailer container transporting radioactive waste to the WIPP.

Today, about 61 million Americans live within 50 miles of a military nuclear waste storage site. By the time the WIPP has been in operation for 10 years, the number should drop to 4 million. Over the next 35 years, barring court challenges, almost 40,000 truckloads of waste will be trucked across the country to the WIPP.

Yucca Mountain

The centerpiece of the geologic disposal of highly radioactive waste is the Yucca Mountain site. The Nuclear Waste Policy Act of 1982 (above) requires the Secretary of Energy to investigate the site and, if it is suitable, recommend to the president that the site be established. The DOE's current objective is to begin disposing of waste in the repository in 2010, 12 years later than originally expected.

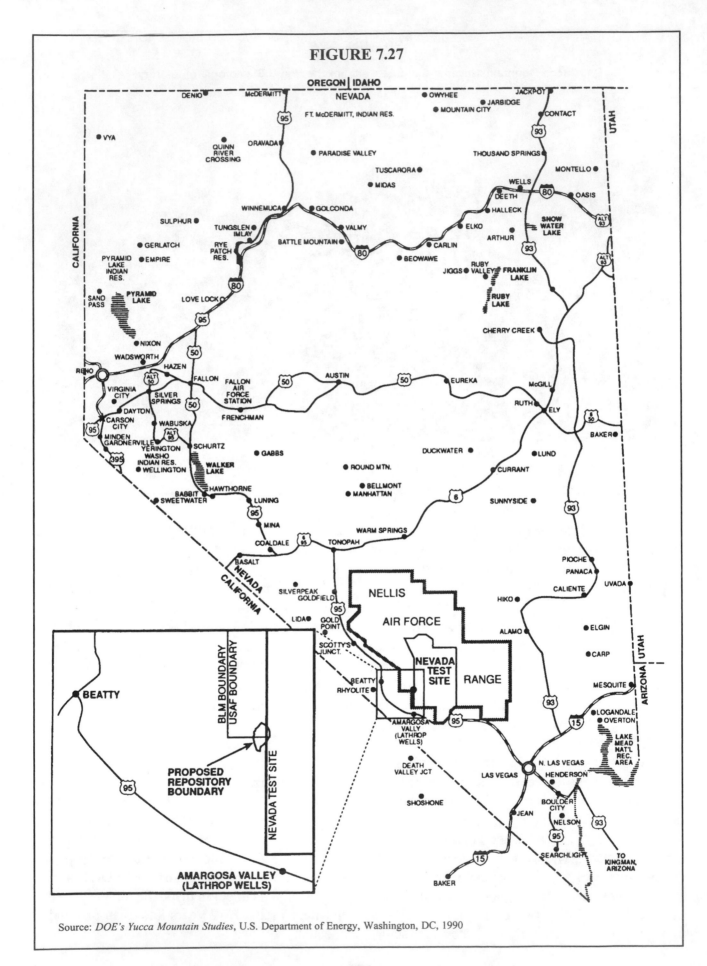

FIGURE 7.27

Source: *DOE's Yucca Mountain Studies*, U.S. Department of Energy, Washington, DC, 1990

It is not clear whether Yucca Mountain (Figures 7.26 and 7.27) is suitable — it is located near volcanic and earthquake activity, and rights to the land are being contested by local Native American tribes. Scientists have discovered areas of "perched water" above the water table (Figure 7.28). Although these areas may not ultimately prove to be a problem, researchers must determine their size and number in order to know. In addition, some western states feel they have long been targeted for hazardous facilities. If the site is found to be acceptable, the President approves it, and a recommendation goes to the Congress, the state of Nevada is expected to file a notice of disapproval.

Can Containment Standards Ever Be Met?

In order for the Yucca Mountain Repository to be built, the DOE must satisfactorily demonstrate to the Nuclear Regulatory Commission (NRC) that the combination of the site and the repository design complies with the standards set forth by the EPA. The EPA's standard is based on a new approach of using numerical probabilities to establish requirements for containing radioactivity within the repository. Their quantitative terms are

- Cumulative releases of radioactivity from a repository must have a likelihood of less than one chance in 10 of exceeding limits established in the standard and a likelihood of less than one chance in 1,000 of exceeding 10 times the limits for a period of 10,000 years.

- Exposures of radiation to individual members of the public for 1,000 years must not exceed specified limits.

- Limits are placed on the concentration of radioactivity for 1,000 years after disposal

from the repository to a nearby source of ground water that 1) currently supplies drinking water for thousands of persons and 2) is irreplaceable.

- Prescribed technical or institutional procedures or steps must provide confidence that the containment requirements are likely to be met.

Crisis in the Industry

The long delay in providing disposal sites for nuclear wastes, coupled with the accelerated pace at which nuclear plants are being retired, has created a crisis in the industry. Several aging plants are being maintained — at a cost of $20 million a year for each reactor — simply because there is no place to send the waste once the plants are decommissioned. Under the Nuclear Waste Policy Act of 1982, the Energy Department was scheduled to begin picking up waste on January 31, 1998. The utilities have been paying a tenth of a cent per kilowatt-hour produced by the reactors to finance a repository.

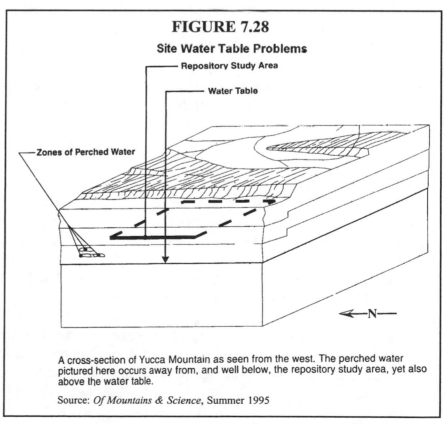

FIGURE 7.28

Site Water Table Problems

Repository Study Area

Water Table

Zones of Perched Water

←—N—

A cross-section of Yucca Mountain as seen from the west. The perched water pictured here occurs away from, and well below, the repository study area, yet also above the water table.

Source: *Of Mountains & Science*, Summer 1995

FIGURE 7.29

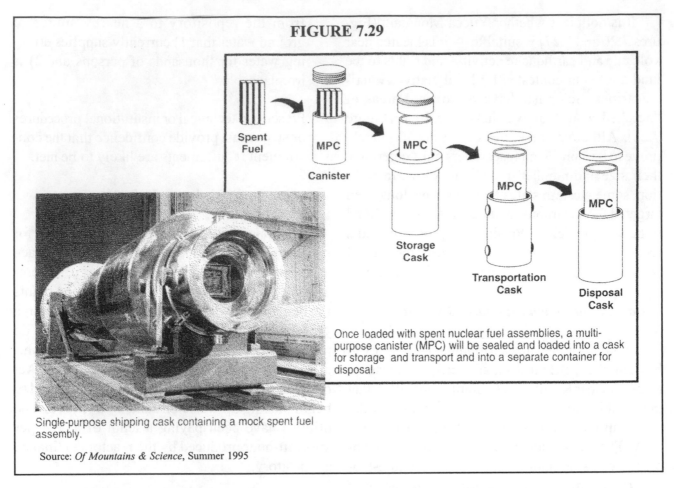

Spent Fuel

MPC
Canister

MPC
Storage Cask

MPC
Transportation Cask

MPC
Disposal Cask

Once loaded with spent nuclear fuel assemblies, a multi-purpose canister (MPC) will be sealed and loaded into a cask for storage and transport and into a separate container for disposal.

Single-purpose shipping cask containing a mock spent fuel assembly.

Source: *Of Mountains & Science*, Summer 1995

Although the 1987 waste amendment designated Yucca Mountain as the site, little progress has been made in approving the project. In 1996, the U.S. Court of Appeals, in *Indiana Michigan Power Co. v. Department of Energy* (88 F.3d 1272 [D.C. Ctr., 1996]), ruled that the nuclear waste act creates an obligation for DOE to start disposing of utilities' waste no later than January 31, 1998. Because the DOE missed the deadline, more than 20 utilities have sued. In Minnesota, state consumer advocate David Sampsel said, "We went into the nuclear power business relying on their [the Department of Energy] assurances that the DOE would have a repository for spent nuclear fuel."

In February 1999, the Energy Department announced that, because it was unable to receive nuclear waste for permanent storage, it would take ownership of the waste and pay temporary storage costs with money the utilities have paid to develop the permanent repository. The waste will stay where it currently is being stored, and the DOE will pay the storage costs.

Both the Senate and the House have passed legislation to build a temporary repository in Nevada. The Clinton Administration, however, opposes the temporary site, claiming that it has not been proven safe and would deflect funds and engineering talent needed to build the permanent facility. Even without the expense of temporary storage, the nuclear waste fund (from the 1 cent per 10 kilowatt-hours of nuclear power generated by the utilities) is many billions short of what Yucca Mountain is expected to cost.

TRANSPORTING HAZARDOUS WASTE

Many of the products humans use daily could not be manufactured without generating hazardous waste. Because these wastes may cause environmental damage, they cannot simply be thrown away like ordinary trash. To avoid human exposure, such wastes must be treated at special facilities that have been built to ensure environmental protection. At present, about 98 percent of the nation's hazardous waste is moved by truck, and the rest is moved by rail.

Since the beginning of this country's nuclear program, there have been more than 2,500 shipments of spent fuel and many more shipments of low-level waste. However, shipments of radioactive waste increased in 1999 when the Waste Isolation Pilot Plant (WIPP) began operation and will rise dramatically when Yucca Mountain opens.

Transportation of nuclear waste is of particular concern to states and Native American reservations along the main transportation routes to possible disposal sites. Several transportation organizations are actively preparing for potential shipments across country. Under the Hazardous Materials Transportation Act of 1975 (PL 93-633), the Department of Transportation and the Nuclear Regulatory Commission (NRC) share responsibility for regulating standards of safety for packaging and transport of hazardous materials by any mode in interstate and foreign commerce.

Spent nuclear fuel and radioactive wastes are solid material shipped in large, heavy metal containers called casks, which are designed to shield radiation and withstand severe accidents without releasing their toxic contents. Such fuel is usually transported by truck or rail. Casks, which are regulated by the NRC, have multiple layers of walls. Each container can hold 14 55-gallon drums. (Figure 7.29 shows the design of a shipping cask.) A satellite tracking system will maintain constant contact with the trucks, and drivers will be tested for safety and trained in emergency response.

TABLE 7.9

Repository Development Status and Estimated Opening Dates in Selected Countries

Country	Earliest anticipated repository opening date	Status
Germany	2008	Constructing underground test facility
United States	2010	Constructing underground test facility
Sweden	2020	Searching for suitable site
Switzerland	2020 or later	Searching for suitable site
France	2020 or later	Developing repository concept
Canada	2025 or later	Reviewing repository concept
Japan	2030	Searching for suitable site
United Kingdom	After 2040	Delaying decision until 2040

Source: *Nuclear Waste: Foreign Countries' Approaches to High-Level Waste Storage and Disposal,* U.S. General Accounting Office, Washington, DC, 1994

INTERNATIONAL APPROACHES TO HIGH-LEVEL WASTE DISPOSAL

In 1997, nuclear power generated 17 percent of the world's electricity. Governments around the world generally believe that deep geologic disposal offers the best option for isolating highly radioactive waste, although no country has yet built an operational facility. In fact, most do not plan to have a repository until 2020 or later. (Tables 7.9 and 7.10 show estimates of repository opening dates in selected countries and the unique features of each nation's program.)

While the United States faces a serious challenge because it has, by far, the largest civilian nuclear power program in the world, other countries are under less pressure because they have temporary storage facilities that will be adequate for decades or, as in France, they are reprocessing their spent fuel.

In 1993, the British government opened a nuclear fuel reprocessing plant, one of only two in the world (the other is in France) that reprocesses used fuel from nuclear power generators around the world. Some Americans fear that the venture will undermine efforts to halt the spread of nuclear arms because the process of transporting such materials increases the possibility for theft or ac-

TABLE 7.10
Comparison of Waste Programs

Country	Number of reactors	Nuclear-generated electricity in 1992 (approx.)	Earliest repository date	Likely geologic medium	Status	Unique features
Canada	22	15%	2025	Granite	Reviewing concept	Province of Ontario has 20 of Canada's 22 reactors
France	56	73%	2020	Granite or clay	Developing concept	Public opposition significantly slowed program
Germany	21	30%	2008	Salt	Constructing test facility	Opposition from state may affect licensing
Japan	43	27%	2030	Not selected	Searching for site	Government plans to increase use of nuclear power
Sweden	12	43%	2020	Crystalline rock	Searching for site	Waste managers plan to use long-lived copper canister
Switzerland	5	40%	2020	Crystalline rock or clay	Searching for site	Government would prefer to use an international repository
United Kingdom	37	23%	2040	Not selected	Delaying decision	Government plans lower-level waste repository
United States	109	22%	2010	Tuff	Constructing test facility	Federal law designated candidate site

Source: Developed by GAO from data provided primarily by foreign officials. Data are as of June 1993.

Source: *Nuclear Waste: Foreign Countries' Approaches to High-Level Waste Storage and Disposal,* U.S. General Accounting Office, Washington, DC, 1994

cident. In 1997, German officials claimed that French reprocessing plants had dumped highly radioactive material in the English Channel. To date, no permanent disposal of high-level waste has taken place in any country. Most countries face political opposition to such facilities. As a consequence, some nations are researching alternatives to disposal and are contracting with other countries for reprocessing services.

In 1997, North Korea, facing famine and desperate for currency, agreed to accept up to 200,000 barrels of nuclear waste from Taiwan in exchange for tens of millions of dollars. Observers fear this offer could pave the way for other countries seek-

ing a disposal site for their nuclear waste. South Korea claims the waste will contaminate ground water, harming South Korea as well, and will break an international practice of disposing of one's own nuclear waste at home. South Korea also fears that shipping radioactive waste could endanger countries along shipping routes.

In 1997, a train carrying nuclear waste to an interim storage depot, guarded by thousands of police officers, drew crowds of protesters as it reached its goal in central Germany. The annual event has drawn increasing numbers of anti-nuclear protesters since the transport of nuclear waste began.

CHAPTER VIII

PUBLIC OPINION AND ENVIRONMENTAL POLICY

HALF OF AMERICANS CONSIDER THEMSELVES ENVIRONMENTALISTS

Although most Americans are concerned about the environment, levels of concern have dropped in the 1990s. In 1991, the Gallup Poll asked people whether they thought of themselves as environmentalists. Seventy-eight percent said they were environmentalists, while only 19 percent indicated they were not. Eight years later, however, support had declined. A 1999 Gallup poll showed Americans evenly divided between those who considered themselves environmentalists and those who did not, suggesting that, in general, concern for environmental issues has dropped. (See Table 8.1.)

Men and women (50 percent each) were about equally likely to identify themselves as environmentalists. Politically, environmentalists were only slightly more likely to identify themselves as liberal (56 percent) than as conservative (52 percent) and were less likely to be Republicans (43 percent) than Independents (52 percent) or Democrats (54 percent).

Mood of the Nation

The Gallup survey found that two-thirds of Americans say they are generally satisfied with the state of environmental protection in the United States, up from half who felt this positively six years ago (Table 8.2). Experts believe this level of contentment with the environment today is likely a re-

TABLE 8.1

Do you consider yourself to be an environmentalist, or not?

99 Apr 13-14

	Yes	No	No Opinion
Gender			
Men	50%	49%	1%
Women	50	48	2
Age			
18-29	50	50	*
30-49	50	48	2
50+	50	47	3

Source: The Gallup Organization, Princeton, NJ

TABLE 8.2

How would you rate your satisfaction with the state of the nation in terms of protection of the environment--are you very satisfied, somewhat satisfied, not too satisfied, or not at all satisfied?

	Very Satisfied	Somewhat Satisfied	Not Too Satisfied	Not at All Satisfied	No Opinion
99 Apr 13-14	10%	59%	22%	8%	1%
97 Jan 10-13	13	50	24	11	2
93 Jan 8-11	8	44	28	18	2

Source: The Gallup Organization, Princeton, NJ

sponse to real improvements in this area, but also reflects a general state of satisfaction with the state of the nation. In 1993, when only 52 percent indicated they were satisfied with environmental protection, overall satisfaction with the condition of the nation stood at only 29 percent. Today, at a time when the economy is strong, employment levels high, and crime declining, Americans are optimistic, and that carries over to their feelings about the environment.

Nonetheless, most Americans still think some sectors of society are not concerned enough about environmental problems. Fifty-seven percent think the American public, as well as the government, is not worried enough about the environment. Criticism of American business and industry remains high, with 74 percent thinking business and industry are not concerned enough, down from 1990, when 85 percent felt that way.

Americans are most concerned about the pollution of drinking water (68 percent). Approximately half are concerned about toxic waste contamination, pollution of rivers, lakes, and reservoirs, and air pollution. Of the issues considered in the 1999 survey, Americans were least concerned (29 percent) about acid rain and global warming (34 percent).

In a 1996 survey *(Environmental Support Softens Amid Economic Uncertainty*, McLean, Virginia, September 1998), Wirthlin Worldwide, a Virginia-based marketing research and consulting company, asked Americans to rate the most important environmental problems. Water and air pollution and replanting forests ranked highest, with concerns over hormone-disrupting chemicals, global warming, and food additives somewhat less worrisome. Garbage and landfills were rated 7.9, moderately high, on their level of concern. (See Table 8.3.)

When asked which industries were "causers" or "solvers" of environmental problems, the chemical and oil and gas industries were ranked worst as

TABLE 8.3

PRIORITY OF ENVIRONMENTAL PROBLEMS
MEAN ON A SCALE OF 1 (LOW PRIORITY) TO 10 (HIGH PRIORITY)

water pollution	8.8	depletion of forest lands	7.3
air pollution	8.4	clear cutting of forests	7.2
planting more new trees than are harvested	8.2	protecting old growth forests	7.2
recycling more material	8.1	ozone depletion	7.0
garbage and landfills	7.9	hormone disrupting chemicals	6.6
depletion of tropical rain forests	7.8	global warming	6.5
alternative fuels for automobiles	7.5	food additives and hormones	6.4

TABLE 8.4

INDUSTRY ENVIRONMENTAL SCORECARD
FIVE YEAR TREND

	INDUSTRY	1993 score*	1996 score*	1998 score*
best	computers	25	11	15
	natural gas	11	-9	7
	electrical utilities	n/a	n/a	-11
	furniture	-29	-19	-15
	steel	n/a	-40	-21
	forest/paper products	-28	-36	-34
	plastics	-38	-36	-35
	nuclear power	-42	-50	-43
	fast food	-69	-43	-45
	automotive	n/a	-50	-56
	oil/gasoline	-59	-69	-65
worst	chemicals	-59	-75	-71

* difference score = % who say this industry has SOLVED environmental problems minus % who say this industry has CAUSED environmental problems. Higher scores are better. "NEITHER" responses are not reflected in the scores.

Source of both tables: *The Wirthlin Report*, September 1998

causers of pollution. The computer and natural gas industries ranked best. (See Table 8.4.)

When asked if their households sort and separate garbage for cans, bottles, or paper to be recycled, 76 percent claimed they did. Among employed respondents, 71 percent indicated their companies sorted and separated office garbage for recycling. Twenty-nine percent of respondents said they had stopped buying a product specifically because the manufacturer pollutes the environment.

Roper Starch Worldwide, in a 1998 study, "The Power of Two: Conservation and Corporate Environmental Responsibility," *The Public Pulse*, reported that Americans looked favorably on corporations that undertake environmental improvement measures. Seventy-eight percent said they had more positive feelings about corporations associated with environmental groups. Three in 4 claimed they would be more likely to buy such a

TABLE 8.5

Which of the following environmental
organizations do you find MOST believable?

Greenpeace	22%
Environmental Defense Fund	2%
Sierra Club	11%
Nature Conservancy	7%
Keep America Beautiful	50%
Don't Know/Refused	8%

Which of these same environmental
organizations do you find LEAST believable?

Greenpeace	28%
Environmental Defense Fund	14%
Sierra Club	17%
Nature Conservancy	12%
Keep America Beautiful	11%
Don't Know/Refused	18%

Source: *The Wirthlin Report*, September 1998

corporation's products, and 2 in 5 said they might invest in a company that partners with an environmental group.

Environmental Organizations

Wirthlin Worldwide's 1998 survey reported that Americans generally viewed environmental action groups as credible organizations, compared to private industry or government agencies. Out of five environmental organizations, survey respondents viewed Keep America Beautiful (50 percent), a consortium of Fortune 500 companies, as most

believable, with Greenpeace (28 percent) judged the least credible. (See Table 8.5).

A MISINFORMED PUBLIC — THE 1997 NATIONAL REPORT CARD

Today's environmental threats are more complex and subtle than when rivers were catching on fire in the 1960s from industrial pollution. Solutions to these new problems must start with a more sophisticated understanding of the issues. Lawmakers, businesses, environmental causes, and most of all the public suffer when people don't understand what needs fixing. — Kevin Coyle, President of NEETF, 1997

The National Environmental Education and Training Foundation (NEETF), a private non-profit organization, was chartered by Congress to serve as a link between public and private sectors to facilitate partnerships in support of environmental education. In 1997, NEETF commissioned Roper Starch Worldwide to conduct the *National Report Card on Environmental Attitudes, Knowledge, and Behaviors*. The survey interviewed 1,501 American adults about their beliefs on environmental issues and questioned respondents about their knowledge on such matters.

Two out of 3 adults failed a simple test on environmental knowledge (Table 8.6). For example, only 1 in 3 knew that burning fossil fuels — coal, natural gas, and oil — produces most electricity. Half the public thought electricity is produced mostly by hydropower, which actually accounts for just 12 percent of U.S. energy. Such misunderstandings may explain why lawmakers often find it difficult to engage the general public in solutions to global warming and maintaining air quality. (Table 8.7 shows how the American public scored on various subjects.)

TABLE 8.6

Report Card			
Subject: Environmental Knowledge			
Student: The American Public			
Grade	Percentage of Total Sample Receiving Grade	Percentage of Men Receiving Grade	Percentage of Women Receiving Grade
A (90 - 100%)	11%	17%	5%
B (80 - 89%)	10%	14%	6%
C (70 - 79%)	11%	12%	9%
F (0 – 69%)	68%	58%	79%

Source: *The National Report Card on Environmental Knowledge, Attitudes and Behaviors*, National Environmental Education and Training Foundation, Washington, DC, 1997

The survey showed that the public, despite considerable ignorance of issues, supports environmental protection by a 2 to 1 majority, even more for air and water quality protection. Sixty percent of respondents were concerned about pollution (Figure 8.1). In addition, 90 percent of people claimed to sometimes engage in at least five of 10 environmental activities, such as saving electricity, buying "green" (good for the environment) products, conserving water, and reducing trash (Table 8.8).

The survey also showed that environmental knowledge contributes to actions to protect the environment. For example, people who knew that vehicles are major contributors to carbon monoxide pollution of the atmosphere were 10 percent more likely to use public transportation when it was available.

The adults who resoundingly failed NEETF/Roper's environmental quiz were unequivocal about wanting their children to do better. Fully 95 percent of adults, including 96 percent of parents, believe environmental education should be taught

TABLE 8.7

Environmental Knowledge Questions and the Percentage of Individuals Answering Each Question Correctly

Content of Environmental Knowledge Question	Percentage Who Answered Question Correctly
The most common source of water pollution	23%
How most electricity in the U.S. is generated	33%
Definition of biodiversity	40%
The primary benefit of wetlands	53%
Protection provided by ozone in upper atmosphere	57%
Disposal of nuclear waste in the U.S.	58%
Recognition of a renewable resource	66%
Knowledge about materials considered hazardous waste	67%
The largest source of carbon monoxide (air pollution) in U.S.	69%
The most common reason for extinction of animal and plant species	73%
Environmental Protection Agency is primary federal agency that works to protect environment	74%
Where most household garbage ends up	83%

Percentages are based on the full sample of 1501 and are rounded to the nearest whole number.

Source: *The National Report Card on Environmental Knowledge, Attitudes and Behaviors*, National Environmental Education and Training Foundation, Washington, DC, 1997

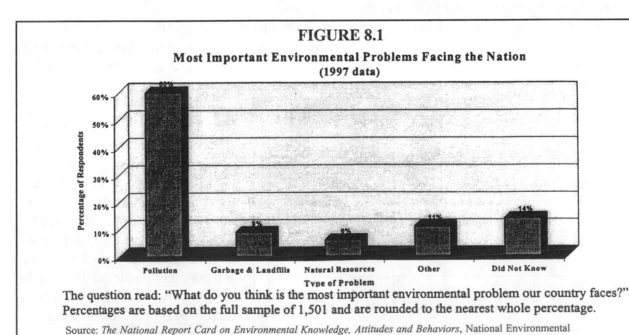

FIGURE 8.1

Most Important Environmental Problems Facing the Nation
(1997 data)

The question read: "What do you think is the most important environmental problem our country faces?" Percentages are based on the full sample of 1,501 and are rounded to the nearest whole percentage.

Source: *The National Report Card on Environmental Knowledge, Attitudes and Behaviors*, National Environmental Education and Training Foundation, Washington, DC, 1997

TABLE 8.8

Percentage of Respondents Who Reported Engaging in Pro-Environmental Activities			
Type of Pro-Environmental Activity	**Frequency of Participation**		
	Frequently	**Sometimes**	**Total**
Conserving Electricity	87%	12%	99%
Watching Environmental Shows on Television	51%	42%	93%
Buying Biodegradable or Recyclable Products	50%	42%	92%
Conserving Water	61%	30%	91%
Reducing Household Trash	58%	32%	90%
Recycling	64%	24%	88%
Avoiding Chemicals in Yard or Garden	40%	30%	70%
Donating Money to Environmental Organizations	11%	49%	60%
Using Alternative Forms of Transportation (Rather than Car)	14%	25%	39%
Doing Volunteer Work for an Environmental Organization	6%	22%	28%

Question Read: "Now I would like to ask you about some of the things you may do in your day-to-day life. For each of the following things, would you please tell me whether you never do it, sometimes do it, or frequently do it." (List of the above items was then read.)

Percentages are based on the full sample of 1501. The "Total" represents the combined percentages of individuals who said they frequently or sometimes participated in an activity. The other individuals replied either "Don't Know" or "Never" when asked how frequently they participated in the activity.

Source: *The National Report Card on Environmental Knowledge, Attitudes and Behaviors*, National Environmental Education and Training Foundation, Washington, DC, 1997

in schools (Figure 8.2). Americans seemed hopeful about the environmental future. Most believed that technology will help solve environmental problems (Figure 8.3).

PROTECTING THE ENVIRONMENT OR ECONOMIC GROWTH

Americans sometimes weigh the benefit of protecting the environment at the expense of economic growth. Gallup's 1999 survey found that 67 percent of respondents thought that the environment should be given priority, even at the expense of curbing economic growth. Just 28 percent thought economic growth should be given priority, even if the environment suffered to some extent. This pro-environment viewpoint has stayed relatively constant, at about two-thirds, since it was first measured in 1984. (See Table 8.9.)

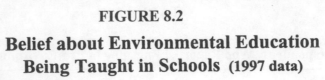

FIGURE 8.2

Belief about Environmental Education
Being Taught in Schools (1997 data)

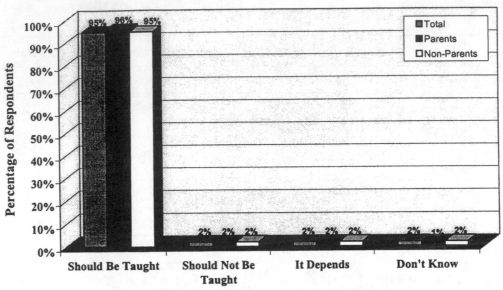

The question read: "Do you think environmental education should be taught in schools?"
Nine individuals did not respond to the question about children, therefore percentages are based on a total of
1,495 individuals. Of these, 563 were classified as parents and 932 were classified as non-parents. Percentages
are rounded to the nearest whole percentage.

Source: *The National Report Card on Environmental Knowledge, Attitudes and Behaviors*, National Environmental
Education and Training Foundation, Washington, DC, 1997

Wirthlin Worldwide (see above) concluded that environmental support in the United States generally moves in accord with the economy. Wirthlin compared U.S. unemployment rates to the data shown in Figure 8.4 and found a statistically significant inverse relationship between the unemployment level and support for environmental protection — when unemployment rises, environmental support falls. The report concluded, "When consumer confidence reflects a good economy, public concerns for social issues is heightened, and pro-environmental sentiments run high. But when the economy is bad, the environment tends to fall to the back burner."

The Wirthlin survey also asked respondents if they believed that economic growth should be sacrificed for environmental quality. Three-fourths of Americans believed there was no need to choose between economic growth and environmental quality.

Similarly, the NEETF study (see above) showed that Americans thought they could find a balance between the need to protect the environment and to have a healthy economy. If forced to choose between the two, 69 percent of the public chose the environment (Figure 8.5).

How Reliable Are Polls
on Environmental Issues?

Some experts suggest that opinion polls are an unreliable guide to how voters actually feel about environmental issues. Although polls of Americans indicate that concern for environmental issues is a great public concern, some observers suggest that people often claim in polls that they are interested in environmental reform, giving the pollster the answer they think she wants to hear, when, in actuality, they may be more interested in the economic cost.

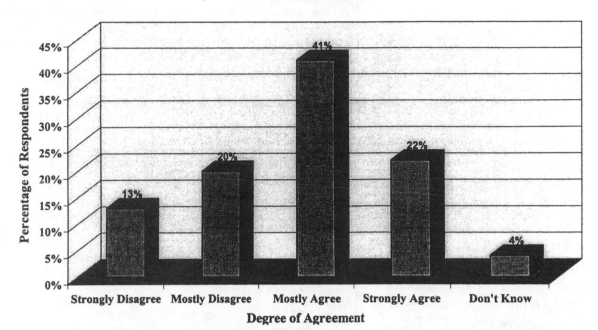

FIGURE 8.3
Technology Will Help Solve Environmental Problems
(1997 data)

The question read: "Please indicate for each of the following statements whether you strongly agree, mostly agree, mostly disagree, or strongly disagree: Technology will find a way of solving environmental problems?" Percentages are based on responses of the full sample of 1,501 individuals. Percentages were rounded to the nearest whole number.

Source: *The National Report Card on Environmental Knowledge, Attitudes and Behaviors*, National Environmental Education and Training Foundation, Washington, DC, 1997

THE ANTI-REGULATORY MOVEMENT

Over the past decade and a half, dissatisfaction with government regulation has grown. In 1994, the newly elected Republican-controlled Congress attempted to strike down a wide variety of federal regulations, including environmental regulations that they considered overly burdensome. Bills were introduced to relax regulations under the Clean Water Act (PL 93-523), Endangered Species Act (PL 93-205), the Superfund Toxic Waste Clean-up Program (PL 96-510), the Safe Drinking Water Act (PL 93-523), and other environmental statutes. Although much of that legislation ultimately failed to pass, budget cuts resulted in a lack of enforcement of many statutes.

Several factors contributed to this reaction to federal regulation. During the early days of the environmental era, the United States was experiencing a post-World War II economic boom, leading Americans to regard regulatory costs as sustainable. But during the 1970s and 1980s, as economic growth slowed, wages stagnated and Americans became uncertain about the future. An increasing number of Americans started to question the costs of environmental protection. The return of a vigorous economy in recent years has generally failed to revive the commitment to environmental issues. In addition, since Vietnam and Watergate, growing numbers of Americans have viewed their government with suspicion and mistrust.

The impact on private property use has also played a very important role. The Endangered Species Act and the wetlands provisions of the Clean Water Act spurred a grass-roots "private property rights" movement. Many people became concerned about legislation that would allow the government to "take" or devalue properties without compen-

185

sation. For example, if federal regulations prohibited a landowner from using his land to build a beach house on protected land, the owner wanted the government to compensate him for making the land worth less. In addition, some observers believe that regulation of the waste industry, among others, has accomplished its goals and that it is time to relax control in favor of economic growth.

COMPARATIVE RISK ASSESSMENT — HOW CLEAN IS CLEAN?

It is hard to translate a public consensus on environmental priorities into the concrete reality of municipal budgets and ordinances. — Tom Arrandale, *Governing*, 1997

The U.S. EPA and many other sources believe that pollution control budgets are badly out of kilter with actual threats to the environment and that when pollution occurs, governments overreact on the theory that the safest thing to do is clean everything up completely. But that is no longer considered practical by many Americans, especially as regulatory agencies begin focusing on smaller and smaller pollution sources. Instead of responding immediately to every potential threat, many experts believe there needs to be a pause for evaluation.

That approach is termed comparative risk assessment. (This concept differs from the scientific discipline of quantitative risk assessment and cost-benefit analysis that some congressmen advocate. Comparative risk assessment factors in more subjective criteria.) A committee of citizens looks into potential pollution problems, reviewing pertinent scientific information about the hazards — including risk assessments and cost-benefit analyses — and then ranks the perils to a city's health, natural

TABLE 8.9

Here are two statements which people sometimes make when discussing the environment and economic growth. Which of these statements comes closer to your own point of view [ROTATE 1-2]: (1) Protection of the environment should be given priority, even at the risk of curbing economic growth, or (2) Economic growth should be given priority, even if the environment suffers to some extent?

	Protection of the Environment	Economic Growth	No Opinion
99 Apr 13-14	67%	28%	5%
99 Mar 12-14	65	30	5
98 Apr 17-19	68	24	8
97 Jul 25-27	66	27	7
95 Apr 17-19	62	32	6
91 Apr	71	20	9
90 Apr	71	19	10
84 Sep	61	28	11

Source: The Gallup Organization, Princeton, NJ

surroundings, and general quality of life. In short, comparative risk assessment asks communities to decide for themselves what environmental problems to take most seriously by factoring into the scientific evidence the quality-of-life concerns that cannot be economically quantified. A number of states have launched comparative assessment projects. Critics of this approach fear it will be used as a way to cloud the issue and make sure nothing gets done either way.

LITIGATION AND ENVIRONMENTAL POLICY

Courts have been an important forum for developing environmental policy because they allow citizens to challenge complex environmental laws and to affect the decision-making process. Individuals and groups can sue after a regulation has been enacted, if an agency fails to enforce a policy, or if they feel the legislature is unsympathetic to their cause. Just the threat of litigation has changed policy within agencies enforcing environmental laws.

An environmental law can be challenged on grounds that it violates the Constitution of the United States. Successful challenges can force the legislature to bring the law into constitutional compliance. A lawsuit can also be filed based on harm to a person, property, or an economic interest, such as major claims involving asbestos, lead, or loss of private property. Lawsuits have also prompted legislation, such as the federal Superfund law and the Toxic Substances Control Act (PL 94-469), requiring agencies to control pollutants.

NORTH AMERICAN AGREEMENT ON ENVIRONMENTAL COOPERATION

The United States, Canada, and Mexico signed the North American Agreement on Environmental Cooperation (NAAEC), the environmental side agreement to the North American Free Trade Agreement (NAFTA), to discourage countries from weakening environmental standards to encourage trade. Other countries may become members of the NAAEC, and a country may withdraw from the agreement and still remain a NAFTA member.

A member country can be challenged in two ways under the NAAEC if one of its states fails to enforce environmental laws. First, a nongovern-

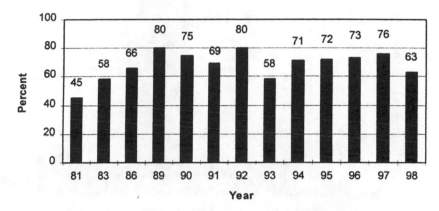

FIGURE 8.4

Environmentalism Takes a Dip:

Percent of Respondents Agreeing with the Statement:
"Environmental Standards Cannot Be Too High, and Continuing Improvements Must Be Made Regardless of Cost."

Source: Data from "Environmental Support Systems Amid Economic Uncertainty," *The Wirthlin Report* 8, no. 9, September 1998, p. 1.

mental agency, such as the Sierra Club or Audubon Society, may petition the commission. This alerts the public to the violation. Second, a member country can initiate proceedings against another member country showing a "persistent pattern of failure ... to enforce its environmental law" that can be directly linked to goods and services traded between the parties. If the conflict is not resolved through initial consultations, arbitration may be required and fines levied for failure to cooperate. If fines are not paid, a complaining party may suspend NAFTA benefits in an amount not exceeding the assessment.

EXPOSING POLLUTERS TO PUBLIC PRESSURE

In 1997, the Clinton Administration and the EPA initiated the Sector Financing Indexing Project (SFIP), a project to inform the public about industries that pollute the environment. The latest in an ambitious campaign to expand "right-to-know" initiatives, SFIP publishes "pollution profiles" on-line on five industrial sectors — oil pro-

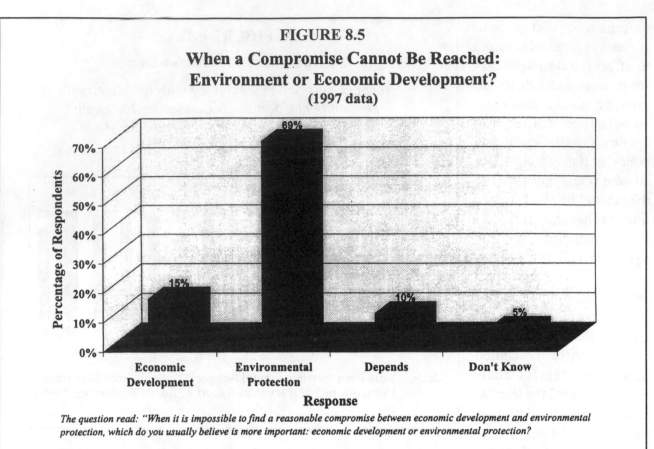

FIGURE 8.5

**When a Compromise Cannot Be Reached:
Environment or Economic Development?**

(1997 data)

The question read: "When it is impossible to find a reasonable compromise between economic development and environmental protection, which do you usually believe is more important: economic development or environmental protection?

Source: *The National Report Card on Environmental Knowledge, Attitudes and Behaviors*, National Environmental Education and Training Foundation, Washington, DC, 1997

duction, steel, other metals, autos, and paper — in hopes of exposing polluters to possible pressure from an informed public.

The profiles include the number of federal inspections, episodes of noncompliance, penalties imposed in recent years, releases of pollutants, pollution spills, injuries and deaths, toxicity of chemicals released, ratios of pollution to production, and demographics (racial and income breakdowns) of neighbors within three miles of a plant. At present, SFIP profiles approximately 640 individual facilities.

IMPORTANT NAMES AND ADDRESSES

Environmental Defense Fund
257 Park Ave. South
New York, NY 10010
(212) 505-2100
FAX (212) 505-2375
www.edf.org

Environmental Industry
Associations
4301 Connecticut Ave. NW, #300
Washington, DC 20008
(202) 244-4700
FAX (202) 966-4818
www.envasns.org

Environmental Protection Agency
401 M St. SW
Washington, DC 20460
(202) 260-4355
www.epa.gov

Foodservice and Packaging
Institute
1550 Wilson Blvd., Suite 701
Arlington, VA 22209
(703) 527-7505
FAX (703) 527-7512
www.fpi.org

Friends of the Earth
1025 Vermont Ave. NW
Suite 300
Washington, DC 20005
(202) 783-7400
FAX (202) 783-8444
www.foe.org

Glass Packaging Institute
1627 K Street NW, Suite 800
Washington, DC 20006
(202) 887-4850
FAX (202) 785-5377
www.gpi.org

Greenpeace USA
1436 U St. NW
Washington, DC 20009
(202) 462-1177
FAX (202) 462-4507
www.greenpeace.org

Izaak Walton League of America
707 Conservation Ln.
Gaithersburg, MD 20878
(301) 548-0150
FAX (301) 548-0146

League of Women Voters
1730 M St. NW, Suite 1000
Washington, DC 20036
(202) 429-1965
FAX (202) 429-0854
www.lwv.org

National Audubon Society
700 Broadway
New York, NY 10003
(212) 979-3000
FAX (212) 979-3188
www.audubon.org

National Consumers League
1701 K. St. NW, Suite 1201
Washington, DC 20006
(202) 835-3323
FAX (202) 835-0747
www.nclnet.org

Natural Resources Defense
Council
40 West 20th St.
New York, New York 10011
(212) 727-2700
FAX (212) 727-1773
www.nrdc.org

Sierra Club
85 Second St., Second Flr.
San Francisco, CA 94105
(415) 977-5500
FAX (415) 977-5799
www.sierraclub.org

Steel Recycling Institute
Foster Plaza 10
680 Anderson Dr.
Pittsburgh, PA 15220
(800) 876-7274
FAX (412) 922-3213
www.recycle-steel.org

U.S. Fish and Wildlife Service
1849 C St. NW
Washington, DC 20240
(202) 208-5634
www.fws.gov

U.S. Geological Survey
12201 Sunrise Valley Dr.
Reston, VA 22092
(703) 648-4460
www.usgs.gov

Worldwatch Institute
1776 Massachusetts Ave. NW
Washington, DC 20036
(202) 452-1999
FAX (202) 296-7365
www.worldwatch.org

RESOURCES

The United States Environmental Protection Agency (EPA) is the most important source of information on garbage and pollution in America. The EPA is responsible for keeping the statistics on pollution, educating the American people about pollution, and making sure that environmental regulations are obeyed. The EPA's *Let's Reduce and Recycle: Curriculum for Solid Waste Awareness* (1990) is a valuable teaching guide to introduce students to recycling and the awareness of pollution in the environment. *The Plain English Guide to the Clean Air Act* (1993) offers a basic introduction to the Clean Air Act and the problems of air pollution. The *Characterization of Municipal Solid Waste in the United States* comes out every other year and tracks how garbage is disposed of in the United States. *The National Air Quality and Emissions Trends Report, 1997* (1998) documents levels of pollutants.

The U.S. Geological Survey (USGS), a branch of the Department of the Interior, has the principal responsibility within the federal government for appraising the nation's water resources and providing hydrologic information. The periodic *National Water Quality Inventory* provides a complete overview of the condition of water in the United States. *Distribution of Major Herbicides in Ground Water of the United States* (1999) studied chemical contamination of American ground water.

The now-defunct Office of Technology Assessment (OTA), a branch of the United States Congress, traditionally provided some of the best studies on scientific problems facing the United States. The OTA's *Saving Energy in U.S. Transportation* (1994) was most helpful for data on automobile fuel economy and alternative fuels. *Green Products by Design* (1992) deals with U.S. hazardous waste and municipal solid waste policy. Other valuable studies include *Managing Industrial Solid Wastes* (1992), *Wastes in Marine Environments* (1987), and *Bioremediation for Marine Oil Spills* (1991).

Other government publications used in the preparation of this book include the U.S. Department of Agriculture's (USDA) *Agriculture and the Environment* (1991) and *Yucca Mountain Studies* (1990), prepared by the U.S. Department of Energy (DOE). The U.S. Department of Energy's Office of Civilian Radioactive Waste Management (OCRWM) publishes the *OCRWM Bulletin* on issues involving hazardous waste disposal. *The Waste Isolation Pilot Plant*, published by the Department of Energy, provided material and photographs on the nuclear waste plant. The Centers for Disease Control and Prevention of the U.S. Department of Health and Human Services publishes *Healthy People 2000* on environmental health and the American people. The U.S. Department

of Justice publishes *Federal Enforcement of Environmental Laws, 1997* (1999) on environmental crime.

The Environmental Industry Associations, the waste management industry's trade association, provides many helpful brochures and booklets on waste management. Information Plus appreciates the right to use graphics from some of these materials, including *Landfill Capacity in North America* (1996), *Interstate Solid Waste Movement in 1995* (1997), and *Municipal Solid Waste Disposal Trends: 1996 Update* (1996).

The Natural Resources Defense Council (NRDC), a private environmental research organization, published *Testing the Waters-1999: A Guide to Water Quality at Vacation Beaches* (1999) and *Testing the Waters: Who Knows What You're Getting Into?* (1996) on the condition of the nation's recreation beaches. Wirthlin Worldwide, a private research and consulting firm in McLean, Virginia, graciously allowed the use of material from its *Wirthlin Report* (1998).

Information Plus would also like to thank *BioCycle*, a journal of composting and recycling, for information on waste disposal from its annual "State of Garbage in America" survey. The League of Women Voters prepares materials on a variety of topics. Information Plus appreciates use of its *Plastic Waste Primer* (1993) and *The Garbage Primer* (1993). The National Conference of State Legislatures' *Farewell to Arms* (1993) was helpful in understanding the cleanup of nuclear weapons facilities. *Dying from Dioxin* (1995), published by the Citizens' Clearinghouse for Hazardous Waste, was the source of data on dioxin in the environment. The Center for the Study of American Business at Washington University in St. Louis, Missouri, provided *Enhancing Environmental Protection While Fostering Economic Growth* (1999). The National Conference of State Legislatures' *Legisbrief*, "New Developments in Environmental Justice" (1999) surveyed state enforcement of environmental laws.

Information Plus also thanks Roper Starch for use of its studies conducted for the National Environmental Education and Training Foundation, "Environmental Attitudes and Behaviors of American Youth" (1994) and the "National Report Card on Environmental Knowledge, Attitudes, and Behaviors" (1997). John C. Ryan and Alan Thein Durning, of Northwest Environmental Watch, published *Stuff — The Secret Lives of Everyday Things* (1997), on consumption in the United States. Susan Strasser's *Waste and Want — A Social History of Trash* (Henry Holt and Company, New York, 1999) is a thorough and entertaining look at the treatment — and role — of garbage through history. As always, Information Plus thanks the Gallup Organization for the use of its surveys.

INDEX

INDEX (Continued)